ALL NEW 100 MATHS LESSONS

Licence

YEAR 5

Yvette McDaniel

Contents

Acknowledgements

Extracts from the National Numeracy Strategy *Framework for Teaching Mathematics* © Crown copyright. Reproduced under the terms of HMSO Guidance Note 8.

Designed using Adobe Inc. InDesign™ v2.0.1

British Library Cataloguing-in-Publication Data
A catalogue record for this book is available from the British Library.
ISBN 0-439-98471-8   **ISBN 978-0439-98471-3**

Published by
Scholastic Ltd
Villiers House
Clarendon Avenue
Leamington Spa
Warks. CV32 5PR

© Scholastic Ltd, 2005
Text © Yvette McDaniel, 2005

Printed by Bell & Bain
456789   678901234

Series Consultant
Ann Montague-Smith

Author
Yvette McDaniel

Editors
Joel Lane and
Dodi Beardshaw

Assistant Editors
Aileen Lalor and
Charlotte Ronalds

Series Designer
Joy Monkhouse

Designers
Catherine Mason, Micky
Pledge and Andrea Lewis

Illustrations
Andy Rob and
Jon Mitchell
(Beehive Illustration)

CD development
CD developed in association
with Footmark Media Ltd

Visit our website at
www.scholastic.co.uk

About the series

100 Maths Lessons is designed to enable you to provide clear teaching, with follow-up activities that are, in the main, practical activities for pairs of children to work on together. These activities are designed to encourage the children to use the mental strategies that they are learning and to check each other's calculations. Many of the activities are games that they will enjoy playing, and that encourage learning.

About the book

This book is divided into three termly sections. Each term begins with a **Medium-term plan** ('Termly planning grid') based on the National Numeracy Strategy's *Medium-term plans* and *Framework for teaching mathematics*. Each term's work is divided into a number of units of differentiated lessons on a specific subject.

Note: Because the units in this book follow the structure of the National Numeracy Strategy's *Framework for teaching mathematics*, the units in each term jump from Unit 6 to Unit 8. The Strategy suggests you put aside the time for Unit 7 for Assess and review.

Finding your way around the lesson units

Each term is comprised of 11 to 12 units. Each unit contains:
- a short-term planning grid
- three to five lesson plans
- photocopiable activity sheets.

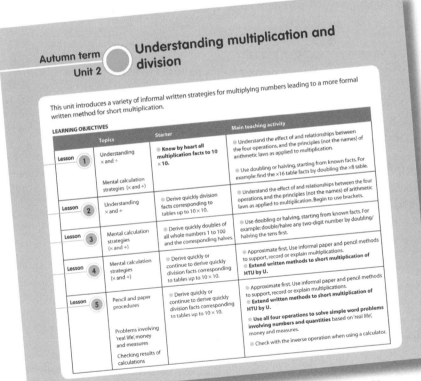

Short-term planning grids

The short-term planning grids ('Learning objectives') provide an overview of the objectives for each unit. The objectives come from the Medium-term plan and support clear progression through the year. Key objectives are shown in bold, as in the Yearly Teaching Programme in the NNS *Framework for teaching mathematics*.

Lesson plans

The lessons are structured on the basis of a daily maths lesson following the NNS's three-part lesson format: a ten-minute **Starter** of oral work and mental maths, a **Main teaching activities** session with interactive teaching time and/or group/individual work and a **Plenary** round-up including **Assessment** opportunities. In some lessons, differentiated tasks are supplied for more able and less able pupils.

However, this structure has not been rigidly applied. Where it is appropriate to concentrate on whole-class teaching, for example, the lesson plan may not include a group-work session at all. The overall organisation of the lesson plan varies from unit to unit depending on the lesson content. In some units all the plans are separate, though they provide different levels of detail. Elsewhere you may find a bank of activities that you can set up as a 'circus', or instruction and support for an extended investigation, either of which the children will work through over the course of several days.

Most units of work are supported with activity pages provided in the book, which can also be found on the accompanying CD. In addition to these core activity sheets, the CD contains differentiated versions for less able and more able ability levels. Some are available as blank templates, to allow you to make your own further differentiated versions.

How ICT is used

Ideas for using ICT are suggested wherever appropriate in *100 Maths Lessons*. We have assumed that you will have access to basic office applications, such as word-processing, and can email and research using the Internet. The QCA's *ICT Scheme of Work for Key Stages 1 and 2* has been used as an indicator of the skills the children will be developing formally from Year 1 and their progression in the primary years.

While some lessons use dataloggers or floor robots, we have avoided suggesting specific software, except for the games and interactive teaching programs (ITPs) provided by the NNS. If you do not already have them, these can be downloaded from the NNS website at: http://www.standards.dfes.gov.uk/numeracy

How to use the CD-ROM

System requirements

Minimum specification:
- PC with a CD-ROM drive and at least 32 MB RAM
- Pentium 166 MHz processor
- Microsoft Windows 98, NT, 2000 or XP
- SVGA screen display with at least 64K colours at a screen resolution of 800 x 600 pixels

100 Maths Lessons CD-ROMs are for PC use only.

Setting up your computer for optimal use

On opening, the CD will alert you if changes are needed in order to operate the CD at its optimal use. There are two changes you may be advised to make:

Viewing resources at their maximum screen size

To see images at their maximum screen size, your screen display needs to be set to 800 x 600 pixels. In order to adjust your screen size you will first need to **Quit** the program.

If using a PC, select **Settings**, then **Control Panel** from the **Start** menu. Next, double click on the **Display** icon and then click on the **Settings** tab. Finally, adjust the **Screen area** scroll bar to 800 x 600 pixels. Click **OK** and then restart the program.

Adobe® Acrobat® Reader®

Acrobat® Reader® is required to view Portable Document Format (PDF) files. All of the unit resources are PDF files. It is not necessary to install **Acrobat® Reader®** on your PC. If you do not have it installed, the application will use a 'run-time' version for the CD, i.e. one which only works with the 100 Maths Lessons application.

However if you would like to install **Acrobat® Reader®**, version 6 can be downloaded from the CD-ROM*. To do this, right-click on the **Start** menu on your desktop and choose **Explore**. Click on the + sign to the left of the CD drive entitled '100 Maths Lessons' and open the folder called **Acrobat Reader Installer**. Run the program contained in this folder to install **Acrobat® Reader®**. If you experience any difficulties viewing the PDF files, try changing your **Acrobat® Reader®** preferences. Select **Edit**, then **Preferences**, within **Acrobat® Reader®**. You will then be able to change your viewing options.

(*Please note that **Acrobat® Reader®** version 6 is not compatible with some versions of Windows 98. To download version 5 or for further information about **Adobe® Acrobat® Reader®**, visit the **Adobe®** website at www.adobe.com.

Getting started

The *100 Maths Lessons CD-ROM* program should auto run when you insert the CD-ROM into your CD drive. If it does not, use **My Computer** to browse the contents of the CD-ROM and click on the '100 Maths Lessons' icon.

From the start up screen there are three options: Click on **Credits** to view a list of acknowledgements. You must then read the **Terms and conditions**. If you agree to these terms then click **Next** to continue. **Continue** on the start up screen allows you to move to the Main menu.

Main menu

Each *100 Maths Lessons* CD contains:
- core activity sheets – with answers, where appropriate, that can be toggled by pressing the 'on' and 'off' buttons on the left of the screen
- differentiated activity sheets for more and less able pupils (though not necessarily both more and less able sheets in every instance)
- blank core activity sheets for selected core activity sheets – these allow you to make your own differentiated sheets by printing and annotating
- general resource sheets designed to support a number of activities.

You can access the printable pages on the CD by clicking:
- the chosen term ('Autumn','Spring' or 'Summer')
- the unit required (for example,'Unit 2: Place value and ordering)
- the requisite activity page (for example,'Numbers to 10';'Less able').

To help you manage the vast bank of printable pages on each CD, there is also an 'Assessment record sheet' provided on the CD that you can use to record which children have tackled which pages. This could be particularly useful if you would like less able children to work through two or three of the differentiated pages for a lesson or topic. The termly planning grids found on pages 6-7, 82-83 and 152-153 have also been supplied on the CD in both **PDF** and **Microsoft Word** formats to enable you to incorporate the 'All New 100 Maths Lessons' units into your planning or to adapt them as required.

CD navigation

- **Back**: click to return to the previous screen. Continue to move to the **Menu** or start up screens.
- **Quit**: click **Quit** to close the menu program. You are then provided with options to return to the start up menu or to exit the CD.
- **Help**: provides general background information and basic technical support. Click on the **Help** button to access. Click **Back** to return to the previous screen.
- **Alternative levels**: after you have accessed a CD page, you will see a small menu screen on the left-hand side of the screen. This allows you to access differentiated or template versions of the same activity.

Printing

There are two print options:
- The **Print** button on the bottom left of each activity screen allows you to print directly from the CD program.
- If you press the **View** button above the **Print** option, the sheet will open as a read-only page in **Acrobat® Reader®**. To print the selected resource from **Acrobat® Reader®**, select **File** and then **Print**. Once you have printed the resource, minimise or close the **Adobe®** screen using _ or **x** in the top right-hand corner of the screen.

Viewing on an interactive whiteboard or data projector

The sheets can be viewed directly from the CD. To make viewing easier for a whole class, use a large monitor, data projector or interactive whiteboard.

About Year 5

Much of the work in Year 5 focuses on the progression from informal calculating methods to more formal standard methods. The Year 5 programme is designed to give step-by-step guidance through these methods and includes a number of practice activities for reinforcement and assessment. There is also a variety of games and puzzles to encourage children to learn and apply mental calculating strategies to ensure that the learning process is both challenging and fun. It is important at this stage that children are able to make informed and appropriate choices about the methods and strategies they use and there are a number of opportunities in the book for practising this.

EVERY DAY: Practise and develop oral and mental skills (eg, counting, mental strategies, rapid recall of × and ÷ facts)

- Read and write whole numbers in figures and words, and know what each digit represents.
- Add or subtract the nearest multiple of 10 or 100, then adjust.
- Recognise and extend number sequences.
- Consolidate knowing by heart addition and subtraction facts for all numbers to 20.
- Derive quickly all two-digit pairs that total 100.
- Derive quickly doubles of all whole numbers to 100, and the corresponding halves.
- Add several numbers (e.g. four or five single digits).
- Use known number facts and place value to add or subtract mentally.
- **Know by heart multiplication facts up to 10 × 10.**
- Derive quickly division facts corresponding to tables up to 10 × 10.
- Multiply any positive integer up to 1000 by 10 and understand the effect.
- **Round a number with one or two decimal places to the nearest integer.**

Units	Days	Topics	Objectives
1	3	Place value, ordering, and rounding	Read and write whole numbers in figures and in words, and know what each digit represents. **Multiply and divide any positive whole integer up to 10 000 by 10 or 100 and understand the effect.** (eg 9900 ÷ 10, 737 ÷ 10, 2060 ÷ 100). Use the vocabulary of comparing and ordering numbers, including symbols such as <, >, =. Give one or more numbers lying between two given numbers.
		Using a calculator	Develop calculator skills and use a calculator effectively.
2–3	10	Understanding × and ÷	Understand the effect of and relationships between the four operations, and the principles (not the names) of arithmetic laws as they apply to multiplication. Begin to use brackets.
		Mental calculation strategies (× and ÷)	Use doubling/halving, starting from known facts. For example: double/halve any two-digit number by doubling/halving the tens first; double one number and halve the other multiply by 25, multiply by 100 then divide by 4; find the ×16 table facts by doubling the ×8 table; find sixths by halving thirds.
		Pencil and paper procedures (× and ÷)	Approximate first. Use informal pencil and paper methods to support, record or explain multiplications and divisions. **Extend written methods to:** **short multiplication of HTU or U.t by U.**
		Problems involving 'real life', money and measures	**Use all four operations to solve simple word problems involving numbers and quantities** based on 'real life' money and measures **(including time),** using one or more steps, including making simple conversions of pounds to foreign currency and finding simple percentages.
		Making decisions	Choose and use appropriate number operations to solve problems, and appropriate ways of calculating: mental, mental with jottings, written methods, calculator.
		Checking results of calculations	Estimate by approximating (round to nearest 10 or 100), then check result. Check with the inverse operation when using a calculator.
4–5	10	Fractions, decimals and percentages ratio and proportion	Use fraction notation, including mixed numbers, and the vocabulary numerator and denominator. Change an improper fraction to a mixed number (e.g. change 13/10 to 1 3/10). Recognise when two simple fractions are equivalent, including relating hundredths to tenths (e.g. 70/100 = 7/10). **Use decimal notation for tenths and hundredths.** Know what each digit represents in numbers with up to two decimal places. Begin to understand percentage as the number of parts in every 100, and find simple percentages of small whole-number quantities (e.g. 25% of £8). Solve simple problems using ideas of ratio and proportion ('one for every...' and 'one in every...').
6	8	Handling data	Discuss the chance or likelihood of particular events. Solve a problem by representing and interpreting data: in bar line charts, vertical axis labelled in 2s, 5s, 10s, 20s, or 100s, first where intermediate points have no meaning (e.g. scores on a dice rolled 50 times), then where they may have meaning (e.g. room temperature over time). Find the mode of a set of data.
		Using a calculator	Develop calculator skills and use a calculator effectively.
7	2	Assess and review	

EVERY DAY: Practise and develop oral and mental skills (eg counting, mental strategies, rapid recall of + and – facts)	
• Read and write whole numbers in figures and words, and know what each digit represents. • Recognise and extend number sequences. • **Round a number with one or two decimal places to the nearest integer.** • Consolidate knowing by heart addition and subtraction facts for all numbers to 20.	• Use known number facts and place value to add or subtract mentally. • Know by heart multiplication facts up to 10 × 10. • Derive quickly division facts corresponding to tables up to 10 × 10. • Derive quickly doubles of all whole numbers to 100, and the corresponding halves. • Use known number facts and place value to multiply integers by 10.

Units	Days	Topics	Objectives
8–10	15	Shape and space	**Recognise properties of rectangles**. Classify triangles (isosceles, equilateral, scalene), using criteria such as equal sides, equal angles, lines of symmetry. Recognise positions and directions: read and plot co-ordinates in the first quadrant.
		Reasoning and generalising about numbers or shapes	Explain methods and reasoning orally and in writing. Solve mathematical problems or puzzles, recognise and explain patterns and relationships, generalise and predict.
		Measures	Understand, measure and calculate perimeters of rectangles and regular polygons. Measure and draw lines to the nearest millimetre. Use, read and write standard metric units (km, m, cm, mm, kg, g, l, ml) including their abbreviations and relationships between them. Convert larger to smaller units (eg km to m, m to cm or mm, kg to g, l to ml). Know imperial units (mile, pint, gallon). Use units of time on 24-hour digital clock and use 24-hour clock notation, such as 19.53. Use timetables. Suggest suitable units and measuring equipment to estimate or measure length, mass or capacity. Record estimates and readings from scales to suitable degree of accuracy.
		Problems involving 'real life', money and measures	**Use all four operations to solve simple word problems involving numbers and quantities** based on 'real life', money and measures (**including time**), using one or more steps, including making simple conversions of pounds to foreign currency and finding simple percentages.
		Making decisions	Choose and use appropriate number operations to solve problems, and appropriate ways of calculating: mental, mental with jottings, written methods, calculator.
11	5	Mental calculation strategies (+ and –)	Find differences by counting up through next multiple of 10, 100, or 1000, eg **calculate mentally a difference such as 8006 – 2993.** Partition into H, T, and U, adding the most significant digits first.
		Pencil and paper procedures (+ and –)	Use informal pencil and paper methods to support, record and explain additions and subtractions. **Extend written methods to: column addition/subtraction of two integers less than 10 000.**
		Problems involving 'real life', money and measures	**Use all four operations to solve simple word problems involving numbers and quantities** based on 'real life' and money and measures (**including time**), using one or more steps, including making simple conversions of pounds to foreign currency and finding simple percentages.
		Making decisions	Choose and use appropriate number operations to solve problems, and appropriate ways of calculating: mental, mental with jottings, written methods, calculator.
		Checking results, including using a calculator	Check with the inverse operation when using a calculator.
12	5	Properties of numbers and number sequences	Recognise and extend number sequences formed by counting from any number in steps of a constant size, extend beyond zero when counting back. For example: count on in steps of 25 to 1000, and then back; count on or back in steps of 0.1, 0.2, 0.3 … Know squares of numbers to at least 10 x 10. Find all the pairs of factors of any number up to 100.
		Reasoning and generalising about numbers	Solve mathematical problems or puzzles, recognise and explain patterns and relationships, generalise and predict.
13	2	Assess and review	

Place value and ordering

This unit is designed to develop confidence with place value and ordering numbers. It uses calculators to observe the effect of multiplying and dividing by 10 or 100.

LEARNING OBJECTIVES

	Topics	Starter	Main teaching activity
Lesson 1	Place value Using a calculator	● **Know by heart all multiplication facts up to 10 × 10.**	● Read and write whole numbers in figures and words, and know what each digit represents. ● Develop calculator skills.
Lesson 2	Place value and ordering	● Read and write whole numbers in figures and words, and know what each digit represents.	● Use the vocabulary of comparing and ordering numbers. ● Give one or more numbers lying between two given numbers.
Lesson 3	Place value Using a calculator	● **Multiply and divide a positive integer up to 10 000 by 10 or 100 and understand the effect. Know by heart all multiplication facts up to 10 × 10.**	● **Multiply and divide any positive integer up to 10 000 and understand the effect.** ● Develop calculator skills.

Lessons   overview

Preparation
Photocopy 'Number fan cards 0–9', 'Place value chart' (two sheets) and '0–9 digit cards' onto card. Make the number fans, arrow cards and digit cards. For the arrow cards, it will be helpful if the units, tens, hundreds and so on are on different colours to assist with selection and recombining. Photocopy 'Place value chart' onto A3.

Learning objectives
Starter
● **Know by heart all multiplication facts to 10 × 10.**
● Read and write whole numbers in figures and words, and know what each digit represents.
● **Multiply and divide a positive integer up to 10 000 by 10 or 100 and understand the effect.**
Main teaching activities
● Read and write whole numbers in figures and words, and know what each digit represents.
● Use the vocabulary of comparing and ordering numbers.
● Give one or more numbers lying between two given numbers.
● Develop calculator skills.
● **Multiply and divide a positive integer up to 10 000 by 10 or 100 and understand the effect.**

Vocabulary
units, tens, hundreds, thousands, ten thousand, hundred thousand, million, digit, place, place value, less than, greater than, between, worth, sign.

You will need:
Photocopiable pages
'Number line shuffle', see page 11, and 'Multiplication bingo', one for each child OR for teacher's/LSA's reference, see page 12, one per pair.

CD pages
'Number fan cards 0–9', 'Place value arrow cards', one set of cards per pair; 'Place value chart', copied to A3; '0–9 digit cards', for teacher's/LSA's use (see General resources). 'Number line shuffle' and 'Multiplication bingo', less able and more able versions for both and 'Multiplication bingo' template (see Autumn term, Unit 1).

Equipment
Calculators; pencils and rough paper; counters.

Lesson

Starter

Call out a range of multiplication facts (two, three, five and ten times) using a variety of vocabulary: *5 × 3… 6 lots of 2… multiply 4 by 10… what is 10 times bigger than 8?…* Ask the children to show you the answer with their number fans when you say *'Show me'.*

Main teaching activities

Whole class: Display the 'Place value chart' and indicate how the place value of each digit moves one place to the left as you move up the chart. Revise the vocabulary of place value to ensure that everyone is clear about it – for example, point to 300 and ask the children to identify the names of all the numbers in that row, then repeat for 30 000 or 3000.

Talk about how digits can be combined to build up any number. Use the arrow cards to build a number. Start with a four-digit number and invite four children to hold up the correct arrow cards (for example, 2000, 400, 30 and 1 to make 2431). Ask these children to read out each digit individually, then combine the arrows to make the number and read out the whole number together. Invite someone to write it in words on the board. Repeat, choosing different digits. Try a five-digit number.

Group work: The children work in pairs, using a set of arrow cards. They select one card from each place value set at random, then record them as (for example):

60 000 + 4000 + 200 + 10 = 64 210 Sixty-four thousand, two hundred and ten.

Differentiation

Less able: Make four-digit or possibly three-digit numbers.
More able: Make six-digit numbers.

Plenary & Assessment

Give out calculators and ask the children to put in the number 1024 (say *one thousand and twenty-four*). Ask them what they have displayed. How did they get the 1 into the thousands column? What did they have to remember to put in? (The 0 for no hundreds.) What would the display have read if they had forgotten the 0? (One hundred and twenty-four.) Ask the children to clear the display and repeat with ten thousand and forty-six.

Lesson

Starter

Write a five-digit number (such as 65,213) on a piece of paper and hide it from the children. Write up the digits of your number in a random order on the board. The children ask you questions to which the answer may be *Yes/No* and *higher/lower*. For example: 'Is the 5 digit in the tens column?' *No, higher.* The children have 20 questions to work out the position and place value of each digit in order to find the number.

Main teaching activities

Whole class: Play 'Human digit cards'. Draw a number line on the board. Invite four children to select a digit card each. Ask the rest of the class to arrange these children so as to make the smallest possible number. Write this number on the left of the number line. Repeat to make the largest number possible from the same digits. What do the children notice? (The order is reversed.) Write this number on the right of the number line.

Ask the children to make two more numbers with the same digits. Together, estimate the position of each number on the line by discussing halfway points. Record both numbers on the line.

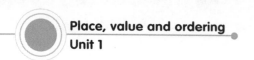
Finally, introduce or revise the symbols < (less than) and > (greater than), and put them between the numbers on the line:

2479_<__2497_____4297_____<_____9742

Group work: Working in pairs, the children use a set of digit cards to generate four- or five-digit numbers. They can record the smallest and greatest possible numbers at either end of the number lines provided on the 'Number line shuffle' activity sheet, then make two more numbers and estimate their positions. They should use the < symbol to write a number sentence as above.

Differentiation

Less able: Use the version of the sheet with three given digits and complete the number sentences provided.

More able: Use the version that involves making six-digit numbers. Complete the follow-up challenge (answers: two numbers with two digits, six with three digits, 24 with four digits).

Plenary & assessment

Draw a number line:

1359_____9531

Ask: *How can we find the midpoint of this number line by rounding and estimating?* (From 1 500 to 9 500 is 8 000, so the midpoint is 4 000 + 1 500 = 5 500.) *How could this help us to divide the line into quarters?* (Half of 4 000 is 2 000, so the quarters are at 3 500 and 7 500.) Repeat for 2 422 and 9 470, or for 12 321 and 20 854.

Lesson

Starter

Question the children about how we multiply by 10 and 100 (as covered in Year 4): to multiply by 10, move the digits one place to the left. Ask: *How can this help us to multiply by 20?* (Multiply by 10 and double.) Try 5 × 20: 5 × 10 = 50 and double 50 = 100. Now try 15 × 20 (= double 150 = 300). Go on to 6 × 10; 6 × 100; 16 × 20.

Main teaching activities

Whole class: Distribute calculators. Ask the children to key in 24 × 10 and note the answer, clear the display, then key in 24 × 100. *What is happening?* (The place value is moving to the left, with the spaces filled by 0.)

Group work: Introduce the 'Multiplication bingo' activity sheet. Check that the children understand the rules. Discuss strategies, including doing approximate mental calculations to help in choosing numbers.

Differentiation

Less able: Use the version of 'Multiplication bingo' with single digits, 10 and 100.
More able: Use the version that includes decimal numbers.

Plenary & assessment

Ask: *If we multiply a decimal number by 10 or 100, does the same place value rule apply as for a whole number?* (Yes.) Demonstrate: 0.5 × 10 is 5; 0.2 × 100 is 20. Show why 'add a 0' is not a good rule here: 0.5 × 10 is 5, not 0.50. *Does the same theory apply when we divide a number by 10 or 100? For example, what is 640 divided by 10? Can anybody describe what has happened to the digits this time? What about if we divided by 100? Can we suggest a rule that we could always apply when multiplying and dividing by 10 or 100?* (The digits stay the same, but the place value moves to the **left** when multiplying and to the **right** when dividing.) Chant this as a class.

Name	Date

Number line shuffle

1. Take four digit cards. Arrange them to make the smallest possible number. Write it at the left-hand end of the number line below.

2. Rearrange the cards to make the largest possible number. Write it at the right-hand end of the number line.

3. Can you make two more numbers from the digits and estimate their positions on the number line?

4. Complete a number sentence using either < or > symbols.

_____

Number sentence: _____

_____

Number sentence: _____

_____

Number sentence: _____

5. Now try making some five-digit numbers with the digit cards.

_____

Number sentence: _____

_____

Number sentence: _____

Challenge: Draw some more number lines on the back of the sheet, using a ruler, and use them to create some more number sentences.

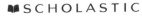

Name	Date

Multiplication bingo

A game for two players.

You need a calculator between you and four counters each (choose a different colour from your partner).

Take turns to choose two numbers from:

200	100	40	30	20	10	5	4	3	2	1

Multiply your two chosen numbers together on the calculator. If the answer is one of the numbers in the grid, cover it with one of your counters.

The winner is the first player to cover four numbers in a straight line (in any direction) with their counters.

5	80	40	6	40	20 000
4000	1000	30	160	2	20
60	10	150	2000	600	300
90	3000	6000	500	300	15
200	120	12	80	50	800
8	100	1200	400	3	8000

Understanding multiplication and division

This unit introduces a variety of informal written strategies for multiplying numbers leading to a more formal written method for short multiplication.

LEARNING OBJECTIVES

		Topics	Starter	Main teaching activity
Lesson	1	Understanding × and ÷ Mental calculation strategies (× and ÷)	● **Know by heart all multiplication facts to 10 × 10.**	● Understand the effect of and relationships between the four operations, and the principles (not the names) of arithmetic laws as applied to multiplication. ● Use doubling or halving, starting from known facts. For example: find the ×16 table facts by doubling the ×8 table.
Lesson	2	Understanding × and ÷	● Derive quickly division facts corresponding to tables up to 10 × 10.	● Understand the effect of and relationships between the four operations, and the principles (not the names) of arithmetic laws as applied to multiplication. Begin to use brackets.
Lesson	3	Mental calculation strategies (× and ÷)	● Derive quickly doubles of all whole numbers 1 to 100 and the corresponding halves.	● Use doubling or halving, starting from known facts. For example: double/halve any two-digit number by doubling/halving the tens first.
Lesson	4	Mental calculation strategies (× and ÷)	● Derive quickly or continue to derive quickly division facts corresponding to tables up to 10 × 10.	● Approximate first. Use informal paper and pencil methods to support, record or explain multiplications. ● **Extend written methods to short multiplication of HTU by U.**
Lesson	5	Pencil and paper procedures Problems involving 'real life', money and measures Checking results of calculations	● Derive quickly or continue to derive quickly division facts corresponding to tables up to 10 × 10.	● Approximate first. Use informal paper and pencil methods to support, record or explain multiplications. ● **Extend written methods to short multiplication of HTU by U.** ● **Use all four operations to solve simple word problems involving numbers and quantities** based on 'real life', money and measures. ● Check with the inverse operation when using a calculator.

Lessons   overview

15 16 35 21
  36 12 24
18 20 14

Preparation
Prepare an A3 copy of the 'Blank multiplication grid'. Write a list of multiples of two, three, four and five times table (for example, see illustration) on the board. Copy the three 'Number cards 1–100' sheets onto card and cut out a set of cards.

Learning objectives
Starter
● **Know by heart all multiplication facts to 10 × 10.**
● Derive quickly division facts corresponding to tables up to 10 × 10.
● Derive quickly doubles of all whole numbers 1 to 100 and the corresponding halves.
Main teaching activities
● Understand the effect of and relationships between the four operations, and the principles (not the names) of arithmetic laws as applied to multiplication. Begin to use brackets.
● Use doubling or halving, starting from known facts. For example: find the ×16 table facts by doubling the ×8 table; double/halve any two-digit number by doubling/halving the tens first.

Vocabulary
multiply, multiple, times, lots of, divide, double, halve, inverse, factor, digit, significant digit, partition, square number

You will need:
Photocopiable pages
'Tricky times', see page 18, one for each child.

CD pages
'Blank multiplication grid', one for each child and copied to A3 or OHT; 'Number cards 1–100', '1–9 Digit cards', for teacher's/LSA's reference (see General resources). 'Tricky times', less able and more able versions (see Autumn term Unit 2)

Equipment
Rough paper and pencils.

Lesson ①

Starter

Display the blank multiplication grid. Complete with 10 × 10 factors along margins. Cover up the vertical section that shows times tables 6 to 10. Ask the children to look at the numbers on the board. Remind them what a **multiple** is: a multiple of 5 is a number in the 5 times table, or several lots of 5. Ask the children to decide where the numbers fit on the grid as multiples. Demonstrate by writing 15 in the square that intersects the 3 row and the 5 column. Invite suggestions. If an incorrect answer is offered, ask the class to count up in the appropriate times table.

Main teaching activities

Whole class: Explain that since we already know some multiplication facts, we can use them to find more difficult ones. Reveal the rest of the grid. Explain how we can double the 2 × table to find the 4 × table. Demonstrate that if 6 × 2 = 12, then 6 × 4 = 24. Repeat with some examples of 3× doubled to make 6× or 4× doubled to make 8×. Ask for ways to find multiples of 7 and 9 (for example, 3× + 4× = 7× and 10× − 1× = 9×). Fill in a few examples for each times table. Ask the children to remind you how to find the remaining tables (6 to 10). Write a list of their suggestions on the board.

Individual work: Give each child a copy of the 'Tricky times' activity sheet. Ask the children to complete the blank times tables grid (part 1), using tables facts they know and the rules you have just discussed.

Differentiation

Less able: Use the version of 'Tricky times' with paired grids for 2× and 4×, 5× and 10×, 3× and 6×.
More able: Use the version where the multiples include HTU numbers. Look for further patterns. Can the children suggest any alternative methods using known table facts? (For example, the 9× could be made by tripling 3×.)

Plenary & assessment

Challenge the children to think of questions using a variety of multiplication and division vocabulary. Ensure that the various words are understood and used correctly, for example: 'How many 6s in 54?' 'How many lots of 8 in 56?' 'What is the product of 4 and 5?' Use the children's answers to complete your main grid. This will get harder as more questions are needed. Now ask: *Can you think of a method of finding multiples larger than 10 that we might try? How might this help us when we multiply bigger numbers?* (Partitioning and recombining allows us to solve more difficult multiplications using known facts.)

Lesson ②

Starter

Use the grid completed yesterday to look for division facts as the inverse of multiplication facts. Ask: *What is 42 divided by 6?* Find 42 on the grid, then find its factors (6 and 7) by tracing back with your finger. Invite individuals to challenge the class with a variety of division fact questions.

Main teaching activities

Whole class: Explain that the children are going to use the methods they used in Lesson 1 to help them multiply bigger numbers that are not usually in the times tables they know. They will also write down how the answer was found, using brackets.

Ask the children to use the grid to help them find 15 × 8. Write on the board:

$$15 \times 8 = (10 \times 8) + (5 \times 8) = 80 + 40 = 120$$

Explain that 10, 8 and 5 are **factors** of 120 and can be multiplied in any order. The brackets make it clear what should be multiplied, what should be added and in what order (whatever is in the brackets should be done first). Now try 18×7, 23×7 and 29×6.
Individual work: Complete part 2 of 'Tricky times', using the completed grid.

Differentiation

Less able: Use the version of 'Tricky times' part 2 that has smaller numbers and multiples of 2, 3, 4, 5 and 10 only. This group may need support in using brackets.
More able: Use a 'Blank multiplication grid' to include more challenging numbers. The children could double 6×, 7×, 8× and 9× to find 12×, 14×, 16× and 18×. Could they extend their grid to include multiples of 100?

Plenary & assessment

Share some answers and ask the children to explain the strategies they used. Ask individuals to demonstrate their methods on the board. These may include:
- Partitioning and adding known times tables
  eg $14 \times 4 = (10 \times 4) + (4 \times 4) = 40 + 16 = 56$
- Using a multiple of 10 and adjusting
  eg $18 \times 9 = (20 \times 9) - (2 \times 9) = (10 \times 9) + (10 \times 9) - (2 \times 9) = 90 + 90 - 18 = 180 - 18 = 162$
- Doubling known times tables
  eg $7 \times 12 = (7 \times 6) + (7 \times 6) = 42 + 42 = 84$

Ask: *How could we use this method for HTU numbers?* Work out 179×5 on the board. Take suggestions for methods. Explain that sometimes partitioning creates such a long string of calculations that errors are likely, and so we need to find a better way of organising the calculations (such as using a multiplication grid).

Lesson

Starter

Pick a number card 1–50 at random. Ask the class to call out its double. Try others. Ask: *Which ones are easy or well-known?* (20, 50…) *Which are more difficult? Why?* (16, 17, 18, 19, 26… because they cross the next ten and are harder to visualise.) Repeat using the 50–100 cards and halving. Ask: *Which ones do not have answers that are whole numbers?* (The odd numbers.)

Main teaching activities

Whole class: Explain that you are going to build together on your knowledge from the last two days. You are going to partition numbers and use doubling to solve TU × U problems. Ask: *How can we double 47?* Explain that you can partition it into 40 and 7, double each part, then recombine by adding. Demonstrate using brackets:
$$47 \times 2 = (40 \times 2) + (7 \times 2) = 80 + 14 = 94$$

Practise with some more examples. Now ask: *If we know this, how could it help us to multiply by 4?* Explain that this means doubling and doubling again:
$$47 \times 4 = (47 \times 2) \times 2 = 94 \times 2$$
$$= (90 \times 2) + (4 \times 2) = 180 + 8 = 188$$

Individual work: Ask the children to generate their own doubling problems by picking cards from a set of two-digit number cards (10–99) and doubling the numbers. You might want to give some children numbers less than 50 and other children numbers greater than 50. The children should record their work by writing number sentences, using brackets.

Differentiation

Less able: The children could double only multiples of 5 and 10 to begin with.
More able: The children could try multiplying numbers by 4.

Plenary & assessment

Ask individuals appropriately differentiated questions, such as: *How would you double 26? … 58? … halve 54… halve 96?*

Revise the children's multiplication strategies. *How would you work out 27 × 4?* (partition into 20 × 4 and 7 × 4, then add) *…36 × 6?* (partition into (10 × 6) × 3 and 6 × 6, then add) *…16 × 7?* (find 8 × 7, then double).

Ask the children: *Look at the following calculation and decide which method has been used. Is the method correct? If not, can you explain where it has gone wrong?*
16 × 8 = (8 × 8) × 2 = 64 × 2 = 124

Lessons   overview

Preparation

Write up some differentiated examples of TU × U and HTU × U problems on the board. For Lesson 4, prepare TU and U problems on grid paper

Learning objectives

Starter

● Derive quickly, or continue to derive quickly, division facts corresponding to tables up to 10 × 10.

Main teaching activities

● Approximate first. Use informal pencil and paper methods to support or explain multiplication methods.
● **Extend written methods to short multiplication of HTU by U.**
● **Use all four operations to solve simple word problems involving numbers and quantities** based on 'real life', money and measures.
● Check with the inverse operation when using a calculator.

Vocabulary

grid method, short multiplication (also see vocabulary list for Lessons 1–3.x)

You will need:

Photocopiable pages
'Different ways to multiply', see page 19, one for each child.

CD pages
'Number cards 1–10', one for each group (see General resources). 'Different ways to multiply', less able and more able versions (see Autumn term, Unit 2).

Equipment
Calculators, dice for each group.

Lesson

Starter

Play 'Division Lotto'. Give each group six number cards at random from a 1–10 set. Call out division questions such as *What is 35 ÷ 5?* or *How many lots of 3 in 18?* The children look for the answer among their cards and, if they find it, turn the card over. The first group to have turned all its cards over wins.

Main teaching activities

Whole class: Explain that the children are going to use partitioning to multiply larger numbers – but they can avoid having long, confusing strings of brackets by using a grid method. Write on the board (see left):

94	X 3
X	3
90	270
4	12
=	282

Remind the children about place value in relation to multiplying by 10 and 100: *90 × 3 is the same as 9 × 3 × 10.* The children will use multiples of 10 and 100 when partitioning. Remind them that extra care is needed when recombining the numbers: *It's no use getting the multiplying correct if your adding is wrong. To add the numbers, look at the most significant digit (the one with the highest place value) first. So to add 270 and 12: Keep 270 in your head, add 10, then add 2.*

Individual work: Ask the children to create TU x U problems throwing a 6-sided dice. Solve them by using the grid method. They should check each answer by dividing, using a calculator.

Differentiation

Less able: The children can use a version of the activity that involves multiplying numbers 20–25 and 30–35 by 2 or 5, as defined by the teacher.

More able: The children can create their own examples where the target answer is between 800 and 1000 (for example, 41 × 20 or 274 × 3). This requires them to estimate first.

Plenary & assessment

Invite individuals to demonstrate some examples on the board. Write on the board an example containing some errors. Ask: *Can you spot the mistakes and put it right?*

Place value forgotten: 42 has not been × by 10.
The 6 should be used to multiply, not added in with the answer.

174	× 6
×	6
100	600
70	42
4	24
=	672

Lesson ⑤

Starter

Play 'Division Lotto' as in Lesson 4. Keep a record of the division facts you ask in order to judge the children's accuracy at the end of the game

Main teaching activities

Whole class: Give each child a copy of the 'Different ways to multiply' activity sheet. Read through some of the problems together. Talk about the methods of multiplication you have tried this week. Remind the children about using known table facts and doubling. Revise partitioning and using brackets for TU × U, and using the grid method for more difficult numbers. Explain that knowing a variety of methods is better than relying on one. Go through the questions on the sheet, identifying together the method that is most suitable in each case and marking it on the sheet.

Individual work: The children work through the problems on the sheet. Encourage checking using inverse calculations, with a calculator if necessary.

Differentiation

Less able: Use the version of the activity sheet that reinforces multiplying by 10 and partitioning two-digit numbers, using TU × U examples.

More able: Use the version of the activity sheet that includes HTU × U and TU × TU examples. Then challenge the children to write some word problems of their own. Can they write both a one-step problem and a two-step problem? (For example: 'Jane saves £1.50 pocket money for 6 weeks. How much has she saved?' or 'Fred has 38 football stickers. He buys a new pack of 5 every week. How many stickers will he have after 6 weeks?')

Plenary & assessment

Work through a selection of the problems from the activity sheet. Choose an example of each multiplication method and discuss why some methods are more appropriate for a given calculation than others. For example:

- 6 × 5 is a mental calculation using known facts.
- 18 × 4 is a mental calculation using doubling. It may be helpful to use informal jotting.
- 28 × 7 is best done using partitioning with brackets as an informal jotting, since the numbers are too big and unwieldy to hold in your head.
- 176 × 6 should be done using the grid method, because there are several parts to the calculation and they need to be presented in an organised way to avoid errors.

Name	Date

Tricky times

1. Complete this multiplication grid, using the times table facts you know to help you with the more difficult ones. Some answers have been put in to help you.

×	2	3	4	5	6	7	8	9	10
2	4		8						
3									
4				20					40
5									
6		18							
7									
8									
9			36						
10									

2. Use the completed grid above to help you partition these multiplication problems and write the answers. Don't forget to use brackets.

$18 \times 3 = (10 \times 3) + (8 \times 3) = 30 + 24 = 54$

$16 \times 4 = (\underline{\quad} \times \underline{\quad}) + (\underline{\quad} \times \underline{\quad}) = \underline{\qquad\qquad}$

$17 \times 5 = \underline{\qquad\qquad\qquad\qquad}$

$15 \times 9 = \underline{\qquad\qquad\qquad\qquad}$

$23 \times 4 = \underline{\qquad\qquad\qquad\qquad}$

$26 \times 7 = \underline{\qquad\qquad\qquad\qquad}$

$34 \times 6 = \underline{\qquad\qquad\qquad\qquad}$

$41 \times 8 = \underline{\qquad\qquad\qquad\qquad}$

Name	Date

Different ways to multiply

Can you solve these multiplication questions?

Before you try, decide which is the best method for each question. Record the code letter of your chosen method in the box. Do your working out on another sheet of paper if necessary.

Write **M** for mental calculation, **XD** for known times tables that you can double, **P** for partitioning with brackets or **G** for a written method such as the grid method.

Problem	Method
$16 \times 8 =$	
$70 \times 6 =$	
$47 \times 7 =$	
$78 \times 3 =$	
$6 \times 7 =$	
Andrew is sponsored 5p for every length of the swimming pool he swims. If he does 25 lengths, how much money will he collect?	
Andrew has 9 sponsors. How much money will he make altogether?	
My car does 17 miles for every litre of petrol. If I put in 8 litres, how far can I travel?	
There are 48 tables in a restaurant. 6 people can sit at each table. How many people can sit in the restaurant at the same time?	
There are 6 biscuits in each packet and 6 packets on the shelf. How many biscuits are there on the shelf?	
The school cook can fit 9 pudding dishes on one tray. If she has 34 trays, how many puddings has she made?	
I have 14 goldfish, but Liam has 4 times as many. How many fish does Liam have in his pond?	

Written multiplication

Continuing written methods for multiplication, giving the teacher choice about when pupils are ready to move on to standard written methods. Opportunities for pupils to put their calculating skills into practise using word problems.

LEARNING OBJECTIVES

	Topics	Starter	Main teaching activity
Lesson 1	Properties of number sequences	● Round a number with one or two decimal places to the nearest integer.	● Know squares of numbers to at least 10 × 10.
Lesson 2	Pencil and paper procedures (× and ÷)	● Know squares of numbers to at least 10 × 10.	● **Extend written methods to short multiplication of HTU or U.t by U.**
Lesson 3	Pencil and paper procedures (× and ÷) Checking results of calculations	● Derive quickly all two-digit pairs that total 100. ● **Know by heart all multiplication facts up to 10 × 10.** ● Continue to derive quickly division facts corresponding to tables up to 10 × 10.	● Approximate first. Use informal pencil and paper methods to support, record or explain multiplications and divisions. ● Estimate by approximating (round to nearest 10 or 100), then check result.
Lesson 4	Pencil and paper procedures (× and ÷) Problems involving 'real life', money and measures	● Derive quickly all two-digit pairs that total 100. ● **Know by heart all multiplication facts up to 10 × 10.** ● Estimate by approximating (round to nearest 10 or 100), then check result.	● Approximate first. Use informal pencil and paper methods to support, record or explain multiplications and divisions. ● **Use all four operations to solve simple word problems involving numbers and quantities** based on 'real life', money and measures.
Lesson 5	Problems involving 'real life', money and measures Making decisions Checking results of calculations	● Recognise and extend number sequences formed by counting from any number in steps of constant size.	● **Use all four operations to solve simple word problems involving numbers and quantities** based on 'real life', money and measures. ● Choose and use appropriate number operations to solve problems, and appropriate ways of calculating: mental, mental with jottings, written method, calculator. ● Estimate by approximating (round to nearest 10 or 100), then check result.

Lessons overview

Preparation
For Lesson, make an A3 copy of OHT of the 'Multiplication square' sheet for display. Cut up a sheet of squared paper into squares (see above).

Learning objectives
Starter
● Round any integer up to 10 000 to the nearest 10, 100 or 1000.
Main teaching activities
● Know squares of numbers to at least 10 × 10.

Vocabulary
square number, square root, round up, round down, nearest

You will need
Photocopiable pages
'Making square numbers', see page 25, one for each child.

CD pages
'Place value arrow cards', for teacher's/LSA's use; 'Multiplication square' copied to A3 or OHT, for teacher's/LSA's use (see General resources). 'Making square numbers', less able and more able versions (see Autumn term, Unit 3).

Equipment
A sheet of squared paper cut into 2 × 2 and 4 × 4 squares; coloured pens; scissors; adhesive; additional squared paper.

Lesson

Starter

Use the arrow cards to make a three-digit number such as 372. Ask the children to read out the number. Write it on the board and ask individuals to round it to the nearest 10 (370) or the nearest 100 (400). To demonstrate this more clearly, draw a number line with a difference of 10 (370–380 in this case) and place the number on the line. Repeat with hundreds (a number line 300–400). Repeat with more three-digit and four-digit numbers.

Main teaching activities

Whole class: Display the enlarged multiplication table. Explain that today you are going to look at special multiples: numbers that are multiplied by themselves, or square numbers. Ask volunteers to shade in on the multiplication table numbers that are obtained by multiplying a number by itself – for example, 4 or 49. Can the children see the pattern on the grid? (The square numbers form a diagonal line.) Explain that they are called *square numbers* because when one of these numbers is arranged as squares or dots, it makes a square. Demonstrate with squared paper squares showing 2 × 2 and 4 × 4. Ask children to count the individual squares: 2 × 2 = 4 and 4 × 4 = 16. The inverse or opposite of a square is known as a square root – for example, 4 is the square root of 16.

Individual work: The children can use the 'Making square numbers' activity sheet to make and solve jigsaws of square numbers, count or calculate each square number and write the relevant multiplication fact beneath each jigsaw square. They can use the enlarged multiplication table to check their answers.

Differentiation

Less able: These children may only find the square numbers of 2, 3, 4 and 5. They can count the squares on the jigsaw pieces to calculate the square numbers.

More able: These children should be able to complete the squares quickly. They can go on to calculate the squares of 11, 12 and 13 and, using squared paper, create the jigsaws for a friend.

Plenary & assessment

Check the results of the jigsaw puzzles and the square numbers calculated. Ask questions such as: *What is the square of 4? What is the square root of 25?* Invite the children to demonstrate the square numbers by using themselves to form a square 'grid' of bodies: 4 × 4, 5 × 5 and so on.

Lesson  overview

Learning objectives

Starter
- Know squares of numbers to at least 10 × 10.

Main teaching activities
- **Extend written methods to short multiplication of HTU or U.t by U.**

Vocabulary
times, lots of, multiple

You will need

CD pages
'0–9 digit cards' (see General resources), a set for each group.

Equipment
Rough paper and pencils (or individual whiteboards and pens if available).

Lesson

Starter

Play 'Square root bingo'. Give each group six different single-digit cards from 2 to 9. Call out questions such as *What is the square root of 36?* The groups who have the correct digit (6) turn it face down. The winning group is the first to turn over all its cards.

Main teaching activities

Whole class: Provide each child with paper and pencil or an individual whiteboard and pen. Explain that you are going to revise the grid method for multiplying large numbers and also show them two more compact methods. Emphasise that no method is 'better': the children must choose the method with which they feel most comfortable and which gives the most accurate results. Provide opportunities for the children to attempt each method on their paper or board and hold it up to show you their calculations. Discuss the following methods of doing the calculation 134×5. Then try some further examples.

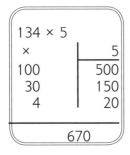

The grid method
- Approximate first: $\sim 150 \times 5 = 750$. This will give you an idea of the size of the answer.
- Draw the grid and partition the number into H, T and U.
- Multiply each part carefully, aligning the place value of each answer.
- Add the numbers back up, starting with the most significant digit: '500 in your head, add 100, gives us 600, add 50 is 650, add 20 equals 670.'

The expanded vertical method
This method is similar to the grid method and is a natural development from it. However, it relies on secure place value understanding.
- Write the calculation vertically.
- Multiply the most significant digit first (the hundreds): 100×5
- Multiply the tens: $30 \times 5 = 150$
- Multiply the units: $8 \times 5 = 20$
- Add up, counting on from the most significant digit as before.

It is possible to take the development onward another stage by using the expanded method above, but starting with the least significant digit (units) and thus inverting the recording. This prepares the children for:

```
  H T U
  1 3 4
×     5
─────────
  5 0 0
  1 5 0
    2 0
─────────
  6 7 0
```

The compact standard method
This is vertical multiplication, but multiplying the smallest digit (units) first and carrying the next place value over. Not every child will be able to cope with this method, and you may choose to teach it only to one group in your group teaching time.
- Write the calculation vertically.
- Multiply the units first: $4 \times 5 = 20$. Write the 0 units in the units column and carry the 2 tens to underneath the tens column.
- Multiply the tens: $5 \times 3 = 15$. Add the extra 2 tens, making 17. Write 7 in the tens column and carry over 1 hundred.
- Multiply the hundreds: $1 \times 5 = 5$. Add the extra hundred, making 6.

```
  H T U
  1 3 4
×     5
─────────
  6 7 0
  1 2
```

Group work: Write three or four examples for groups to attempt using their (or your) chosen method. For example: 146×2; 231×5; 315×3. The children should complete each calculation individually, but then share their answers with the group. The group can then discuss any differences in method or answer.

Differentiation
Less able: The children could use the grid method only. They may only manage TU × U problems.
More able: The children could work through to the compact standard method.

Plenary & assessment
Discuss the methods used and problems encountered. Make this more fun by dividing the class into three groups, each representing a different calculating method. The children have five minutes to jot down reasons why they believe their chosen method to be the best and most accurate one. They then present their reasons to the class, with opportunities for questioning and debate.

Lessons   overview

Learning objectives

Starter

● Derive quickly all two-digit pairs that total 100.

● **Know by heart all multiplication facts up to 10 × 10.**

● Continue to derive quickly division facts corresponding to tables up to 10 × 10.

● Estimate by approximating (round to nearest 10 or 100), then check result.

Main teaching activities

● Approximate first. Use informal pencil and paper methods to support, record or explain multiplications and divisions.

● Estimate by approximating (round to nearest 10 or 100), then check result.

● **Use all four operations to solve simple word problems involving numbers and quantities** based on 'real life', money and measures.

● Choose and use appropriate number operations to solve problems, and appropriate ways of calculating: mental, mental with jottings, written methods, calculator. Divide, share, share equally, altogether, lots of, each, inverse.

You will need

Photocopiable pages

'Written division skills', see page 26, one for each child.

CD pages

'0–9 digit cards' and completed 'Multiplication square', both for teacher's/LSA's use (see General resources). 'Written division skills', less able and more able versions (see Autumn term, Unit 3).

Equipment

Rough paper and pencils or individual whiteboards and pens; calculators.

Lesson

Starter

Write a number on the board, such as 24. Ask the children to suggest number sentences that give that answer, such as 6 × 4, 12 + 12, 25 – 1, 48 ÷ 2… Record this as a web, with the number in the centre and lines radiating from it leading to number sentences. Repeat with 36, 18 and 32.

Main teaching activities

Whole class: Explain that, since we have seen that multiplication and division are closely linked – one is the *inverse* or opposite of the other, we are now going to use multiplication facts we know to help us divide numbers that are bigger than our known table facts. For example: *What is 62 ÷ 4?* Encourage the children to estimate first: *4 ×10 is 40, too small. 4 × 20 is 80, too big. So we know the answer is between 10 and 20.* Go on to demonstrate the 'chunking' method:

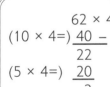

● Write the division question: 62 ÷ 4.

● Find a known × fact (10 × 4).

● Subtract that 'chunk', leaving 22.

● Find the next nearest × fact to 22 (5 × 4).

● Subtract that, leaving a remainder of 2.

● Answer: 15 (lots of 4) remainder 2

Repeat, asking the children to show you this method. Try 78 ÷ 5 and 56 ÷ 3.

Group work: The children can attempt more examples (such as 59 ÷ 3, 67 ÷ 4, 76 ÷ 5), individually in their books or on whiteboards, then discuss the results in groups.

Differentiation

Less able: Children may find the activity very difficult if they do not know many multiplication facts. Try to create some division questions using only divisors 2 and 5 (for example, 27 ÷ 2 and 68 ÷ 5).

More able: Ask these children to attempt HTU division, using larger 'chunks'. For example: 124 ÷ 8, 129 ÷ 9, 131 ÷ 7. Remind them to estimate the range first.

Plenary & assessment

Check the children's understanding of the method by writing up one of the questions they have attempted on the board. For example, write 59 ÷ 3. Display the digit cards 3, 0, 2, 9, 2, 7, 2, 1, 9, 2 close by. Explain that all of these digits appear in the solution: the children have to decide where they fit and their appropriate place values, using the 'chunking' method of division. So a child might say: 'The first chunk is $10 \times 3 = 30$, so I need the 3 and the zero. Take 30 away from 59 and I'm left with 29, so I need a 2 for the tens and a 9 for the units. The next chunk is $9 \times 3 = 27$, so I need the 2 and the 7. Subtracting 27 from 29 leaves a remainder of 2, so the answer is 19 remainder 2.' Ask a volunteer to write up one of his or her calculations on the board, and to choose digit cards for the rest of the class to place.

Lesson ④

Starter
Repeat the starter from Lesson 3, using the numbers 100, 42, 20 and 48.

Main teaching activities
Whole class: Explain that the children will be using pencil and paper methods to solve division word problems. Read the questions on the 'Written division skills' activity sheet together. Work through the first example on the board with the children's help.
Individual work: Ask the children to complete the 'Written division skills' sheet.

Differentiation
Less able: Provide the version of the activity sheet that involves dividing TU numbers by 2 and 5.
More able: Provide the version that involves dividing HTU numbers by numbers up to 9.

Plenary & assessment
Go through some of the questions and discuss the methods used. Ask children to explain which method they chose each time and why. Ask: *Is there someone who used a different method? Can you explain it?* Write up a calculation that has been solved incorrectly. Ask: *Can you see where the error has occurred? Can you explain what Dean has done wrong?*

Lesson ⑤

Starter
Challenge the children to spot and continue number patterns – for example: *75, 100, 125, what comes next?... 45, 60, 75... 440, 420, 400...* Once the pattern has been spotted, let the children continue each sequence by 'passing it on' around the room.

Main teaching activities
Whole class: Explain that the children will be solving mixed multiplication and division problems from 'Mixed word problems'. Read through the sheet highlighting the vocabulary that suggests or denotes whether the problem is to be multiplied or divided. Turn this into a game where you read the question and the children stand up if they hear a word suggesting multiplication and sit down if they hear a word suggesting division.
  Discuss also the fact that simpler calculations such as 6×5 do not need a written method.
Individual work: Provide some word problems for the children to complete.

Differentiation
Less able: Provide some simple word problems that involve multiplying and dividing by 2, 3, 5 and 10.
More able: Provide some word problems that involve multiplying and dividing by numbers to 9.

Plenary & assessment
Conclude the lesson as for Lesson 4.

Name	Date

Making square numbers

This sheet provides square jigsaws of different sizes. Each jigsaw shows a square number. Cut the jigsaws out carefully, then cut up each jigsaw along the thick lines.

Now put the jigsaws back together. Stick them down on another sheet of paper. Label each jigsaw with the relevant table fact, for example $2 \times 2 = 4$.

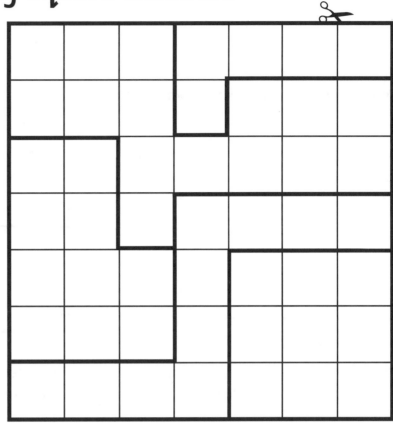

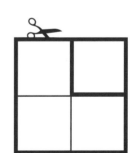

Name	Date

Written division skills

Solve these division problems.

You need to write out each problem in numbers on another sheet, and solve it using the 'chunking' method you have practised in class. You do not need to write out the words!

You can use a multiplication square to help you.

Here is an example:

Gloria has 26 stickers to put in an album.

She can fit 2 stickers on each page.

How many pages will she use?

```
26 ÷ 2        26
            – 20     (10 × 2)
              6
            –  6     (3 × 2)
   Answer:       13
```

1. A class of 52 children sit in groups of 4. How many groups are there?

_____

2. Our class library has 78 group reading books. The books are in sets of 6. How many sets of group reading books do we have?

_____

3. Samir saves £3.00 of his pocket money every week, because he wants to buy a new computer game. He has saved £51 so far. How long has he been saving?

_____

4. Rolls are sold in packs of 4. The shop 'The Dusty Baker' has 88 rolls to sell on a Saturday morning. How many packs is that?

_____

5. A shoe shop has 54 shoes in its sale bin. How many pairs is that?

_____

6. 'There are 64 wheels in this car park,' says the attendant. How many 4-wheeled cars are parked there?

_____

7. Apple juice cartons are sold in boxes of 6 in the supermarket. The supermarket's computer says they have 84 cartons left to sell. How many boxes is that?

_____

8. Ann has earned £95 in 5 weeks. How much does she earn each week?

_____

9. The chairs in the hall have to be put into rows of 5. There are 89 chairs. How many rows will there be? Will there be any chairs left over?

_____

10. George has 83 football cards to stick into a book. He can fit 6 cards on each page. How many pages will he use?

_____

Fractions, decimals and percentages

This unit provides opportunities to recognise links between fractions, decimals and percentages and use these to calculate.

LEARNING OBJECTIVES

	Topics	Starter	Main teaching activity
Lesson 1	Fractions, decimals and percentages	● Recognise multiples of 6, 7, 8, 9, up to the 10th multiple.	● Use fraction notation, including mixed numbers and the vocabulary numerator and denominator.
Lesson 2		● Derive quickly all pairs of multiples of 50 with a total of 1000 (eg 350 + 650).	● Change an improper fraction to a mixed number (eg change 13/10 to 1 3/10). **● Use decimal notation for tenths and hundredths.**
Lesson 3		● Continue to derive quickly all two-digit pairs that total 100 (eg 43 + 57).	● Recognise when two simple fractions are equivalent, including relating hundredths to tenths (eg 70/100 = 7/10). **● Use decimal notation for tenths and hundredths.**
Lesson 4		● Continue to derive quickly doubles of all whole numbers 1 to 100 (eg 78 × 2) and the corresponding halves.	**● Use decimal notation for tenths and hundredths.** ● Know what each digit represents in numbers with up to two decimal places. ● Begin to understand percentage as the number of parts in every 100.
Lesson 5		● Continue to derive quickly division facts corresponding to tables up to 10 × 10.	● Begin to find simple percentages of small whole-number quantities (eg 25% of £8).

Lessons   overview

Preparation

For Lesson 1: write on one side of the board random multiples of 6, 7, 8, 9 and 10, and on the other side a colour key such as red = 6×, blue = 7×, black = 8×, green = 9×. For Lesson 2: write on the board random multiples of 50 up to 1000.

Learning objectives

Starter
● Recognise multiples of 6, 7, 8, 9, up to the 10th multiple.
● Derive quickly all pairs of multiples of 50 with a total of 1000 (eg 350 + 650).

Main teaching activities
● Use fraction notation, including mixed numbers and the vocabulary numerator and denominator.
● Change an improper fraction to a mixed number (eg change 13/10 to 1 3/10).
● Use decimal notation for tenths and hundredths.

Vocabulary

fraction, divide, part, equal parts, half, quarter, third, fifth, sixth, eighth, tenth, hundredth, numerator, denominator, equivalent, proper/improper fraction, mixed number

You will need

Photocopiable pages
'Bits and pieces', see page 30, one for each child.

CD pages
'Number fan cards 0–9', one for each child (see General resources). 'Bits and pieces', less able and more able versions (see Autumn term, Unit 4).

Equipment
Three or four paper circles to represent cakes (or use real cakes); Multilink cubes; counters; Blu-Tack; calculators; a long strip of card; a marker pen.

Lesson ①

Starter
Show the children the jumble of multiples of 6, 7, 8, 9 and 10 and the colour key you have written on the board. Ask them to sort the multiples into the correct times tables by telling you which colour to circle each multiple in. Ask them why some numbers have more than one colour circling them.

Main teaching activities
Whole class: Display a small cake or cake shape and cut it in half. Hold up one half and ask the children how much of the cake you have in your hand. Explain that one half is written as 1/2 because it is one piece out of a possible two. Repeat this process with another cake, using the same language, for 1/4, 1/3 and 1/6. Write up the fraction ½; explain that the top number is called the **numerator** (the number of pieces you have) and the bottom number is called the **denominator** (the total number of pieces there are). Hold up 2/3, 3/4, 5/6 and so on, repeating the same language.

Ask what fraction has a numerator of 3 and a denominator of 5. Now ask how much you would be holding if you had 5/4. Show this using the 'cake'. Explain that this is called an **improper fraction**, because it is more than a whole. Demonstrate wholes such as 2/2 and 4/4. 5/4 is one whole cake and one quarter, so it can be written as 1 1/4 . This is called a **mixed number**, since it combines a whole number and a fraction.

Individual work: Create a worksheet of shapes divided into fraction pieces. Explain that the children need to write, shade or draw fractions, including improper fractions.

Differentiation
Less able: Create a worksheet of shapes for children to colour simple fractions up to one whole.
More able: This worksheet should provide the opportunity to match equivalent shape and number fractions.

Plenary & assessment
Hold up 2/4 and 1/2 of a 'cake'. Ask what the children notice. (They are equivalent.) Ask them which fraction they would prefer. Now ask: *Would you rather have 1/2 or 1/3? 1/10 or 1/5? What helps you decide? If I cut one cake into 10 pieces, what fraction would each piece be? If I cut it into 5 pieces, what fraction would each piece be? How do you know which fraction is bigger?* Invite the observation that the bigger the denominator, the smaller the fraction (if the numerator is the same). *If I divided this cake up so that everybody can have a piece, what fraction would each person get?* Share the 'cakes'.

Lesson ②

Starter
Point to one of the multiples of 50 on the board. Ask the children to show you, using their number fans, the number that would make 1000 when added to it. They can work in pairs to display the numbers, showing one digit each.

Main teaching activities
Whole class: Revise how many fractions there are in a whole: 2/2, 3/3 and so on. Discuss how 6/5 must be more than a whole. Demonstrate this using Multilink cubes. Make a tower of 5 red cubes and say this is a whole chocolate bar. Now make a tower of 6 red cubes, compare it to the original and record it as '6/5 or 1 1/5'.

Write '11/10' on the board. Count out 11 counters and stick them to the board with Blu-Tack. Explain that each counter is 1/10 of a packet of sweets, so we must have more than one whole packet. Draw a circle around 10 counters, then write '1 1/10'. Ask the children to enter 11 ÷ 10 into a calculator. The display will show 1.1. Explain that the first decimal place represents tenths, so the calculator shows that 11/10 is greater than 1 whole.

Now write '15/6'. Use the counters to illustrate that this improper fraction contains 2 wholes or lots of 6/6. Demonstrate that this can be calculated by dividing the numerator by the denominator: 15 ÷ 6 = 2.5 = 2 1/2. Repeat using 13/4.

Individual work: Distribute copies of the 'Bits and pieces' activity sheet. Explain that this sheet gives practice in changing improper fractions to mixed numbers and vice versa.

Differentiation

Less able: Use the version of 'Bits and pieces' that provides diagrams for the children to shade before they write the answers.

More able: Use the version with larger numerators to provide multiple whole numbers and more challenging calculations.

Plenary & assessment

Ask the children to convert 3 ¾ to an improper fraction. (15/4) Ask: *How did you do that? What about 5 2/3? What do you have to multiply? What must you remember to add? Can anyone come and write a rule saying how to do this, so we can display the rule to remind us what to do?* (Provide the card strip and marker pen for this.) Ask: *Which is bigger, 10/3 or 12/4?* (10/3 = 3 1/3 and 12/4 = 3.) *Can you explain how you worked it out? Can you convert 82/10 to a mixed number? Can anyone draw this on the board as cakes?*

Lessons   overview

Preparation
Make up the set of cards from the General resources (see 'CD pages'). Make an A3 copy or OHT of 'Blank multiplication grid'.

Learning objectives
Starter
Continue to derive quickly:
- all two-digit pairs that total 100 (eg 43 + 57).
- doubles of whole numbers 1 to 100 (eg 78 × 2) and the corresponding halves.
- division facts corresponding to tables up to 10 × 10.

Main teaching activities
- Recognise when two simple fractions are equivalent, including relating hundredths to tenths (eg 70/100 = 7/10).
- **Use decimal notation for tenths and hundredths.**
- Know what each digit represents in numbers with up to two decimal places.
- Begin to understand percentage as the number of parts in every 100.
- Begin to find simple percentages of small whole-number quantities (eg 25% of £8).

Vocabulary
Percentage, per cent, %, in every, equivalent, decimal, decimal point, decimal place.

You will need
Photocopiable pages
'Percentages to find', see page 32, one for each child.

CD pages
'Number fan cards 0–9', one for each child; '0–9 digit cards', 'Number cards 10–90', 'Fractions, decimals and percentages' cards, one for each pair; 'Blank multiplication grid', copied to A3 or OHT, for teacher's/LSA's reference (see General resources). 'Percentages to find', less able and more able versions (see Autumn term, Unit 4).

Equipment
Multilink cubes and/or counters; calculators.

Lesson

Starter
Using number cards, hold up a two-digit number such as 22, 34 or 53. Ask the children to use their number fans to show you the number that would add to your number to total 100.

Main teaching activities

Whole class: Talk about the word *equivalent*, meaning the 'same value as'. Give an example, such as 2/4 and 1/2. Demonstrate this using Multilink cubes or drawing a circle on the board and dividing it. Look at 70/100. Explain that this number could be simplified by dividing both the numerator and the denominator by 10 to make them smaller. The total amount stays the same. So 70/100 is equivalent to 7/10. Use the blank 100 square to demonstrate: colour in 70 squares, then overshade 7 lots of 10. You use the same number of squares. Write '30/100' and '90/100' on the board and invite simplification to equivalent fractions (3/10 and 9/10).

Now explain that we can sometimes find a decimal equivalent to a fraction, because decimal numbers show 10ths and 100ths. Ask the children to put 70 ÷100 into the calculator and say what the answer (0.7) means. Now ask them to put in 7 ÷ 10. The answer is the same, showing that 70/1000 and 7/10 are equivalent. Repeat this with 3/10 and 30/100. Explain that in a decimal everything has to be written as tenths or hundredths, though fractions can have any numbers. Ask the children to put 1 ÷ 2 into the calculator. The answer is 0.5. Can they explain why? Use the calculator to show that 1/2 = 2/4 = 3/6 = 4/8 = 5/10 = 0.5.

Paired work: Give a set of fractions and decimals cards to each pair. Ask the children to look at each fraction, use the calculator to discover the equivalent decimal, then arrange their cards in pairs on the table.

Differentiation

Less able: Ask the children to match up only the 'tenths' fractions and decimals.
More able: Ask the children to generate further fractions and their decimal equivalents, for example 3/4, 4/5, 2/5, 7/8…

Plenary & assessment

Compare the children's sets of paired cards. Ask each pair of children to hold up the fraction and decimal cards representing one half. Say: *We know ½ = 0.5 and ¼ = 0.25. What do you think ¾ is? How can we work it out? How many lots of 0.25 do we need?* Count together in 0.25s: 0.25, 0.50, 0.75… *What comes next? What fraction is 1 equivalent to?* Play 'Fraction Snap': call out a fraction or decimal and the children hold up the equivalent card. Alternatively, split the class into two teams: one team holds up fraction cards, the other team holds up decimal cards. Call out fractions and decimals alternately.

Lesson 4

Starter

Hold up a digit card. Go round the room, asking each child to double the number until 100 is passed. Give that table a point. Hold up the next digit card and continue. The first table/group to score five points is the winner.

Main teaching activities

Whole class: Revise tenths and hundredths, asking for equivalent decimals: 1/10 = 0.1; 2/10 = 0.2… Introduce the concept of percentages as parts of 100. Use the blank hundred square to shade in 10 squares (= 10% or 10 out of 100). Show that 35 out of 100 = 35%. Show how percentages are linked to fractions and decimals: 1/10 = 0.1 = 10/100 = 10%. Use fractions, decimals and percentages cards to start a class table of equivalents on the board:

Fraction	Decimal	out of 100	Percentage
1/10	0.1	10/100	10%

Paired work: Ask the children to work through a set of fractions cards, finding the equivalent decimals with a calculator, then write the percentages.

Differentiation

Less able: The children could work only with tenths.

More able: The children could include 1/4, 1/5, 1/8, 3/4 and so on.

Plenary & assessment

Ask: *How would you obtain 1/10 of a cake?* (Cut it into 10 pieces.) *What would 1/10 be equivalent to? How would you find 10% of a cake? What about 50% of a cake, or 25% of a bag of sweets?* Repeat the 'Pairs' game from yesterday, with one team holding up the fraction card and the other team holding up the percentage card as you call out each decimal.

Lesson  5

Starter

Ask the children to spot the link between the number fact 35 ÷ 5 = 7 and the question *What is 1/5 of 35?* They should be able to see that a fraction of a number can be found by using division. Ask some division fraction questions, such as *What is 1/2 of 18?… 1/3 of 90… 1/4 of 36… 1/7 of 42?* Discuss how fractions are linked to dividing up a number or a shape.

Hold up a digit card. Go round the room, asking each child to double the number until 100 is passed. Give that table a point. Hold up the next digit card and continue. The first table/group to score five points is the winner.

Main teaching activities

Whole class: Explain that finding a percentage of a number is also linked to division, and it can be helpful to remember the equivalent fraction. Demonstrate by saying: *What is 100% of 50? What is 10% of 50? Remember that from our table yesterday, 10% is equivalent to 1/10. To find 1/10 of a number we divide by 10. So to find 10% of a number we divide by 10. So 10% of 50 =5. From this, I can find 20% (twice as much). What is 20% of 50?* Now ask whether anyone can remember the equivalent fraction for 50%. This can help us to find 50% of a number. *How can this help us find 25%?* (25% = ¼, so we can divide by 4.)

Explain that any percentage can be found by using fractions. 75% of 36 can be found by adding 50% (18) and 25% (9) to get 27. We can find harder percentages: 13% of 30 can be made up by finding 10% (3) and 3 lots of 1% (0.3 × 3) and adding them to get 3.9.

Individual work: Ask the children to complete the 'Percentages to find' activity sheet, using the equivalents table from Lesson 4. Remind them to record which fraction they used each time, and show how they calculated the answers.

Differentiation

Less able: Provide the version of the sheet that involves finding only 10% and 50%.

More able: Provide the version that involves finding percentages such as 13% by calculating them in parts.

Plenary & assessment

Ask questions that link fractions and percentages, such as: *Which is greater, 50% of 60 or half of 60? Which would you prefer, 25% of £10 or 1/5 of £10? Why?* (Because 25% is equivalent to 1/4, which is bigger than 1/5.) Ask the children to think of a comparison question that uses equivalents they have learned. Split the class into two teams to challenge each other. Keep the score, and ask the children to explain their reasoning.

Name	Date

Bits and pieces

1. Change these improper fractions to mixed numbers – that is, whole numbers and fractions.

$\frac{3}{2}$	$\frac{5}{3}$	$\frac{6}{4}$

$\frac{7}{5}$	$\frac{8}{7}$	$\frac{6}{5}$

$\frac{9}{4}$	$\frac{6}{3}$	$\frac{7}{3}$

2. Now change these mixed numbers to improper fractions.

$1\frac{1}{2}$	$1\frac{1}{3}$	$1\frac{2}{3}$

$1\frac{2}{5}$	$1\frac{3}{4}$	$2\frac{1}{4}$

$2\frac{3}{4}$	$2\frac{4}{5}$	$2\frac{2}{6}$

3. Write four equivalent improper fractions and mixed numbers of your own.

Name	Date

Percentages to find

There's an easy way to find percentages! Just find an equivalent fraction. Divide the number by the denominator and, if necessary multiply by the numerator. For example, 50% $= \frac{1}{2}$, so to find 50% of 10 you divide 10 by 2.

You can find 25% ($\frac{1}{4}$), 10% ($\frac{1}{10}$) and 1% ($\frac{1}{100}$) in the same way. You can find most percentages by using division facts!

Find the following percentages. Work it out as shown in the first example. Remember to show which fraction you used.

1. 50% of 18 $= \frac{1}{2}$ of 18 = 18 ÷ 2 = 9

2. 50% of 32 = _____

3. 10% of 60 = _____

4. 10% of 90 = _____

4. 20% of 90 = _____

5. 25% of 32 = _____

5. 25% of 48 = _____

6. 1% of 200 = _____

7. 1% of 50 = _____

8. 20% of 25 = _____

9. 2% of 300 = _____

10. 60% of 30 = _____

Fractions, ratio and proportion

This unit uses 'real life' contexts for understanding problems of ratio and proportion.

LEARNING OBJECTIVES

		Topics	Starter	Main teaching activity
Lesson	1	Fractions, ratio and proportion	● Continue to derive quickly division facts corresponding to tables up to 10×10.	● Change an improper fraction to a mixed number (eg change 13/10 to 1 3/10).
Lesson	2		As for Lesson 1.	● Solve simple problems using ideas of ratio and proportion ('one for every…' and 'one in every…').
Lesson	3		As for Lesson 1.	As for Lesson 2.
Lesson	4		As for Lesson 1.	As for Lesson 2.
Lesson	5		As for Lesson 1.	As for Lesson 2.

Lesson ① overview

Preparation
Make a class set of 'Fraction questions and answer cards' (see General resources). Draw a number line 0–3 on the board, as shown below:

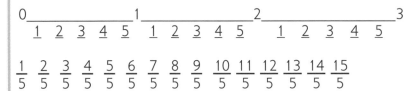

Learning objectives
Starter
● Continue to derive quickly division facts corresponding to tables up to 10×10.
Main teaching activities
● Change an improper fraction to a mixed number (eg change 13/10 to 1 3/10).

Vocabulary
mixed number, improper fraction, equivalent, denominator, numerator

You will need
Photocopiable pages
'Improper fractions and mixed numbers', see page 37, one for each child.

CD pages
'Fractions question and answer cards', one for each child (see General resources). 'Improper fractions and mixed numbers', more able version (see Autumn term, Unit 5).

Equipment
Multilink cubes in different colours; circles of paper for folding; rough paper and pencils or whiteboards and pens for jotting.

Lesson ①

Starter

Split the class in half. Distribute the fraction questions to one group and the answers to the other. The groups take turns to read out a question, the child with the answer responds and the pair are matched. Either pair up the children or stick the pairs of cards up on the board.

Main teaching activities

Whole class: Ask the children to identify some simple fractions, using folded paper circles and cubes: *2 cubes are green and 3 are blue. What fraction is blue?* (3/5). Then show them shapes or cube towers that are all one colour: *6 cubes are blue. What fraction is that?* (6 or 1 whole.) Now hold up 7/6 using your circles. Ask: *How many sixths is that?* Write it on the board and explain that this is called an improper fraction. *How else could we say this fraction?* (1 whole and 1/6.) Repeat using 5/3 and 13/5.

Indicate the prepared number line. Show that it is divided into fifths. Count the fifths out loud together: *one fifth, two fifths… 1 whole or five fifths.* Demonstrate that we can then count on in fifths (*six fifths, seven fifths…*) or in whole numbers and fifths (*one and one fifth, one and two fifths…*). Use the number line to find more equivalent fractions, such as: *What is the same as 7/5?* (2 and 2/5.)

Individual work: Distribute copies of the 'Improper fractions and mixed numbers' activity sheet . Explain that it presents shapes and number lines for the children to identify as improper fractions and mixed numbers. (For an ICT link, look at the similar examples on www.visualfractions.com.)

Differentiation

Less able: The children could use Multilink to model the number lines shown on the activity sheet.
More able: The children could complete the version of the activity sheet that involves converting written improper fractions to mixed numbers and vice versa, and suggesting a rule for the conversion. (For example: 33/5 = 33 ÷ 5 = 6 3/5.)

Plenary & assessment

Ask the children to convert some improper fractions (such as 15/6) to mixed numbers (2 3/6). Ask: *Do you notice anything about that fraction?* Remind them that sometimes fractions can be further simplified because they are equivalent: *3/6 =1/2, so 15/6 = 2 1/2.*

Divide the class into groups of 4–6 and play 'Speedy equivalents'. Give each group a whiteboard and pen or paper and pencil. You call out a mixed number, such as 2 and 4/8, and ask the groups to write down as many equivalent fractions as they can in 2 minutes. Compare their answers, which may include 2 1/2 , 20/8, 10/4, 15/6, 2 3/6 and so on. Ask children to explain how they decided on some of the more unusual fractions. Repeat with 1 3/4.

Lessons overview

Preparation
For Lesson 2, make up four or five Multilink sticks in different ratios, such as two blue to three red and one green to four pink. For Lesson 4, write some fraction word problems (see lesson plan) on the board or OHT.

Learning objectives
Starter
● Continue to derive quickly division facts corresponding to tables up to 10 × 10.
Main teaching activities
● Solve simple problems using ideas of ratio and proportion ('one for every…' and 'one in every…').

Vocabulary
ratio, proportion, part, in every, for every (Also see the vocabulary list for Lesson 1.)

You will need
Photocopiable pages
'Ratio and proportion problems', see page 38, one for each child.

CD pages
'Number fan cards 0–9', one for each child, and '0–9 digit cards', one for each child (see General resources). 'Ratio and proportion problems', less able and more able versions (see Autumn term, Unit 5).

Equipment
Multilink cubes; rough paper and pencils or individual whiteboards and pens; a 6-sided or a 10-sided dice for each pair of children.

Lesson

Starter
Ask some simple fraction questions, such as 1/3 of 30; ¼ of 24… Then ask: If we know 1/3 of 30 is 10, what is 2/3 of 30? How did you work it out? (2 lots of 1/3.) Ask some similar questions: 1/5 of 25, 2/5 of 25; 1/3 of 27, 2/3 of 27; ¼ of 24, ¾ of 24.

Main teaching activities
Whole class: Introduce the word 'ratio' as meaning 'one for every…'. Say: *If I have 1 blue cube for every 3 red ones, then the ratio is 1:3. That means 1 blue for every 3 red.* Display a suitable Multilink stick. *What fraction of this stick is blue?….red?* (1/4, ¾) Explain that a fraction expressed in this way is called a 'proportion'. Demonstrate several examples with Multilink to help the children see the relationship between ratio and proportion. Encourage them to use cubes to produce the ratios visually. Ask them to consider a ratio of 2 blue cubes for every 4 red ones. *What is the proportion of blue cubes?* (2/6) Remind the children what they already know about simplifying fractions: 2/6 could also be expressed as 1/3.

Paired work: Ask the children to look at the Multilink patterns that you have prepared (see 'Preparation') and to identify the ratio and then the proportion of each colour. It may help them to draw and colour each pattern on squared paper, then record the ratio and proportions.

Differentiation
Less able: The children will probably need adult support. They could use cubes to build the examples for themselves.
More able: The children could go on to create examples of their own and record the ratios and proportions.

Plenary & assessment
Discuss the results of the paired work to assess the children's level of success. Play 'Human ratios' to consolidate the ideas of ratio and proportion. Ask 4 boys and 3 girls (or 4 children with brown hair and 3 with fair hair) to stand up. Ask: *What is the ratio? What is the proportion of boys?* Add 4 more boys and 3 more girls, then repeat the questions. Add 1 more boy and girl, 2 more and so on. Keep asking about the ratio and the proportions, and simplify the fractions as appropriate. You could have a 'scribe' to keep a record of the ratios and proportions you have created.

Lesson ③

Play 'What is the question?' Arrange the children into teams of 4 or 5. Hold up a single-digit card and ask the children to suggest a fraction question with this answer. Give one point (a counter or Multilink cube) for a simple fraction and two points for a multiple fraction. For example, the answer 6 could match the question 'What is 1/5 of 30?' (1 point) or 'What is 2/3 of 9?' (2 points).

Main teaching activities

Whole class: Explain that just as fractions have equivalents, so do ratios. Distribute paper and pencils or individual whiteboards and pens. Show a stick of 2 yellow and 3 green cubes. Explain that these represent a packet of 5 sweets. The manufacturer always produces sweets in this ratio. Ask the children to draw this packet. Now say that the manufacturer has decided to bring out a bumper packet, double the size. Ask: *How many yellow and green sweets are in each packet? Draw what you think and show me.* (4 yellow and 6 green.) *How many would be in a giant packet that had 10 yellow sweets?* (15) Show how the answers can be multiplied up, as with fractions.

Individual work: Draw some sweet bags and give the total number of sweets and the ratio of colours for the children to identify by drawing and shading the correct number in each packet.

Differentiation

Less able: The children can use Multilink cubes to build the ratios before recording on the sheet.
More able: Ask the children to draw three sizes of bags of sweets, using the same ratio of colour that provides an opportunity to explore equivalent ratios.

Plenary & assessment

Set a problem: *There are 30 children in a class. There is a ratio of 2:1 girls to boys. How many girls and how many boys are there?* (20 girls, 10 boys.) *What strategies did we use to solve this?* (Working out that 1/3 of the class are boys and 1/3 of 30 is 10.) *As well as the ratio, what other information did we need?* (The number of children in the class.)

Play 'Human Ratios' again. This time, have a group of 12 children: 6 boys and 6 girls. Ask the rest of the class to suggest ratios and proportions that they could make from this group, and all the different ways that they could represent these (using 2, 4, 6, 8, 10 or all of the children). Repeat this using different numbers.

Lesson ④

Ask fraction word problems: **1.** There are 33 children in a class. 1/3 of them have brown hair. What fraction do not have brown hair? How many children is that? **2.** There are 40 children at a youth club. 1/4 wear sweatshirts, the rest wear T- shirts. How many children wear T-shirts? **3.** There are 55 people at a meeting. 2/5 of them have lace-up shoes. How many do not? **4.** Out of the 108 children in a cross-country race, 1/9 finish in less than 20 minutes. How many children took longer than that? Discuss the strategy of finding a simple fraction and then multiplying by the numerator to find a multiple fraction such as 2/3 or 3/4. Talk about alternative strategies, such as finding 1/9 and subtracting it from the total to find 8/9.

Main teaching activities

Whole class: Say that you are going to discuss problems using ratio and proportion. Say: *In a tea shop, there are seven cakes or biscuits on each plate. They are in a ratio of 3:4 biscuits to cakes.* Draw the plate to demonstrate this. Ask: *What is the fraction or proportion of cakes?* (3/7) Now show how the

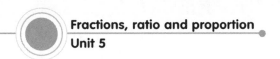

calculation can be reversed: *In another teashop, the proportion of cakes on each plate is 5/7. What is the ratio of cakes to biscuits?* Ask for a volunteer to draw them. Repeat using different proportions and ratios, such as: 3:4; 4:6; 3/8; 5/9.

Paired work: The children work in pairs with a 10-sided dice to generate more ratios of biscuits to cakes, draw them and write the proportion of cakes on each plate.

Differentiation

Less able: The children can use a 6-sided dice to generate ratios and draw them.
More able: The children can use a 10-sided dice to generate proportions of cakes, putting the smaller number as the numerator and the larger number as the denominator. They can then work out the ratio of cakes to biscuits in each case (for example, 2/9 → 2 out of 9 items are cakes → the ratio is 2:7 cakes to biscuits.

Plenary & assessment

Say: *I have 15 cakes. 2/3 of them are iced buns, the rest are gingerbread men. What is the ratio of gingerbread men to iced buns?* (5:10 or 1:2.) Remind the children that some ratios can be simplified.
    Play 'Human Ratios', using groups of 6 or 8 children (mixed boys and girls). Say a ratio that needs simplifying, such as 4:6, 5:10 or 15:3, and ask the children in each group to arrange themselves into the simplest form of that ratio. (Some children may sit down, leaving the required number standing.) Each time, ask one of the groups to explain how they simplified the ratio and another to name the proportion of girls (or boys).

Lesson

Starter

Ask quick-fire percentage questions, such as: *10% of 30; 20% of 60; 15% of 40; 25% of 24; 50% of 32; 11% of 120. The children use their number fans to show the answers.*

Main teaching activities

Whole class: Continue the discussion of ratio and proportion problems. Say: *I have 20 cakes on a plate and 1/5 of them are chocolate. The rest are plain. How many cakes are plain?* (1/5 of 20 = 4, 20 – 4 = 16) *What is the ratio of chocolate to plain cakes?* (4:16 = 1:4) *If I have 30 cakes in a ratio of 1:4 chocolate to plain, how many of each do I have?* (1/5 are chocolate, which is 30 ÷ 5 = 6 cakes, so there are 30 – 6 = 24 plain cakes.)
Individual work: Ask the children to complete the 'Ratio and proportion problems' activity sheet.

Differentiation

Less able: The children could use the version of the activity sheet that suggests using cubes to support making ratios.
More able: The children could work on the version with more challenging calculations. They could create further ratio questions to challenge a friend.

Plenary & assessment

Ask the children to give you a definition of ratio ('one for every…') and proportion ('one in every...'), and to tell you how they are linked (add the ratio numbers together to find the denominator of the proportion fraction, and each ratio number can be the numerator). For example, 3:4 → 3 biscuits for every 4 cakes → proportions of 3/7 biscuits and 4/7 cakes. Ask: *If I have a bag of sweets with a ratio of 3:2 toffees to fruit gums and nothing else, how many sweets might there be in the bag?* (Any multiple of 5.) Ask for a volunteer to demonstrate some possibilities on the board by drawing the sweets. Repeat this question with different ratios, such as 6:7, 4:3 and 3:8.

Name	Date

Improper fractions and mixed numbers

1. Write the fraction shown in the circles as an improper fraction and a mixed number.

_____

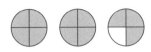

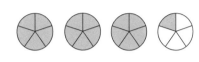

_____

_____

2. Look at the number lines below. Write the improper fraction and the mixed number shown by each letter.

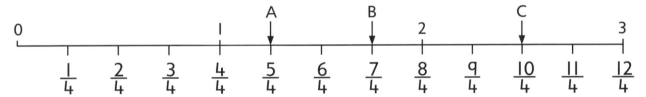

A = _____   B = _____   C = _____

D = _____   E = _____   F = _____

G = _____   H = _____   I = _____

Name	Date

Ratio and proportion problems

1. To make a profit, a tea shop needs to provide more plain biscuits than chocolate ones. They experiment with various ratios.

For each ratio of chocolate to plain biscuits, draw the biscuits and write the proportion of chocolate biscuits.

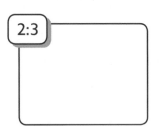 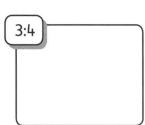 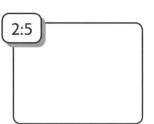 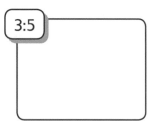

Proportion of biscuits that are chocolate:

2. Different shades of green are mixed at the paint shop. The higher the ratio of yellow to blue, the paler the shade is.

Look at these ratios of yellow to blue. For each one, work out the proportions. Write the ratios in order from the palest shade to the darkest. Are any the same?

Ratio yellow: blue	2:3	1:4	2:5	3:5	1:2
Proportions: yellow					
Proportions: blue					

Ratios in order:					

3. To make purple paint, red and blue paint are mixed in the ratio of 3 tins of red to 4 tins of blue.

> 3 red + 4 blue = 7 tins of purple paint

How many tins of each colour do I need to make 14 tins of purple paint?

_____ red + _____ blue

I decide to change the proportion of red paint to $\frac{2}{5}$. I need 25 tins of purple paint in this new shade. What is the ratio of red to blue? _____

How many tins of red and blue do I need? _____ red + _____ blue

Autumn Term
Unit 6
Handling data

A variety of charts and graphs are used in this unit to help children to understand that data is represented pictorially in order to show comparisons or to show a large amount of information on one image. Scales have been chosen to give experience of reading between two numbers. Children learn that different types of graphs have different functions.

LEARNING OBJECTIVES

	Topics	Starter	Main teaching activity
Lesson 1	Handling data	● Continue to derive quickly doubles of all whole numbers 1 to 100 (eg 78 × 2).	● Solve a problem by representing and interpreting data: in bar line charts, vertical axis labelled in 2s, 5s, 10s, 20s or 100s, where intermediate points have no meaning (eg scores on a dice rolled 50 times).
Lesson 2	Handling data Using a calculator	● Recall addition and subtraction facts for each number up to 20.	● Solve a problem by representing and interpreting data: in bar line charts, vertical axis labelled in 2s, 5s, 10s, 20s or 100s, first where intermediate points have no meaning (eg scores on a dice rolled 50 times). ● Find the mode of a set of data. ● Develop calculator skills and use a calculator effectively.
Lesson 3	Handling data	● **Know by heart all multiplication facts up to 10 × 10.** ● Continue to derive quickly division facts corresponding to tables up to 10 × 10.	● Solve a problem by representing and interpreting data: in bar line charts, vertical axis labelled in 2s, 5s, 10s, 20s or 100s, first where intermediate points have no meaning (eg scores on a dice rolled 50 times).
Lesson 4	Handling data	● Recognise and extend number sequences formed by counting from any number in steps of constant size, extending beyond zero when counting back. For example: count on in steps of 25 to 1000, and then back.	● Solve a problem by representing and interpreting data: in bar line charts, vertical axis labelled in 2s, 5s, 10s, 20s or 100s, first where intermediate points have no meaning (eg scores on a dice rolled 50 times). ● Discuss the chance or likelihood of particular events.

Lessons   overview

Preparation
Draw a blank tally chart for the numbers 1–21 on the board.

Learning objectives

Starter
- Continue to derive quickly doubles of all whole numbers 1 to 100 (eg 78 × 2).
- Recall addition and subtraction facts for each number up to 20.
- **Know by heart all multiplication facts up to 10 × 10.**
- Continue to derive quickly division facts corresponding to tables up to 10 × 10.
- Recognise and extend number sequences formed by counting from any number in steps of constant size, extending beyond zero when counting back. For example: count on in steps of 25 to 1000, and then back.
- Recognise multiples of 6, 7, 8, 9 up to the 10th multiple.

Main teaching activities
- Solve a problem by representing and interpreting data on a bar line chart where the vertical axis is labelled in 2s, 5s, 10s, 20s or 100s, where the intermediate points have no meaning (eg scores on a dice rolled 50 times).
- Find the mode of a set of data..
- Discuss the chance or likelihood of particular events.
- Develop calculator skills and use a calculator effectively.

Vocabulary
data, table, chart, graph, represent, bar chart, bar line chart, tally chart, axis, axes, label, title, mode, range

You will need

Photocopiable pages
'Doubles in a minute', see page 46, one for each child, and 'Lazy Larry's ice cream', see page 47, one for each child.

CD pages
'Number fan cards 0–9', one for each child and 'Number cards 1–20', for teacher's/LSA's use (see General resources). 'Doubles in a minute' less able version and 'Lazy Larry's ice cream', less able and more able versions (see Autumn term, Unit 6).

Equipment
Paper and pens; calculators; two dice for each pair of children; a spreadsheet program such as *Excel* or *Numberbox* (Black Cat Software).

Lesson

Starter

Distribute the 'Doubles in a minute' activity sheet. Look at the set of numbers in Part A. Ask the children to double as many of these as they can in one minute. Say that if one number is more difficult than others, they should miss it out. Afterwards, go through some of the answers, asking the children to explain their strategies. (Recall, partitioning and so on.) Ask which numbers were more difficult and why. (Numbers that bridge a 10.)

Main teaching activities

Whole class: Explain that you want to know how many numbers most of the children can double in one minute. To find this out, the children are going to represent their results as a bar line chart. Emphasise that drawing a chart helps other people to interpret your data.

Revise the use of a tally chart. On the blank chart on the board, fill in the possible scores from zero to the highest number of correct doubles. By a show of hands, fill in the tally chart. For example, part of the chart might show:

Score	0	1	2	3	4	5	6	7
Tally	0	I	II	I	IIII	III	IIII	IIII

Say that a tally chart is quite helpful for examining data, but a graph gives a clearer visual impression of the data. Show the children the blank axes on Part B of the 'Doubles in a minute' sheet. Agree on what the axes represent and label them together. (The x-axis is 'Number of correct doubles', the y-axis is 'Number of children'.) Emphasise that a graph without labels has no meaning. Give the graph a title, such as: 'A graph to show the scores of Year 5's doubles in a minute competition'. Suggest that the y-axis should be labelled in 2s, with 2 people for every square and the number of scores filled in along the bottom (from 0 to the highest score). Ask: *What happens when we want to record 3 people?* (The level on the y-axis will be halfway between 2 and 4.)

Decide whether all your class are capable of coping with a bar line chart (each value shown by a vertical line ending with a cross), or whether some of them would be more comfortable using solid bars. **Individual work:** Ask the children to complete the graph, using the tally chart data.

Differentiation

Less able: The children can use the version of 'Doubles in a minute' with easier numbers to double. They can draw a bar chart with support (especially to check that they are representing odd-numbered values correctly as coming halfway up a square on the y-axis).

More able: When the children have completed their chart, ask them what the graph would have looked like if they had used 5 squares per person or one square per person. *Why is getting the scale right important? Would we have used 2 people per square if we had collected this data from the whole school? Why? What would have been a better scale?* (Too much space for each unit means the chart will not fit on the page, too little space means the difference in the bar lines is too difficult to see.)

Plenary & assessment

Look at and compare the children's graphs. Are they consistent? Begin to use the graphs to extract information by asking, for example: *Which score did the most people get? Did a greater number of people score more or less than 7?How many people scored above 10? What can we say about Year 5's doubling ability? Is there a trend? Did more people score above 10 than scored below 10?* Now ask: *Why are graphs used to represent and compare data? Where might you see graphs? Are they all the same kind as ours?*

Lesson

Starter

Give a number card from 1–20 to each group or table, with a large sheet of paper and pens. The children must write down at least five addition and subtraction number sentences with that answer, in the form of a starburst or cloud with the number in the middle and the number sentences around it. The children then hold up their results for others to check.

Main teaching activities

Whole class: Build on the plenary session from Lesson 1. Explain that a graph or chart provides information visually and so makes it easy to extract. Introduce the concept of the **mode** or most popular result: the tallest bar or bar line. Encourage the children to investigate questions such as: 'Did more people score higher than the mode or lower?' They can use the calculator to check, adding all of the bars above the mode score and all of those below. They can also calculate the range: the difference between the highest and lowest scores.

Individual work: Ask the children to write six questions to elicit information from the chart, then swap questions with a partner and answer them.

Differentiation

Less able: The children can concentrate on reading off straightforward facts such as '8 people scored 5 doubles'.

More able: The children should be able to make comparisons and create questions that require a calculation, such as: *How many more people scored more than the mode? How many people scored more than 6 but less than 15?*

Plenary & assessment

Ask some children to read out one of their questions; the other children can try to answer them by interpreting their graph. Discuss the importance of carefully drawn, accurate graphs. Emphasise the importance of adding labels and a title. Ask questions to assess the children's level of understanding: *What is the x-axis showing? What about the y-axis? Why would this graph be unhelpful if it did not have titles and labels? Pretend that the titles and labels are missing – what could this graph be about?* (For example, shoe sizes, age, pets.) *What is the range? What is the mode?*

Lesson ③

Starter

Call out multiplication and division facts, using a range of vocabulary: *7 × 3… six lots of 4… How many lots of 7 are there in 14?… What is 10 times smaller than 90?… ¼ of 24…* Ask the children to show you the answer using their number fans when you say *Show me*.

Main teaching activities

Whole class: Explain that the scale used on the Y-axis of a graph is very important. Firstly, it has to fit on the page. Secondly, because graphs and charts present information visually, changing the scale can produce graphs that look very different, and this can be misleading.

Distribute the 'Lazy Larry's Ice Cream' activity sheet. Explain that the chart of figures shows the number of ice creams a van driver has sold over an eight-month period. He is hoping for a bonus, so he wants the graph that he presents to his boss to look as impressive as possible. On the first graph, the Y-axis (representing the number of ice creams sold) is marked in 2s; on the second, it is marked in 20s. Ask the children to put the data onto both graphs in the form of a bar chart or bar line graph.

Individual work: The children complete both graphs from the information given in the chart, then answer the questions.

Differentiation

Less able: Provide the version of the activity sheet with the second graph already drawn; the children can draw the first graph and concentrate on answering the question given.

More able: Provide the version that asks the children more challenging questions about the two graphs.

Plenary & assessment

Discuss the visual impact of each graph, emphasising that both versions display the same data. Ask the children which graph makes the salesman look more hardworking and successful. (Graph 1, because the upward trend of the graph is steeper.) Ask: *How many more ice creams did Larry sell in June than in January? Is this what you would expect? Why? Do you think he may have taken some secret days off during the summer? What excuses might he have for not increasing his sales more during the summer? Do you think his boss will be very impressed? How can you explain the difference between the two graphs?*

Lesson ④

Starter

Ask the children to count out loud together in even steps, from various starting numbers. For example: Count on from 10 in steps of 20 until we reach 150. Count back in twos from 20 to minus 20. Count on and back in fives from 5 to 100. Can you count in fives from 2? Count on in 10s from 1 until we reach 101, then count back.

Main teaching activities

This activity can be done using ICT. The Black Cat Software program *Numberbox* allows the computer to 'throw a dice' randomly as many as 500 or 1000 times, which will increase the accuracy of the conclusions. Any of the graphs in this unit could be drawn with a spreadsheet program such as *Excel*.

Whole class: Explain that the children are going to investigate the probability or likelihood of making one total more often than any other when they throw two dice. Discuss which is likely to produce more accurate results: throwing the dice twice, ten times or 100 times. Create a tally chart together on the board for the children to copy and use for their own recording.

Explain that the children will need to draw a bar line graph to display their results. Discuss what scale might be suitable for the Y-axis (this will depend on how many throws each pair decide to do). Remind the children to give their graph a title and label the axes.

Paired work: The children throw the dice a minimum of 50 times and record the totals on a tally chart. They represent the data in a bar line chart, choosing a suitable Y-axis scale and writing labels and a title. This work will continue in the next lesson.

Differentiation

Less able: The children will need help with drawing the chart axes and choosing a scale. You might like to ask an adult helper to do this for them.

More able: The children should be able to decide independently what scale to use.

Plenary & assessment

Ask the children: *What is the mode of your results?* (It should be 6 or 7.) *Why is this?* (There are more combinations of two dice scores that add up to 6 or 7 than add up to any other number.) *Why is there no bar line for 1?* (Impossible with two dice.) *How could we make this investigation more reliable and accurate? Why would a sample of 500 throws give a more accurate result? What about 5000? Was your investigation fair? How could you standardise your method of throwing the dice* (unless the children used a computer)*? Is this like the way you work in a science investigation?*

Name	Date

Doubles in a minute

PART A

How many of these numbers can you double in one minute?

15	24	12	34	17	22	27
45	50	29	39	46	13	18
26	38	16	25	19	10	37

Tally chart of scores

Score	0	1	2	3	4	5	6	7	8	9	10	11	12	13	14	15	16	17	18	19	20	21
Tally																						

PART B

Using this information, draw a bar line graph to show the scores.

Use one square for every 2 children on the vertical axis (the 'y-axis').

Don't forget to label the axes and give the graph a title.

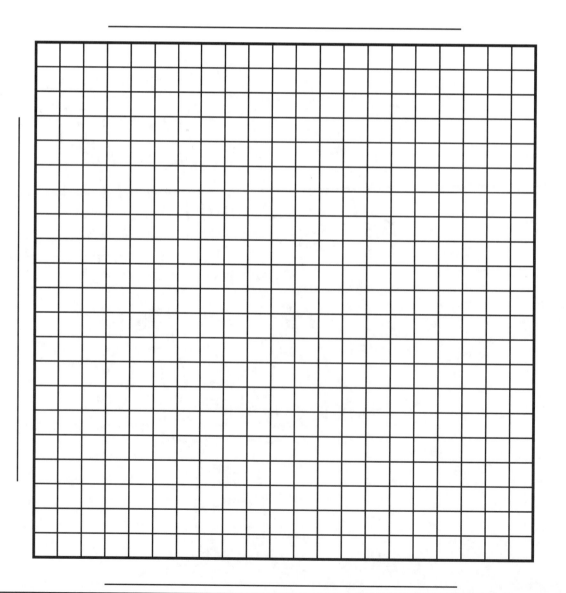

Name

Date

Lazy Larry's ice creams

Larry the ice cream salesman needs to create a graph that will make his sales figures for January to August look good.

Transfer the data from his sales chart onto the two graphs provided below. They have different scales.

Month	Jan	Feb	March	April	May	June	July	Aug
Ice creams sold	162	166	164	170	170	176	174	178

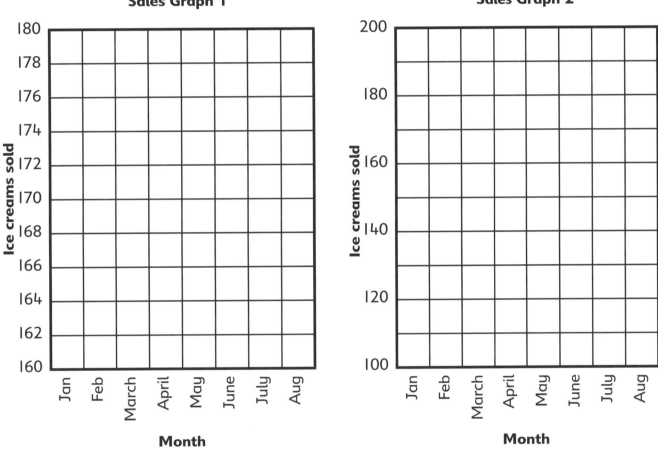

Sales Graph 1

Sales Graph 2

Which graph shows the sales figures in the best light? _____

Reasoning about shapes

This unit provides criteria for sorting and classifying triangles and rectangles according to their properties. This knowledge is then used to plot positions using co ordinates.

LEARNING OBJECTIVES

	Topics	Starter	Main teaching activity
Lesson 1	Shape and space Reasoning and generalising about numbers or shapes	● Recognise and extend number sequences formed by counting from any number in steps of constant size, extending beyond zero when counting back. For example: count on in steps of 25 to 1000, and then back.	● Classify triangles (isosceles, equilateral, scalene) using criteria such as equal sides, equal angles, lines of symmetry. ● Solve mathematical problems or puzzles, recognise and explain patterns and relationships, generalise and predict.
Lesson 2		As for Lesson 1.	As for Lesson 1, plus: ● Explain methods and reasoning, orally and in writing.
Lesson 3	Shape and space	● Round any integer up to 10 000 to the nearest 10, 100 or 1000.	● **Recognise properties of rectangles.**
Lesson 4	Shape and space Reasoning and generalising about numbers or shapes	● Read and write whole numbers in figures and words, and know what each digit represents.	● **Recognise properties of rectangles.** ● Recognise positions and directions: read and plot co-ordinates in the first quadrant. ● Solve mathematical problems or puzzles, recognise and explain patterns and relationships, generalise and predict.
Lesson 5	Shape and space	As for Lesson 4.	As for Lesson 4.

Lessons   overview

Preparation
On the board, draw one each of an equilateral triangle, an isosceles triangle, a scalene triangle and a right-angled triangle. On dotted paper, draw two different triangles. Display some enlarged blank dotted paper on the board or as an OHT.

Learning objectives
Starter
● Recognise and extend number sequences formed by counting from any number in steps of constant size, extending beyond zero when counting back. For example: count on in steps of 25 to 1000, and then back.
Main teaching activities
● Classify triangles (isosceles, equilateral, scalene) using criteria such as equal sides, equal angles, lines of symmetry.
● Solve mathematical problems or puzzles, recognise and explain patterns and relationships, generalise and predict.
● Explain methods and reasoning, orally and in writing.

Vocabulary
equilateral triangle, isosceles triangle, scalene triangle, right-angled, side, symmetrical, angle, acute, obtuse, equal

You will need
Equipment
A selection of different 2-D triangle shapes; dotted paper; adhesive; scissors; rulers; protractors; paper and pencils or individual whiteboards and pens.

Lesson

Starter

Ask the children to count around the room in steps of 25. Each group or table calls out the next number in the sequence until 300 is reached. Ask them to count on from 0, 1 and 2 and count back from 200, 127 and 122 to –100.

Main teaching activities

Whole class: Indicate the four triangles you have drawn on the board. Explain that these are all triangles because they are closed shapes with three straight sides. Tell the children that you want them to think of definitions that will separate these four triangles. They will have to consider the angles (acute, obtuse or right angles), length of sides (equal or not) and lines of symmetry (whether the halves would match exactly if we folded the triangle in half). Ask for observations and record appropriate ones on the board:

Equilateral triangle: 3 sides of equal length; 3 equal angles, always acute; 3 lines of symmetry.
Isosceles triangle: 2 sides of equal length, one of a different length; 2 equal angles (acute) and one different (can be obtuse or acute); one line of symmetry.
Scalene triangle: 3 sides of different lengths; 3 different angles (one may be obtuse), no lines of symmetry.
Right-angled triangle: Can be either isosceles or scalene; one right angle; can have one line of symmetry.

Individual work: Ask the children to copy the definitions they have just created onto a sheet of paper under the headings: 'Equilateral triangle'; 'Isosceles triangle' and 'Scalene triangle'. Then, on a separate piece of paper, they should draw two examples of each triangle. Exchange with a pair and cut out, then measure them carefully with a ruler and a protractor (you may need to revise the use of this) and stick them in the correct column.

Differentiation

Less able: The children may need more support when measuring, and when discussing the criteria.
More able: Ask the children to draw and classify more triangles of their own.

Plenary & assessment

Ask: *Why can't a right-angled triangle also be an equilateral triangle?* (Three equal angles of 90º wouldn't make a triangle.) Ask the children, in groups, to look around the room for right angles and angles that are greater or less than a right angle. They should note these on their whiteboards. Invite feedback. Ask: *What do you notice about the angles in buildings? Which angle did you observe most frequently? Why was that?*

Lesson ②

Starter

Explain that you are going to start counting in a pattern; the children have to spot the pattern and join in together, then stop when you clap your hands Try: *2, 4, 6…; 3, 6, 9…; 90, 80, 70…; 15, 30, 45…; 65, 60, 55…; 2, 1, 0, –1, –2…*

Main teaching activities

Whole class: Explain that you have drawn a triangle on some dotted paper, because it helps you draw accurately. Ask for a volunteer to come and draw the triangle from your description alone. For example: *My triangle has 2 sides that are 4 dots long and one that is 3 dots long. It has a right angle joining the 2 equal sides. Or: My triangle has 3 sides that are 5 dots long. One of the lines runs along the bottom of the page, so that one line of symmetry runs vertically down the page.* Show your original drawings to the class. Has the volunteer drawn the same shapes? Discuss how you might also have to describe which way up the triangle is and which way round it is. Ask the children to think about any differences from the original drawings. Can they explain these differences?

Paired work: Give each child a sheet of dotted paper. One child should draw a triangle and then describe it to their partner, who tries to draw it too; then the two swap roles. Under each triangle drawing, they should write the type of triangle (and how they know it is that type).

Differentiation

Less able: Instead of drawing the triangles, the children could select one of the 2-D triangle shapes and describe it to their partner, who has to find a matching one. They could then record by drawing around the shape and naming it.

More able: The children could describe only the angles, not the lines, and write their observations about the type of triangle created.

Plenary & assessment

Ask for some descriptions of triangles for you to draw. Ask: *Did anyone draw a triangle with an obtuse angle?* Play a triangle recognition game. You hold up or draw a triangle and the children, without speaking, perform an action to show what type of triangle it is. For scalene triangles, hands on heads; for isosceles triangles, fingers on noses; for equilateral triangles, fold their arms; for right-angled triangles, stand up. So for a right-angled isosceles triangle, the children would stand up with their fingers on their noses. Discuss any shapes that the children are getting wrong.

Lessons   overview

Preparation

Draw a 100–1000 number line on the board and mark in division lines for the 1000s. Write the following numbers elsewhere on the board: 84, 203, 256, 745, 350, 618, 491. Make an A3 copy or OHT of 'Drawing quadrilaterals'.

Learning objectives

Starter

● Round any integer up to 10 000 to the nearest 10, 100 or 1000.
● Read and write whole numbers in figures and words, and know what each digit represents.

Main teaching activities

● **Recognise properties of rectangles.**
● Recognise positions and directions: read and plot co-ordinates in the first quadrant.
● Solve mathematical problems or puzzles, recognise and explain patterns and relationships, generalise and predict.

Vocabulary

quadrilateral, rectangle, square, bisect, parallel

You will need

Photocopiable pages

'Drawing quadrilaterals', see page 53, copied to A3 or OHT, and 'Quadrilateral battleships', see page 54, one for each child.

CD pages

'0–9 digit cards', for teacher's/LSA's use (see General resources). 'Drawing quadrilaterals' and 'Quadrilateral battleships', less able and more able versions (see Autumn term, Unit 8).

Equipment

Paper and pencils or individual whiteboards; a selection of 2-D rectangles; coloured pencils.

Lesson ③

Starter

Indicate the number line and list of numbers on the board. Point to one of the numbers and ask the children to round it to the nearest 100. Ask a volunteer to come and write it on the appropriate place on the number line. Repeat with the same number, but rounding to the nearest 10. Repeat with the other numbers.

Main teaching activity

Whole class: Show the children the selection of 2-D rectangle shapes. Ask them to define a rectangle in terms of sides, angles, diagonals and symmetry. Take suggestions from the class and write up a class definition. This should state that a rectangle must have: 2 pairs of parallel sides with each parallel pair the same length; 4 right angles; diagonals that bisect in the middle; two lines of symmetry.

Individual work: Ask the children to copy the definition of a rectangle onto a sheet of paper, then draw several examples of different rectangles and label their features.

Differentiation

Less able: The children can draw around 2-D rectangle shapes and label them.

More able: The children can explain why a square is a special type of rectangle (it has 4 equal sides and 4 lines of symmetry).

Plenary & assessment

Explain that any four-sided shape is called a **quadrilateral**. Ask the children to visualise and then draw (on their whiteboards) a quadrilateral with one of the criteria for a rectangle present and the rest missing. For example, say: *Draw a quadrilateral with only 1 pair of parallel lines of the same length.* Ask: *Is it possible for this shape to have 4 right angles? How many right angles could it have? How many bisecting diagonals does your shape have? Do they bisect in the middle? Hold up your shape to show the rest of the class.* Repeat with another shape: *Visualise and draw a quadrilateral with diagonals that bisect anywhere but in the middle.* Compare and discuss the children's drawings.

Lesson ④

Starter

Ask each group to write the headings TTH, TH, H, T, U on their whiteboard or paper. Explain that they are playing the 'highest number' game. You will hold up five digit cards in turn; the children write them down and then decide which place value to give each digit. The teams with the highest final number get a point.

Main teaching activities

Whole class: Using a –10 to +10 bisecting cross of axes, demonstrate the use of co-ordinates in the first quadrant. Remind the children that the X co-ordinate should be given first, then the Y co-ordinate. They are written in brackets with a comma between them, as in: (2,3). Mark some co-ordinates on the grid, using small crosses, and join them up with a ruler. (Do not use the co-ordinates given on the sheet.)

–10 ┼ 10 **Individual work:** Distribute copies of 'Drawing quadrilaterals' for the children to complete individually. Make sure they understand what to do.

Differentiation

Less able: The children can use the version of 'Drawing quadrilaterals' with alphanumeric co-ordinates (letters and numbers).

More able: The children can use the version with co-ordinates across two quadrants, using negative numbers on the X-axis.

Plenary & assessment

Call out a list of co-ordinates for children to mark with a small cross on the second grid on the activity sheet: (8,10), (6,10), (5,9), (5,7), (6,6), (8,6). Reinforce the importance of putting the x co-ordinate first. Ask the children to join up these points. *What shape have you made?* Discuss what would happen the co-ordinates were the wrong way round. (The shape would be turned on its side.) Check the children's shapes to inform your assessment.

Lesson ⑤

Starter

Repeat the 'highest number' game, this time asking the children to round their final number to the nearest 10, 100 or 1000.

Main teaching activities

Whole class: Using a blank –10 by 10 co-ordinate grid, ask for a volunteer to follow your instructions for drawing a quadrilateral. Call out the co-ordinates (3,5), (3,8), (5,5) and (5,8). Explain that today, the children are playing a version of 'Battleships'. Distribute the 'Quadrilateral battleships' activity sheet and go through the instructions for the game.

Paired work: The children play the game in pairs.

Differentiation

Less able: The children can use the version of the sheet with alphanumeric co-ordinates and only three quadrilaterals to find.

More able: The children can use the version with numeric co-ordinates and five quadrilaterals to find.

Plenary & assessment

Revise the criteria for a rectangle. Ask: *Has anybody drawn another quadrilateral that has a name? Can somebody come and draw a parallelogram on the board? Can we use the definition of a rectangle as a model when we are describing this shape?* (Unless it is a rectangle, a parallelogram has: 2 pairs of parallel lines of different lengths, no right angles, no lines of symmetry, diagonals that bisect in the middle. Explain that a rectangle is a special kind of parallelogram that has only right angles) Repeat for a rhombus (a parallelogram where all the lines are the same length) and a kite (2 pairs of sides of equal length with each pair adjoining, 2 angles the same, diagonals cross at right angles).

Name   Date

Drawing quadrilaterals

Use these co-ordinates to draw quadrilaterals on the grid. Label each point with its co-ordinates.

Shape A: (B,3), (B,1), (E,1), (E,3)
Shape B: (B,6), (B,10), (C,10), (C,6)
Shape C: (A,10), (A,5), (G,5), (G,10)
Shape D: (G,5), (E,8), (C,10), (J,7)

Is Shape D a rectangle?

_____

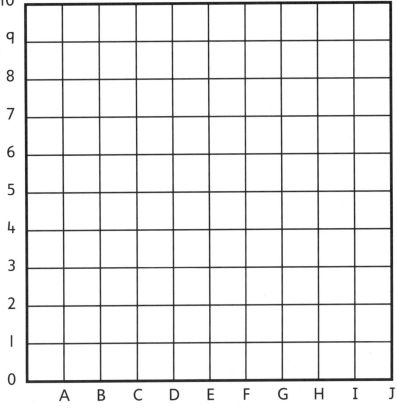

Now write the co-ordinates of the points in each shape drawn below. They are all rectangles.

Shape E: _____

Shape F: _____

Shape G: _____

Shape H: _____

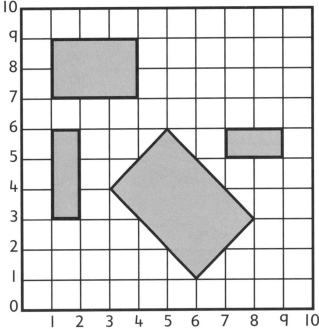

Name   Date

Quadrilateral battleships

On the first grid, draw 5 different quadrilaterals. Colour-code them (all different colours) and label the points with their co-ordinates. Do not let your partner see them.

Take turns with your partner to call out co-ordinates in an attempt to find one of their points. Do not count landing inside one of the shapes: it must be a direct hit on the point itself. If your opponent scores a hit, you must tell them what colour that shape is. Use the second grid to record where you have made guesses and hits on your partner's territory.

The winner is the player who finds all their opponent's shapes first.

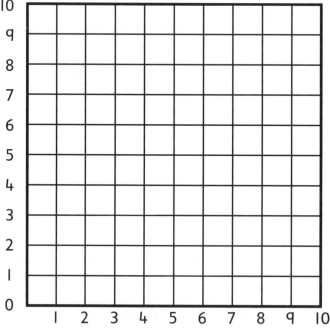

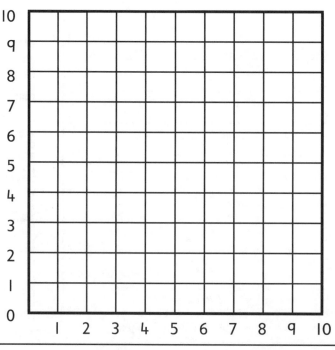

SCHOLASTIC
photocopiable

Autumn Term
Unit 9

Standard measures

Children are given opportunities to understand and use appropriate standard measures for calculating length and apply this knowledge to finding perimeters. Also the unit explores the relationship between equivalent units of measure.

LEARNING OBJECTIVES

		Topics	Starter	Main teaching activity
Lesson	1	Measures	● Derive quickly all two-digit pairs that total 100 (eg 43 + 57).	● Use, read and write standard metric units (km, m, cm, mm, kg, g, l, ml), including their abbreviations, and relationships between them. Convert larger units to smaller units (eg km to m, m to cm or mm, kg to g, l to ml). ● Know imperial units (mile, pint, gallon). ● Suggest suitable units and measuring equipment to estimate or measure length, mass or capacity.
Lesson	2	Measures	As for Lesson 1.	● Use, read and write standard metric units (km, m, cm, mm, kg, g, l, ml), including their abbreviations, and relationships between them. Convert larger units to smaller units (eg km to m, m to cm or mm, kg to g, l to ml). ● Suggest suitable units and measuring equipment to estimate or measure length, mass or capacity.
Lesson	3	Measures	● Use, read and write standard metric units (km, m, cm, mm, kg, g, l, ml), including their abbreviations, and relationships between them. Convert larger units to smaller units (eg km to m, m to cm or mm, kg to g, l to ml).	● Measure and draw lines to the nearest millimetre. ● Understand, measure and calculate perimeters of rectangles and regular polygons.
Lesson	4	Measures	As for Lesson 3.	As for Lesson 3.
Lesson	5	Problems involving 'real life', money and measures	As for Lesson 3.	● **Use all four operations to solve simple word problems involving numbers and quantities** based on 'real life', money and measures, using one or more steps. ● Choose and use appropriate number operations to solve problems, and appropriate ways of calculating: mental, mental with jottings, written methods, calculator.

Lessons   overview

Preparation
Display randomly, on the board, number cards that can be paired to make 100.

Learning objectives
Starter
● Derive quickly all two-digit pairs that total 100 (eg 43 + 57).
Main teaching activities
● Use, read and write standard metric units (km, m, cm, mm, kg, g, l, ml), including their abbreviations, and relationships between them.
● Convert larger units to smaller units (eg km to m, m to cm or mm, kg to g, l to ml).
● Know imperial units (mile, pint, gallon).
● Suggest suitable units and measuring equipment to estimate or measure length, mass or capacity.

Vocabulary
millilitre, litre, gram, kilogram, centimetre, millimetre, metre, kilometre, stone, pound, ounce, mile, gallon, pint, weight, length, distance, capacity

You will need
CD pages
'Number fan cards 0–9', one for each child and 'Number cards 10–90', for teacher's/LSA's use (see General resources).

Equipment
A bucket, several different jugs, measuring cylinders; a metre stick, a tape measure, a trundle wheel, a ruler (showing cm and mm); a spring balance (showing g), a set of stand-on scales (showing kg and stones and pounds).

Lesson ①

Starter

Show the children the jumbled numbers on the board and ask them to find pairs that total 100. Move and match the numbers together.

Main teaching activities

Whole class: Show the children the collection of measuring equipment. Ask them to tell you what could be measured with each one, and in what units. Discuss the need for a range of units of measure. Explain that different types of measuring equipment use different units, and that particular units are more suitable for some things than for others. For example, the spring balance scales would be useful for weighing flour, pencils or raspberries within the range of a few grams to 3 or 4 kilograms. However, standing scales are more appropriate for weighing people in kilograms or stones and pounds, as weighing a person in grams would result in a large and awkward number.

At this point, it is a good idea to address the fact that Britain still has 'imperial' units in common usage, such as pints (for milk and beer), gallons (for the fuel consumption of a car, though petrol has to be sold in litres) and stones and pounds (for people's weight and sometimes foodstuffs – though again, by law, food (whether packaged or loose) must be sold in kilograms. Explain that it is useful to be aware of these imperial units because they are still widely used, but in school we calculate using litres, grams and centimetres.

Individual work:

Provide a variety of items (or pictures) for children to match to appropriate units of measurement.

Differentiation

Less able: The children may find it helpful to have examples of measuring apparatus in front of them, so that they can check the sizes of the units.

More able:

Ask these children to choose appropriate equipment with no units of measure provided, so they have to think of these units without help, and estimate their mass.

Plenary & assessment

Discuss the activity; hear the children's ideas and correct misconceptions. A common error is to think that we measure the distance from Edinburgh to London in metres. Ask: *What would you use to measure petrol for a car?* (Litres.) *So why do people talk about fuel consumption in miles per gallon?* (By law, we must sell petrol in litres; but the gallon is a more familiar unit, and so is still used for comparison.) Ask the children to help you sort all the measuring equipment that you have gathered together into 'length', 'capacity' and 'weight'.

Lesson ②

Starter

Hold up a two-digit number card. Ask the children to find its pair to make 100, then show it to you on their number fans when you say 'Show me'. They could work in pairs, with each child holding up one digit. Repeat for various numbers.

Main teaching activities

Whole class: Explain that while it is important to choose the correct unit of measure, sometimes it is more convenient to use mixed units than just to use one unit. For example, if we want 1.5

kilograms of dried fruit for a cake, it is easier to measure 1kg and 500g than to measure using only grams or kilograms.

In order to measure accurately, it is useful to know the equivalent amounts for each unit. Ask the children to look at the ruler and tell you how many millimetres are equal to 1 centimetre (10); then look at the metre stick and tell you how many centimetres are in 1 metre (100); and so on. (1000 grams = 1 kilogram; 1000 metres = 1 kilometre; 1000 millilitres = 1 litre.) It may help them to remember that 'kilo' means 1000 and 'milli' means 1/1000.

Individual work: Ask the children to create a table of these equivalents and then use it to convert some given measures, for example, 1400 → *1kg 400g*.

Differentiation

Less able: The children can use a calculator to multiply by the appropriate amount. They may need help with putting 2½ (2.5) into the calculator, for example, 1500g → 1.5kg , or 2.5km → 2.5 × 1000 = 2500m.

More able: Ask children to find equivalents of, for example, 7412g → 7kg 412g.

Plenary & assessment

Ask the children: *How many millilitres in 1 litre?… Half a litre?…3.5 litres?… How many metres in 1 kilometre?… 2.5km?… 0.25km?… Which is the most likely distance to the end of our playground: 8.5cm, 88cm, 8m, 18m, 8km? What is the most likely height of a boy in Year 5: 15cm, 1.5m, 15m, 1.5km? How much tea would an average-sized mug hold: 50ml, 500ml, 5 litres? Which is bigger: 5000g or 6 kg? 1500ml or 2 litres? 2750m or 2.5km?*

Lessons   overview

Preparation

Draw some regular polygons (up to eight sides) on an OHT. Write some pairs of equivalent measurements randomly on the board for matching, such as: 2 litres, 500g, 1.5km, 2 000ml, 0.5kg, 1500m, 100cm, 1m, 3.5kg, 4 000ml, 4 litres, 3 500g.

Learning objectives

Starter

● Use, read and write standard metric units (km, m, cm, mm, kg, g, l, ml), including their abbreviations, and relationships between them. Convert larger units to smaller units (eg km to m, m to cm or mm, kg to g, l to ml).

Main teaching activities

● Measure and draw lines to the nearest millimetre.

● Understand, measure and calculate perimeters of rectangles and regular polygons.

● **Use all four operations to solve simple word problems involving numbers and quantities.**

● Choose and use appropriate number operations to solve problems, and appropriate ways of calculating: mental, mental with jottings, written methods, calculator.

Vocabulary

polygon, rectangle, perimeter (Also see vocabulary for Lessons 1 and 2.)

You will need

Photocopiable pages

'Polygon perimeters', see page 60, one for each child, and 'Problems with measures', see page 61, one for each child.

CD pages

'0–9 digit cards', one card for each child (see General resources). 'Polygon perimeters' and 'Problems with measures', less able and more able versions (see Autumn term, Unit 9).

Equipment

Rulers measuring in cm and mm; items to measure (such as an apple, an exercise book, a shoe, a chair, a ball of string, an envelope and so on); an OHT; a clear transparent ruler; paper and pencils or individual whiteboards and pens.

Lesson ③

Starter

Revise the relationships between grams and kilograms, millilitres and litres and millimetres, centimetres, metres and kilometres. Ask questions such as: *How many metres make 4km? How many millilitres in 3 litres? How many millimetres in 8 centimetres? How many millimetres in 1 metre? How many grams in 5.5kg?*

Main teaching activities

Whole class: Ask for a volunteer to draw a shape on an OHT, following your instructions. Explain that today's lesson is about drawing and measuring very accurately, to the nearest millimetre. Revise the properties of a rectangle. Ask your volunteer to draw a rectangle with two 8cm sides and two 4cm sides. Ask for another volunteer to check the accuracy of this. Discuss the need for a sharp pencil when drawing accurately on paper.

Explain that the complete outside edge of a shape is known as the *perimeter*. The perimeter of a field would be the fence around it. The perimeter of a rectangle can be calculated by adding the lengths of all four sides. Ask for a volunteer to do this and write the perimeter (24cm) under the rectangle. Ask the children how we can calculate this in our heads. (8 + 8 + 4 + 4 = 24 or (2 × 8) + (2 × 4) = 24.) Explain that because rectangles always have pairs of sides with the same length, the best way is the second one. Ask children to draw some more rectangles on the board and calculate the perimeter each time – for example, (2 × 6) + (2 × 4) = 20cm.

Individual work: Write up six more rectangle dimensions. Ask the children to draw these on paper and calculate the perimeter each time. For example: *Rectangles of 5cm by 3cm; 6cm by 2cm; 4cm by 7cm; 9cm by 4cm; 3cm by 10cm.*

Differentiation

Less able: The children could draw on 1cm squared paper, following the squares and (if necessary) counting around the perimeter.

More able: Add 0.5cm to each of the dimensions required (see above). This will require greater accuracy in drawing, and increase the challenge of the calculations.

Plenary & assessment

Ask: *If I can calculate the perimeter of a rectangle using a formula or pattern, how could I calculate the perimeter of a square?* (4 × length of one side.) *Or a regular hexagon?* (6 × length of one side.)

Play 'Guess the Lengths'. Say: *If the perimeter of a rectangle is 30cm, what could the lengths of the sides be? Is there only one answer? How did you work that out? Could you tell somebody else a rule for finding the side lengths of a rectangle if you know the perimeter? What about a rectangle with a perimeter of 48cm?* Invite children to demonstrate their thinking on the board, and to think of similar questions to ask the class.

Lesson ④

Starter

Show the children the random measurements written on the board. Explain that each one has a matching equivalent. Ask for volunteers to come and link matching pairs, using a coloured pen line (for example, linking 2 litres to 2 000ml).

Main teaching activities

Whole class: Explain that the children will be finding the perimeters of rectangles and regular polygons. Remind them that regular polygons have sides of equal length. Ask for volunteers to measure the polygons you have prepared on the OHT. Emphasise that they should measure to the nearest mm. Ask the class to calculate the perimeter of each polygon.

Individual work: Distribute copies of the 'Polygon perimeters' activity sheet. Ask the children to measure and label the side lengths for each polygon accurately, and to calculate the perimeter of each shape.

Differentiation

Less able: Provide the version of 'Polygon perimeters' that has only squares and rectangles, with side lengths that are whole cm, drawn on 1cm squared paper.
More able: Provide the version that has regular polygons with side lengths that have to be measured in cm and mm.

Plenary & assessment

Check some of the children's answers and ask the class: *How does our knowledge of shapes help us to calculate a perimeter?* Ask the children to stand in a circle. Give each child a 0–9 digit card. Explain that you will say the perimeter of a rectangle, and each child must find the person with the other side length that will pair with their own to give that perimeter. This game is slightly noisy, but a good way of assessing which children can calculate the lengths quickly!

Lesson

Starter

Hold up a variety of items. Let the children hold them and decide which unit of measure would be suitable to weigh or measure each one.

Main teaching activities

Whole class: Explain to the children that they are going to use their knowledge of equivalent units of measurement to help them solve problems. We sometimes need to convert measurements to the same units in order to work out a problem. For example: *Sally wants to put 3 shelves up in her kitchen. Each shelf is 80cm long. In the DIY store, shelving wood is sold in 2m lengths. How many lengths will she have to buy? How much wood will be wasted?* Work through this problem together on the board:
1. These are mixed units. What needs to be converted to make calculating easier? (2m to 200cm)
2. To turn the problem into a calculation, identify the operation needed to solve it: 200 – 80 = 120cm and 120 – 80 = 40cm. Sally can get 2 shelves from one piece of wood.
3. To make 3 shelves, Sally needs to buy 2 lengths of wood.
4. She will waste 40cm + 120cm = 160cm. (This is not enough for two more shelves!)
Explain that some of the questions on the activity sheet will need formal calculations and some will need informal jottings; but they will all need the word 'converting'. Assess the methods and thought processes the children have used.
Individual work: Ask the children to work through the word problems on the 'Problems with measures' activity sheet.

Differentiation

Less able: Provide the version of 'Problems with measures' with only one-step problems.
More able: Provide the version with a final challenge for the children to try.

Plenary & assessment

Ask for volunteers to talk you through the methods they used to solve some of the problems. Talk about information in word problems that is redundant or irrelevant, as in the question about the race track: you don't need to know how long the track is to work out its width. Provide pairs of children with individual whiteboards or paper and pencils; ask them to write a measures question, including some redundant information, for the others to solve.

Name	Date

Polygon perimeters

Measure these polygons very carefully.

Label each side with its length.

Use the side lengths to calculate the perimeter.

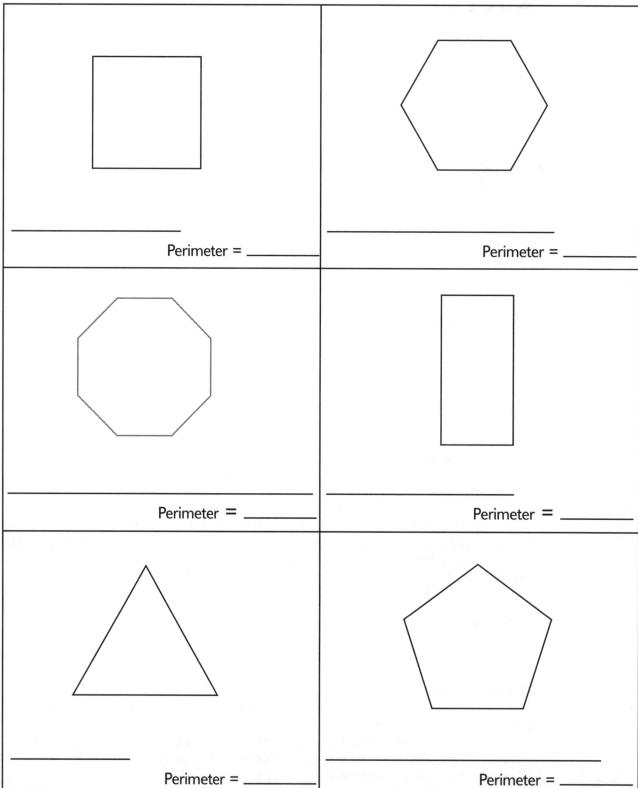

Perimeter = _____

Perimeter = _____

Perimeter = _____

Perimeter = _____

Perimeter = _____

Perimeter = _____

Name	Date

Problems with measures

Solve these word problems. Show how you calculated the answers.

A recipe for scones uses 500g of flour to make 16 scones. How many scones could be made with a 3kg bag of flour?	
Wood can be bought in 2m lengths. Ahmed is making a picture frame that is 45cm by 60cm. How many lengths of wood does he need to buy, and how much will be left over?	
Jon walks 850m to school. His friend Sam walks 1.5km to school. What is the difference between the distances the two boys walk?	
My little sister is 89cm tall. I am 1m 27cm tall. What is the difference between our heights?	
A paper clip uses 3.5cm of wire. How many paper clips could I make from 2m of wire?	
A house is 7m 40cm tall. A ladder is 395cm tall. How much longer would the ladder have to be to reach the top of the house?	
A race track is 100m long. Each lane is 75cm wide. There are 6 lanes. How wide is the race track?	

Using the 24-hour clock

Children are taught to understand both the 12 and 24-hour clock systems and are given opportunities to use digital notation to solve problems involving time.

LEARNING OBJECTIVES

	Topics	Starter	Main teaching activity
Lesson 1	Measures	● **Know by heart all multiplication facts up to 10 × 10.**	● Use units of time; read the time on a 24-hour digital clock and use 24-hour clock notation, such as 19:53.
Lesson 2	Measures Problems involving 'real life', money and measures	● Derive quickly or continue to derive quickly division facts corresponding to tables up to 10 × 10.	● Use units of time; read the time on a 24-hour digital clock and use 24-hour clock notation, such as 19:53. Use timetables. ● **Use all four operations to solve simple word problems involving numbers and quantities** based on 'real life', money and measures **(including time)**, using one or more steps.
Lesson 3		As for Lesson 2.	● Use units of time; read the time on a 24-hour digital clock and use 24-hour clock notation, such as 19:53. Use timetables.
Lesson 4	Measures	● **Multiply and divide any positive integer up to 10 000 by 10 or 100 and understand the effect** (eg 9900 ÷ 10, 737 ÷ 10, 2060 ÷ 100).	● Record estimates and readings from scales to a suitable degree of accuracy.
Lesson 5		As for Lesson 4.	As for Lesson 4.

Lessons   overview

Preparation

Write up a word problem on the board or OHT, such as: *I start watching a programme at 19:30 and it ends at 20:45. How long is the programme?* Also write the times like this:

Programme begins   21:30.
Programme ends   22:15.

Obtain some train and bus timetables. Photocopy these to provide one copy of each type of table for each pair of children. Obtain permission from the station manager before taking the timetables, and contact the travel company to obtain permission before photocopying them.

Learning objectives
Starter
● **Know by heart all multiplication facts up to 10 × 10.**
● Derive quickly or continue to derive quickly division facts corresponding to tables 10 × 10.
Main teaching activities
● Use units of time; read the time on a 24-hour digital clock and use 24-hour clock notation, such as 19:53. Use timetables.
● **Use all four operations to solve simple word problems involving numbers and quantities** based on 'real life', money and measures (including time), using one or more steps.

Vocabulary
24-hour clock, 12-hour clock, digital/analogue clock/watch, hour, minute

You will need
Photocopiable pages
'Steam train times' see page 67, one for each child.

CD pages
'Number cards 0–10', one set for each group; '24-hour clock', one for each child (see General resources). 'Steam train times', less able and more able versions (see Autumn term, Unit 10).

Equipment
Demonstration clock faces (at least one per group), displaying both 12-hour and 24-hour times if possible. Examples of timetables for trains and buses (see 'Preparation').

Lesson

Starter

Tell the children that you are going to set them a quick-fire multiplication quiz, with their table groups as teams. They have to volunteer the answer by being the first to raise a hand. Each correct answer wins a point. Children who have answered a question correctly may not answer again. This ensures that everybody has a try.

Main teaching activities

Whole class: Explain to the children that they are going to use the 24-hour clock to tell the time. There are 24 hours in each day and night, from midnight of one day to midnight of the following day. Instead of using two lots of 12 hours to tell the time, dividing them into 'am' and 'pm' (as we commonly do), the 24-hour clock uses a continuous increase in the number of hours up to 24. So 1:00pm is 13:00 hours, 2:00pm is 14:00 hours and so on. Time in 'am' and 'pm' is modelled on the analogue clock (with hands), which measures only 12 hours. The 24-hour digital clock does not need to have 'am' or 'pm' added.

Ask the children to work out some o'clock times in the 24-hour system: *What is 8pm?… 8am?… 4pm?… 10pm?… 9pm?… 5am?…* Check they understand that to work out the 24-hour equivalent of a 12-hour time, we keep the first 12 hours of the day (from midnight to midday) at exactly the same number, but calculate the second 12 hours by adding 12 to the hour. For example, 4pm is 12 +4 =16:00 hours. Discuss the notation: hours come first, then minutes, so '16:00 hours' means 16 hours and no minutes.

Individual work: Use a circle divided into 24 equal sections, label with 24 hours and explain that the diagram represents a whole day divided into 24 hours. Ask the children to fill in the space for each hour by drawing what they might be doing at that time in a typical school day: eating lunch at 12:00, playing with a friend at 17:00, watching television at 19:00 and so on.

Differentiation

Less able: Give the group a 24-hour clock face to help them convert 12-hour to 24-hour times.
More able: Amend the '24-hour clock' to encourage the children to subdivide the hours into halves and perhaps quarters, so they can indicate times such as 14:30 and 17:45.

Plenary & assessment

Ask the children:
- *What might you be doing at 16:00 hours?… 21:00?… 7:00? What about 10:30?… 18:15?*
- *How many hours are there in a day and a night?*
- *Tell me these times using the 24-hour clock: 6.30am; 5.30pm; 9.45pm; 11.50pm; 4.35am; 7.15pm.*
- *Tell me these times using 12-hour am or pm time: 13:00; 02:45; 16:20; 17:35; 23:15; 19:30; 06:30.* Turn this into a 'Stand up, sit down' game: you say a time and the children stand up if it is in 12-hour time and sit down if it is in 24-hour time. For example, they would sit when you said *0:600* and stand when you said *6.45pm*.

Lesson

Starter

Play 'Division Lotto' as in Term 1 Unit 2 Lesson 4 (see page 16), using 1–10 digit cards.

Main teaching activities

Whole class: Ask the children to look at the prepared word problem on the board or OHP. Ask how they would work out an answer. Take suggestions. Explain that standard written subtraction is not suitable for this problem – it may be tempting when the numbers are written vertically, but it won't give the right answer. Can the children suggest reasons why it doesn't work? (Hours are calculated as multiples of 60 minutes rather than in base 10.) Encourage the children to count on in minutes to the next whole hour from the earlier time, and then count on in hours. Suggest that informal jottings are a good way to keep track for example: 19:30 + 30 minutes = 20:00 and then 45 minutes = 20:45. So time elapsed is 30 + 45 minutes = 1 hour and 15 minutes.' Repeat this with a second example, reminding the children that there are 60 minutes in one hour.

Individual work: Provide some word problems which present questions on time involving the 24-hour clock. The final challenge for the children is to write a time question for a partner to answer.

Differentiation

Less able: Provide some simple word problems that involve calculating in whole and half hours only.

More able: Provide some word problems which require calculations with more difficult numbers of minutes.

Plenary & assessment

Ask the children: *If a train left Waterloo station at 12:35 and arrived at Cambridge 1 hour and 25 minutes later, at what time did it arrive?* Discuss whether in this instance it is easier to add on the hours or the minutes first. Give each pair of children one copy of a timetable. Ask them to calculate the time taken for each stage of a journey, using the counting on method. Go through one timetable as a class, asking individuals to count on aloud.

Lesson

Starter

Play 'Division Lotto' as in Lesson 2. This time, include 'time' questions such as: *The first maths puzzle I did took me 16 minutes. I did the second puzzle in half the time. How long did it take me?*

Main teaching activities

Whole class: Distribute the copies of the timetables you have collected. Discuss with the children how each timetable is arranged, with places and times cross-referenced. You could also discuss how timetables become more complicated when there are weekend and holiday variations. Explain that timetables always use the 24-hour clock to avoid confusion between morning and evening times (for example, 6pm and 6:00 hours). Build the children's confidence in using timetables by asking some simple questions, such as: *What time does the bus leave Warwick? At what time should it arrive at Coventry? How long does the journey take?* Ask the children to make up some questions to challenge the class.

Individual work: Distribute the 'Steam train times' activity sheet. Explain that this sheet presents a timetable; the children have to plan a route and answer some questions, using the 24-hour clock.

Differentiation

Less able: The children can complete the version of 'Steam train times' with a simplified timetable where the journeys take only whole hours and half hours.

More able: The children can complete the version with times that have more awkward numbers of minutes.

Plenary & assessment

Ask for volunteers to describe their planned journey and challenge the rest of the class to calculate how long it will take. Look for consistency in the length of time allocated for a given distance, and sensible judgements about the length of time spent at each place. Check the accuracy of the time calculations (problems often occur with bridging through an hour).

Lessons   overview

Preparation
Write or print a set of cards or labels (one for each item of measuring equipment) saying 'Divisions of _____'.

Learning objectives
Starter
● **Multiply and divide any positive integer up to 10 000 by 10 or 100 and understand the effect** (eg 9900 ÷ 10, 737 ÷ 10 2060 ÷ 100).
Main teaching activities
● Record estimates and readings from scales to a suitable degree of accuracy.

Vocabulary
weight, mass, measuring scale, gram, kilogram, millilitre, litre, second, minute

You will need
Photocopiable pages
'Reading scales', see page 68, for each child.

CD pages
'0–9 digit cards', for teacher's/LSA's use (see General resources). 'Reading scales', less able and more able versions (see Autumn term, Unit 10).

Equipment
A collection of instruments that measure using scales: a top pan balance, a set of bathroom scales, a measuring jug, a measuring cylinder, a stopwatch, a thermometer and so on.

Lesson

Starter
Use a set of 0–9 digit cards to play 'Place Value Shuffle'. Give four different digits (not zero) to four children. They stand at the front of the class and hold up their cards. Ask the rest of the class to read the number displayed. Ask what the number would be if it was multiplied by 10. The children 'shuffle' to display this number, leaving a space. Ask the class what should fit into this space, and ask for a volunteer to hold up that card (zero) in the line. Now ask what the number would be if divided by 100. The children 'shuffle' again. Ask the class what else we need now (a decimal point), and ask for a volunteer to represent it. Carry on multiplying and dividing and discussing the effect. Repeat with different digits and volunteers.

Main teaching activities
Whole class: Show the children the collection of measuring equipment. Explain that they have to decide what units of measure are being used for each item, and how big the divisions are. For example, a top pan balance may measure in divisions of 25g. Ask a child to complete the label: 'Divisions of 25g'. Do this with other items of measuring equipment. Some may have two labels; for example, a stopwatch may measure seconds and tenths of seconds. Explain that the children will need to look for clues on the equipment; for instance, weighing scales often have the weight divisions written on the dial. Noticing the divisions is important for accurate measuring and reading from a scale. It also means that some pieces of apparatus are more appropriate for certain jobs than others; for example, you wouldn't need a scale with 1ml gradations to measure fuel for a car.
Paired work: The children work in pairs to examine the equipment and complete a table to record the unit that each piece of apparatus uses for measurement. For example:

Apparatus	Division of measure
Top pan balance	25g

Differentiation
Less able: Give this group four pieces of equipment with appropriate labels already filled out. Ask them to match each label to the correct item of equipment, then draw and label the items.
More able: Challenge this group to add an extra column to their table, suggesting items that could suitably be measured using each kind of apparatus.

Plenary & assessment

Hold up an item of measuring apparatus, such as a measuring cylinder. Ask: *What division of measure does this scale go up by? What would it be useful to measure?* Repeat this with several more items of equipment. Hold up two different containers that measure in ml, such as a 2 litre jug and a 50ml measuring flask. Ask: *How many of these small flasks would it take to fill this large one?* Repeat using other items, such as a metre stick and a tape measure or a metre stick and a ruler.

Lesson ⑤

Starter

Play 'Place Value Shuffle' as in Lesson 4. Invite the class to create calculations for the human place value shufflers to carry out.

Main teaching activity

Whole class: Explain to the children that they are going to read some scales accurately, using what they know about measuring equipment and units of measurement. Distribute the 'Reading scales' activity sheet and attempt one example of each type of scale together.

Individual work: The children work through the activity sheet. For each picture, they should read the scale and recording the correct value and unit of measure.

Differentiation

Less able: Provide the version of 'Reading scales' where the values to be read on the scale are whole numbers.

More able: Provide the version with a final challenge: to draw a thermometer with a given scale and mark on it a particular temperature measurement.

Plenary & assessment

Talk through the activity sheet, noting some children's answers. Discuss any errors and misconceptions that arise. Ask the children to give their answers both in whole units (eg 2.5kg) and in whole units and smaller ones (2kg 500g). Avoid using terms such as '2½ hours', which do not refer to any actual scale. Sometimes children may become confused by mixed-number measures and say, for example, '2kg and ½kg'. Encourage the children to count on from whole kg or litres in metric steps – for example, 2kg, 2kg 250g, 2kg 500g… or 1 litre, 1 litre 100 ml, 1 litre 200ml…

Name	Date

Steam train times

The following timetable is for a holiday steam train that runs up and down the coast.

Use the timetable to plan a day's excursion, visiting various places on the way.

Answer the questions below the timetable.

Sunnyville Steam Trains

Sunnyville	Depart	10:20	12:30	15:00	Plan your day out. Where would you like to go? Write down your expected arrival times, how long you will stay at each place and your return departure time.
Theme park	Arrive	10:30	12:40	15:10	
	Depart	10:35	12:45	15:15	
Zoo	Arrive	11:25	13:35	16:05	
	Depart	11:30	13:40	16:10	
Beach	Arrive	11:55	14:05	16:35	
	Depart	12:05	14:15	16:45	
Quad bike centre	Arrive	12:20	14:30	17:00	
	Depart	12:25	14:35	17:05	
Bowling	Arrive	12:40	14:50	17:20	
	Depart for Sunnyville	12:50	15:00	17:30	
Sunnyville	Arrive	14:45	16:55	19:25	

Questions to answer

1. How long does it take the train to get from Sunnyville to the theme park? _____

2. How long does it take to get from the zoo to the quad bike centre? _____

3. How long is the entire outward journey to the bowling centre? _____

4. How long does it take to return to Sunnyville from the bowling centre? _____

5. What is the maximum amount of time I can spend at the beach if I am travelling by train from

Sunnyville and back again? _____

Name	Date

Reading scales

Look carefully at the dials and scales below.
Can you see what each mark on the scale represents?

Beneath each picture, write the amount being measured.

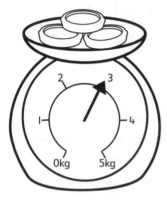   

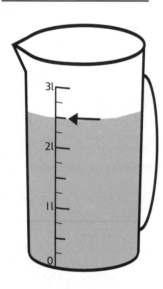 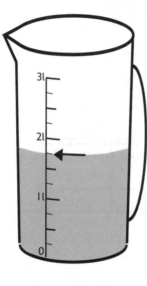 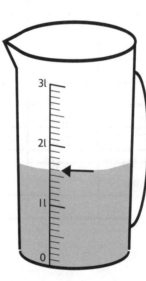 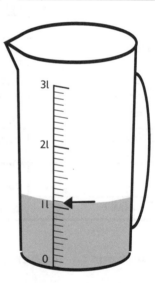

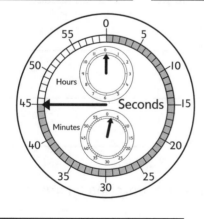 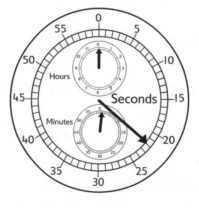 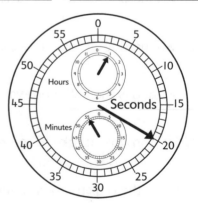

_____   _____   _____

_____   _____   _____

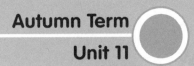

Addition and subtraction strategies

Mental and written calculating strategies to encourage children to understand that there are different appropriate methods for calculating different questions, depending on the size of the numbers involved.

LEARNING OBJECTIVES

		Topics	Starter	Main teaching activity
Lesson	1	Mental calculation strategies (+ and –)	● Recall addition and subtraction facts for each number up to 20. [Year 4 revision]	● Find differences by counting up through the next multiple of 10, 100 or 1000, eg **calculate mentally a difference such as 8006 – 2003**. ● Partition into H, T and U, adding the most significant digits first.
Lesson	2	Pencil and paper procedures (+ and –)	● Derive quickly or continue to derive quickly doubles of all whole numbers 1 to 100 (eg 78 × 2).	● Use informal pencil and paper methods to support, record or explain additions and subtractions. ● **Extend written methods to column addition/ subtraction of two integers less than 10 000.**
Lesson	3	Pencil and paper procedures (+ and –) Checking results of calculations	As for Lesson 2.	As for Lesson 2, plus: ● Check with the inverse operation when using a calculator.
Lesson	4	Pencil and paper procedures (+ and –) Problems involving 'real life', money and measures	● Derive quickly doubles of multiples of 10 to 1000 (eg 670 × 2).	As for Lesson 2, plus: ● **Use all four operations to solve simple word problems involving numbers and quantities** based on 'real life', money and measures, using one or more steps.
Lesson	5	Pencil and paper procedures (+ and –) Problems involving 'real life', money and measures Making decisions	● Know by heart all multiplication facts up to 10 × 10.	● **Extend written methods to column addition/ subtraction of two integers less than 10 000.** ● **Use all four operations to solve simple word problems involving numbers and quantities** based on 'real life', money and measures, using one or more steps. ● Choose and use appropriate number operations to solve problems, and appropriate ways of calculating: mental, mental with jottings, written methods, calculator.

Lessons   overview

Preparation

For Lesson 1, write the difference calculations (see 'Main teaching activities') on the board. For Lesson 2, write up some examples of subtraction questions that require mental calculation or informal jottings, with the two types mixed together. For Lesson 3, write up the questions to be answered (see 'Main teaching activities'). For Lesson 5, write up the word question (see 'Main teaching activities').

Learning objectives

Starters
- Recall addition and subtraction facts for each number up to 20 [Year 4 revision].
- Derive quickly or continue to derive quickly doubles of all whole numbers 1 to 100 (eg 78 × 2).
- Derive quickly doubles of multiples of 10 to 1000 (eg 670 × 2).
- **Know by heart all multiplication facts up to 10 × 10.**

Main teaching activities
- Find differences by counting up through the next multiple of 10, 100 or 1000, eg **calculate mentally a difference such as 8006 – 2003**.
- Partition into H, T and U, adding the most significant digit first.
- Use informal pencil and paper methods to support, record and explain additions and subtractions.
- **Extend written methods to column addition/subtraction of two integers less than 10 000.**
- Check with the inverse operation when using a calculator.
- Use all four operations to solve simple word problems involving numbers and quantities based on 'real life', money and measures, using one or more steps.
- Choose and use appropriate number operations to solve problems, and appropriate ways of calculating: mental, mental with jottings, written methods, calculator.

Vocabulary

add, sum, total, odd, even, multiple of, significant digit, bridging next 10/100, inverse, subtract, take away, difference between, consecutive

You will need

Photocopiable pages
'Work it out', see page 74, one for each child; 'Word problems', see page 75, one per child.

CD pages
'Number fan cards 0–9', one for each child; a set of even number cards 50–100 from 'Number cards 1–100 (see General resources). 'Work it out', less able version and 'Word problems', less able and more able versions (see Autumn term, Unit 11).

Equipment
Individual whiteboards and pens or paper and pencils; calculators; Diennes apparatus.

Lesson

Starter

Give a whiteboard or paper and pencil to each group of about four children. Ask them to write the number 36 in a number cloud in the middle of their page. Allow them 5 minutes to write as many different number sentences as they can around it that have the answer 36. When they have done this, invite some examples. Ask the children to explain how they found some of the more complex answers (for example: '18 × 2. I knew that because I know from the 4 times table that 9 × 4 is 36.')

Main teaching activities

Whole class: Write up on the board the question 3001 – 2785. Ask the children to suggest ways to solve it. They may suggest a written calculation or a number line. Some may suggest counting on. Explain that although these numbers look fairly big, they are not very far apart and so can be calculated by counting on. Explain that subtracting by counting on is easier in many cases than calculating, and should be tried first where appropriate (that is, where the numbers do not have too great a difference).

Draw a number line. Demonstrate counting on in 'jumps':

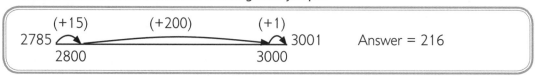

Repeat this method for 4005 – 3826 and 3012 – 2699. Ask the children whether they think these calculations could be done mentally with practice.

Individual work: Ask the children to work out the following calculations, which are written up on the board: 3004 – 2891; 4003 – 3728; 4011 – 3883; 5001 – 4569; 8002 – 7695; 7003 – 5991. They should use the counting on method, drawing a number line to demonstrate their understanding.

Differentiation

Less able: The children can use number lines to calculate the difference between three-digit numbers only, such as 304 – 289; 403 – 372; 401 – 388; 501 – 456; 802 – 769; 703 – 599.

More able: The children will probably not need the visual support of a number line, but should be encouraged to jot down the 'jumps' as they count on in order to avoid mistakes. They could invent some more questions for a partner to solve, finding small differences between four-digit or five-digit numbers by counting on.

Plenary & assessment

Ask individuals to demonstrate on the board how they found some of the differences. Were the 'jumps' the same for everybody? Did some children put different 'jumps' together? For example: 3001 – 2785 = 200 + 215 +1 = 3001. Could they use this method to find larger differences? Ask the children when the method might become too cumbersome. (When the difference to be calculated is very big, and the 'jumps' would be difficult to remember.)

Lesson

Starter

Give one table group a single-digit number. They double it and pass it on. The next group doubles that, and so on until 100 is bridged. The group that bridges 100 receives a point and is given another single digit to start again. The group with the most points at the end wins.

Main teaching activities

Whole class: Remind the children that we can calculate some differences mentally (such as 50 – 17, 100 – 56 or 1008 – 12) and find others by using informal jottings, either with or without a number line (such as 3004 – 2894, 294 – 177 or 9003 – 8895). Indicate the calculations written on the board and ask the children to choose a method to solve each one. Solve them together, either by counting on out loud or with a volunteer using a number line on the board.

Write 751 – 239 on the board. Ask whether the children think this might be too difficult to count on. What about 6383 – 2846? At some point we need a written method to support our calculations, because errors are otherwise too likely. Some individuals will still want to calculate mentally, and may be able to do so; but you need to point out that if the risk of error is high, we need a more 'secure' method to check with.

Individual work: Prepare ten different calculations with their answers. Explain that the children have to decide which method to use to find each of the differences – either just mentally or with informal jottings to support accuracy. Stress that number lines may be used if they are helpful, but none of the subtractions should require a full written method.

Differentiation

Less able: The children could use calculations with numbers up to three digits and number lines provided for support.

More able: The children could use a version with numbers up to five digits and some negative numbers being taken away.

Plenary & assessment

Ask some of the children to explain their methods – for example, with 73 – 38: 'In my head I counted on 2 from 38 to 40, then in tens to 50, 60, 70, then the extra 3, so the difference is 2 + 30 + 3 = 35.' From these explanations, you will be able to judge the children's understanding of informal calculation methods.

Lesson ③

Starter

Play 'Doubles bingo'. Give six even-number cards from the range 50–100 to each group. Call out doubles. For example, if you call out *Double 28*, the group with the 56 card must turn it face down. The game progresses until one group has turned over all of its cards.

Main teaching activities

Whole class: Explain to the class that they are going to look at how we can use written calculation methods to work out subtraction problems with more complex numbers. Using demonstration and asking volunteers to help, go through the expanded method without decomposition and then the expanded method with decomposition. Finally, work towards the standard vertical method. You will have to decide the rate at which your pupils progress through these written methods, according to your school's policy on calculation skills.

Individual work: Ask the children to use the expanded subtraction methods to work out the calculations written on the board: 578 – 243; 659 – 318; 4261 – 2110; 351 – 138; 2422 – 1375.

Differentiation

Less able: The children should practise the expanded method without having to redistribute the numbers. It is important that they are able to partition numbers and understand how this can be used for subtraction. They should try 295 – 123; 379 – 245; 664 – 243; 748 – 326; 754 – 513.

More able: Teach this group the standard method of vertical subtraction (see 'Subtraction and addition methods').

Plenary & assessment

Ask the children to redistribute the number 342 in a variety of ways. Record each way on the board and ask another child to check that it produces the correct number. For example, the children might suggest: 300 + 40 + 2; 300 + 30 + 12; 200 + 130 + 12.

Write the following calculation on the board and ask what is wrong with it:
Establish that the smaller digit has been taken away from the larger one in each column, whereas the correct method would be to take the digit below from the one above.

$$
\begin{array}{r}
631 \\
-\ 342 \\
\hline
311
\end{array}
$$

Lesson ④

Starter

Write a multiple of 10 on the board, such as 560. Ask the children to double it. Repeat with 430, 80, 120, 440, 370, 270 and 190. Discuss the strategy they are using: if they can double a two-digit number such as 43, then doubling 430 involves moving the same digits one place value to the left (making the double 10 times bigger).

Main teaching activity

Whole class: Distribute the 'Work it out' activity sheet. Discuss which of the questions might be calculated mentally, which need informal jottings and which need a written method. Read some of the word questions together and decide how to convert them to calculations, asking questions such as: *Is it an addition or a subtraction problem? Does the maths need a written method?* Revise vertical addition: both the expanded method and, for those you feel are ready, the standard method.

Individual work: Ask the children to work through the mixed addition and subtraction questions on the 'Work it out' sheet, using the most appropriate method. Where the children use informal jottings, ask them to explain how they worked out the answer.

Differentiation

Less able: The children can use the version of 'Work it out' with smaller numbers and easier calculations, requiring no carrying or redistribution in the written methods.

More able: The children should use standard written methods of addition and subtraction.

Plenary & assessment

Hear some of the children's answers and explanations. Iron out any misconceptions.

Write the following calculations on the board. Ask the children: *Is this correct? How can you check? Can you tell me what this person has done wrong? Can you correct the mistakes? How can you advise this person not to make the same mistakes again?* In the first calculation, an upper digit has been taken away from a lower one. In the second calculation, the decomposition is correct, but the 2 from the original number has not been added in.

```
  H  T  U
  2  1  8
+ 1  3  5
  3  0  0
     4  0
     1  7
  3  5  7
```

```
  H  T  U
  4  2  6
+ 2  3  7
  6  6  3
        1
```

Lesson

Starter

Ask quick-fire times tables questions such as *5 × 3, 7 lots of 2* and *double 9*. The children make the answers with their number fans and hold them up when you say *Show me*.

Main teaching activities

```
TH H  T  U
   4  9
   5 0̸11 9̸
-  2  4  7  6
   2  5  4  3
```

Whole class: Write this question on the board. *5019 people attended a rock concert. Because it was late, 2476 people left before the encore. How many were still there at the end?* Ask the children to suggest a method for solving this problem. Work through each method on the board. They may suggest:

- Counting on (using informal jottings): 2476 + 24 makes 2500, another 2500 makes 5000, add 19. Answer is 2543 people.
- Written subtraction. Either:

or:

```
  TH   H    T    U
   5    0    1    9    =   5000 + 0 + 10 + 9     =   4000 + 900 + 110 + 9
-  2    4    7    6    +   2000 + 400 + 70 + 6   =   2000 + 400 + 70 + 6
   2    5    4    3                                  2000 + 500 + 40 + 3
```

Encourage the children to check their answer using the inverse operation (addition).

Individual work: Distribute the 'Word problems' activity sheet. These problems require a mixture of addition and subtraction methods. Ask the children to read through the questions first and decide which method will be best for each problem.

Differentiation

Less able: Provide the version of 'Word problems' with simpler numbers and calculations.

More able: Provide the version using more complex numbers and calculations. Encourage the use of standard written methods.

Plenary & assessment

```
  TH   H    T    U
   2    3    2    0
-  1    4    7    2
```

Hear some of the children's answers and explanations. Iron out any misconceptions. Write up a new calculation, such as:

Ask for two brave volunteers to demonstrate how to solve this, using their own choice of method. Choose one child to demonstrate the standard method and one to demonstrate the expanded version. If the children find the calculation difficult, ask the rest of the class to advise them. Compare the decomposition processes used, and look for and emphasise the similarities between them.

Discuss some common errors when subtracting, for example: taking the top number from the bottom, not checking that the same number remains after redistributing the digits, and so on.

Name   Date

Work it out

Choose the most appropriate calculating method for each of these questions.
Show your thinking by recording with jottings or words or calculations.
Write on another sheet of paper if necessary.

1. 2004 – 1806	**5.** Jake has a collection of 432 bookmarks. His sister gives him her collection of 184 bookmarks. How many bookmarks does Jake have now?
2. 1479 – 1136	**6.** Andrea was reorganising the library. Of the 3005 books, only 2894 fitted onto the shelves. How many books were still on the floor?
3. 72 + 39	**7.** Imran was doing a survey of the car park. He found out that of a possible 1725 spaces, only 237 were unfilled. How many cars were there in the car park?
4. 134 – 85	**8.** Alice counted the people coming into a bowling hall. She counted 46 females and 85 males. How many people went to the bowling hall that evening?

Name		Date	

Word problems

Convert these word problems into calculations. Copy the calculations onto another sheet of paper and work them out. Show how you calculated each answer.

1. After playing two rounds of a computer game, Jay has scored _____ and _____. What is Jay's total score?

2. There are _____ children in a school. One day during a 'flu epidemic, _____ are absent. How many children are in school that day?

3. Asher has _____ stamps in her collection. She gives away _____ of them. How many stamps does she have now?

4. A traffic survey showed that on Monday _____ cars entered the town centre, and on Tuesday there were _____ .
a) What was the total number of cars over the two days?
b) What was the difference between the numbers on the two days?

5. An animal sanctuary calculated that last Christmas they had taken care of _____ animals, of which _____ had been found new homes. How many were still waiting to be rehoused?

6. A farmer had _____ sheep in his flock. He has bought _____ more.
How many does he have now?

7. The shopkeeper bought a supply of _____ chocolate novelties. _____ of them were chocolate teddy bears. The rest were chocolate snowmen.
a) How many chocolate snowmen did she buy?
b) She sold all but _____ teddies and _____ snowmen. How many chocolate novelties did she sell?

8. _____ people visited an exhibition over the Bank Holiday. _____ people visited it during the rest of the week.
a) What was the difference between the numbers of visitors over the two periods?
b) How many people visited the exhibition that week?

Number patterns and sequences

This unit encourages children to investigate patterns in a set of numbers and to create their own.

LEARNING OBJECTIVES

		Topics	Starter	Main teaching activity
Lesson	1	Properties of numbers and number sequences	● Use, read and write standard metric units (km, m, cm, mm, kg, g, l, ml) including their abbreviations, and relationships between them. Convert larger to smaller units (eg km to m, m to cm or mm, kg to g, l to ml).	● Recognise and extend number sequences formed by counting from any number in steps of constant size, extending beyond zero when counting back. For example: count on in steps of 25 to 1000, and back; count on or back in steps of 0.1, 0.2, 0.3…
Lesson	2		● Recognise and extend number sequences formed by counting from any number in steps of constant size, extending beyond zero when counting back. For example: count on in steps of 25 to 1000, and then back.	As for Lesson 1, plus: ● Know squares of numbers up to at least 10 × 10.
Lesson	3		● Continue to derive quickly all two-digit pairs that total 100 (eg 43 + 57).	● Find all the pairs of factors of any number up to 100.
Lesson	4	Reasoning and generalising about numbers	● **Know by heart all multiplication facts up to 10 × 10.** ● Continue to derive quickly division facts corresponding to tables 10 × 10.	● Solve mathematical problems or puzzles, recognise and explain patterns and relationships, generalise and predict.
Lesson	5		● **Know by heart all multiplication facts up to 10 × 10.**	As for Lesson 4.

Lessons   overview

Preparation
For Lesson 1, draw a blank ladder grid on the board . Modify a 6-sided dice to read 2, 3, 4, 5, 10 (or 11). For Lesson 2, write the number patterns on the board (see 'Main teaching activity').

Learning objectives
Starter
● Use, read and write standard metric units (km, m, cm, mm, kg, g, l, ml) including their abbreviations, and relationships between them. Convert larger to smaller units (eg km to m, m to cm or mm, kg to g, l to ml).
● Recognise and extend number sequences formed by counting from any number in steps of constant size, extending beyond zero when counting back. For example, count on in steps of 25 to 1000, and then back.
● Continue to derive quickly all two-digit pairs that total 100 (eg 43 + 57).
Main teaching activities
● Recognise and extend number sequences formed by counting from any number in steps of constant size, extending beyond zero when counting back. For example: count on in steps of 25 to 1000, and back; count on or back in steps of 0.1, 0.2, 0.3…
● Know squares of numbers up to at least 10 × 10.
● Find all the pairs of factors of any number up to 100.

Vocabulary
sequence, pattern, rule, continue, next

You will need
Photocopiable pages
'Investigating factors', see page 81, one for each child.

CD pages
'Multiplication square', one for each less able child (see General resources). 'Investigating factors', less able and more able versions (see Autumn term, Unit 12).

Equipment
6-sided and 10-sided dice (one of each per pair).

Lesson

Starter

Ask questions about changing units of measure to larger equivalents, such as: *How many grams in a kilogram?… in 1.5kg?… in 4.5kg?… in 0.25kg? How many millilitres in a litre?… in 3 litres?…in 5.5 litres? How many cm in a metre?… In a kilometre?… In ¼ of a metre?* Ask the children to raise their hands to answer.

Main teaching activities

Whole class: Explain to the class that in this week's lessons, they are going to use and investigate number patterns. Point to the ladder grid and explain that one roll of a 10-sided dice will decide how big your steps are. Ask for two volunteers to count up the number pattern. Roll the dice: if it shows a 6, explain that the children must count in constant steps of 6. Roll the dice again to give a starting number, such as 4. The children take turns to add to the number pattern: 4, 10, 16, 22… The first child to cross 100 gets a point for their group or team. Repeat with two more volunteers, using a new starting point and constant step.

Paired work: Working in pairs, the children use a 10-sided dice to create number patterns from random starting points. They should keep a record of the constant step in each pattern, and the numbers they make.

Differentiation

Less able: The children can use a modified 6-sided dice that gives steps of 2, 3, 4, 5 and 10 (or 11).
More able: The children can add the constant step and then multiply by 2. So if the constant step is 3 and the starting point is 2, 2 + 3 = 5 and 5 × 2 = 10. A point goes to the first child to reach 200.

Plenary & assessment

Ask whether anyone can spot the pattern – and predict the next three numbers. Say: *2, 5, 8, 11, 14, 17…* (+3) and *5, 11, 23, 47…* (Double and +1). Invite some children to begin a number pattern for the others to identify. Count together up to or over 100 and back to zero, using that sequence.

Lesson

Starter

Start chanting number patterns, inviting the children to join in when they recognise the pattern. Clap your hands to change the direction from counting on to counting back or vice versa. Say: *1, 3, 5, 7, 9… 25, 20, 15, 10, 5, 0, –5, –10… 4, 8, 12, 16, 20… 24, 21, 18, 15, 12, 9, 6, 3, 0, –3…*

Main teaching activities

Whole class: Explain that there are many kinds of number sequence: they don't all count on or back in whole-number steps of constant size. Other kinds of regular step are possible as well as adding or subtracting a constant number. Ask: *Can you spot the pattern? 1, 4, 9, 16, 25, 36, 49, 64, 81, 100.* Establish that this is the sequence of square numbers. Remind the children that a square number is a number multiplied by itself. Ask the children to consider *0.2, 0.4, 0.6, 0.8 1.0, 1.2…* (Jumps of 0.2.) *What about 1, 0, –1, –2, –3?* (Counting back in ones, past zero into the negative numbers.)

Explain that a number pattern rule can have more than one step, as long as the pattern follows the rule faithfully. Look at the rule 'Double it and add 1': start at 1, double it is 2 and add 1 is 3. So the pattern begins 1, 3… Apply the rule again: double 3 is 6 and add 1 is 7. So the pattern is 1, 3, 7… Ask the children to think of the next three numbers in the pattern. Ask whether anyone can invent a new rule for the class to try. Apply it on the board together.

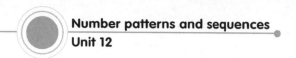
Individual work: Provide a number of starts of number patterns. Explain that this is a page of puzzling number sequences. The children must identify the rule for each sequence, then continue it for the next three numbers.

Differentiation

Less able: Provide a number of starts of number patterns with simple one-step rules only.
More able: Provide a number of starts of number patterns with some more challenging sequences.

Plenary & assessment

Go through some of the trickier patterns from the sheets. Ask the children to explain the pattern or rule. Ask: *What do you look for when solving a pattern? Do the rules always involve finding a difference?* Explain that a number sequence can follow any mathematical rule that gives a constant pattern.

Lesson ③

Starter

Ask the children to imagine that they have £1.00 to spend. *How much change would you have if you spent…* *52p; 58p; 23p; 45p; 91p; 33p; 17p; 29p; 67p?* The children should raise a hand to volunteer the answer.

Main teaching activities

Whole class: Explain that this lesson is about factors. Ask: *What is a factor? What are the factors of 12?* (1, 2, 3, 4, 6, 12.) *Do some numbers have more than two factors?* (Yes.) *What do we call numbers that are only divisible by themselves and 1?* (Prime numbers.) Explain that the children are going to make a list of the factors of various numbers. They have to work out all the factors for the numbers given, then circle the prime numbers.
Individual work: Distribute the activity sheet 'Investigating factors'. Explain that a table has been started on the sheet to list the factors of all numbers from 1 to 50. The children must complete the list.

Differentiation

Less able: The children can use the version of 'Investigating factors' that involves finding the factors of the numbers 1–20. They can use the times tables square to help them.
More able: The children can use the version with a further challenge. From the factors they have found, can they think of a quick and easy way to find the factors for the even numbers from 50 to 100? (Halve each number, list the factors of the half, then double these.)

Plenary & assessment

Ask: *What is a prime number? What are the prime numbers from 1 to 50?* (1, 2, 3, 5, 7, 11, 13, 17, 19, 23, 31, 37, 39, 41, 43, 47.) *Can we make any generalisations about them?* (They are all odd numbers apart from 2.) *What are the factors of 42?… 49?… 36?…*

Play 'Goose'. Ask the children to sit in a circle, and one person starts the count. Explain that they have to count in ones around the circle from 1 to 50 – but every time they come to a prime number, they have to say 'Goose' instead of the number. Play continues until someone makes an error – then the direction of play is reversed. This can be played as a knockout game, where a player is 'out' if he or she makes an error.

Lessons   overview

Learning objectives

Starter
- Know by heart all multiplication facts up to 10 × 10.
- Continue to derive quickly division facts corresponding to tables 10 × 10.

Main teaching activities
- Solve mathematical problems or puzzles, recognise and explain patterns and relationships, generalise and predict.

Vocabulary
predict, relationship, rule

You will need

CD pages
'Number fan cards 0–9', one for each child; '0–9 digit cards' and 'Number cards 12–90' for teacher's/LSA's use (see General resources).

Lesson

Starter

Use a range of vocabulary to test the children's recall and understanding of multiplication and division facts. Ask questions such as: *How many 6s in 42? How many is 4 lots of 3? If I know 10 × 4 is 40, what is 20 × 4 or 40 × 4? Divide 18 by 3. What is the product of 8 and 6?* The children find the answers on their number fans and hold them up when you say *Show me*.

Main teaching activities

Whole class: Explain that the children are going to investigate number pyramids. Using digit cards 1–9, put three different digits in a row. Find the differences between each pair of digits and put these in the second row, then find the difference between these to give the top number. For example:

		0				4		
	1		1		2		6	
3		4		5	1		3		9

Ask the children to investigate these questions:
- *What is the highest number you can get at the top of the pyramid?*
- *Is there a systematic way of finding the answer?*

Individual work: The children investigate the pyramid questions, using reasoning and trial and error. This work will continue in Lesson 5.

Differentiation

Less able: The children may find it helpful to use digit cards to make the pyramids.
More able: Look for independent work and a systematic approach. Extend the investigation by allowing two-digit numbers (up to 20) along the bottom row. Does this change the range of possible numbers at the top of the pyramid?

Plenary & assessment

Ask the children for a progress report on their investigation. *What is the highest top number anyone has found? Can you describe your strategy? What would happen if you used the same digit in all three bottom spaces? What would be the result? Would it be the same no matter which digit you used? Would it be easier or harder if I said that you had to use three different digits in the bottom row?*

Lesson ⑤

Starter

Hold up number cards such as 42, 36, 8, 24, 12 and 15, saying: *Show me the factors of…* The children work in pairs, each pair using number fans to display a pair of factors for the number.

Main teaching activities

Whole class: Continue the number pyramid investigation from Lesson 4. Ask the children: *Is it possible to get a 9 at the top? Can you suggest a strategy for getting the highest possible number at the top? Why does this work?* Explain that this time you would like the children to try out some of the ideas you discussed in the plenary of Lesson 4. *Try using the same digit all along the bottom row. What happens? Is this true whatever digit you use? Try using three different digits in the bottom row. What effect does this have?*

Individual work: Ask the children to write in their recording books or files about what they have found out. They should write a sentence for each thing they have found out.

Differentiation

Less able: The children may find it helpful to use digit cards to make the pyramids.

More able: Look for independent work and a systematic approach. Ask the children to add another row of four single digits at the bottom. Does this change the range of possible numbers at the top of the pyramid?

Plenary & assessment

Hear the results of the children's investigation. Ask: *How did you decide what numbers to put at the bottom of the pyramid? Did you choose digits with large differences or small ones? If I want to have a large number at the top, can you suggest a strategy to help me? Would using two-digit numbers along the bottom/having an extra row of digits at the bottom increase the top number?*

(Actually, the best method of solving this problem is to work in reverse and experiment with possible top numbers. Using the number range 1–9 it is not possible to get a difference of 9 at the top, nor on the second row, which means that the highest top number is 7. This can be obtained in a number of ways, one of which is shown below.)

| Name | Date |

Investigating factors

Find the factors for all the numbers from 1 to 50.

Circle the prime numbers.

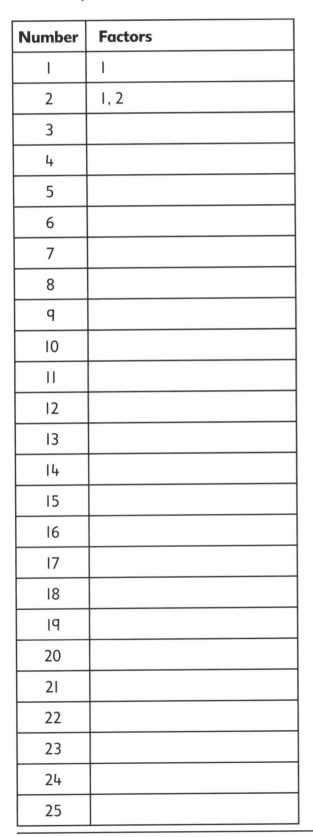

Number	Factors
1	1
2	1, 2
3	
4	
5	
6	
7	
8	
9	
10	
11	
12	
13	
14	
15	
16	
17	
18	
19	
20	
21	
22	
23	
24	
25	

Number	Factors
26	
27	
28	
29	
30	
31	
32	
33	
34	
35	
36	
37	
38	
39	
40	
41	
42	
43	
44	
45	
46	
47	
48	
49	
50	

EVERY DAY: Practise and develop oral and mental skills (eg counting, mental strategies, rapid recall of × and ÷ facts)

- Read and write whole numbers to at least 10 000 in figures and words, and know what each digit represents.
- Develop further the relationship between additon and subtraction.
- Recognise and extend number sequences formed by counting from any number in steps of constant size, extending beyond zero when counting back.
- Continue to derive quickly doubles of all whole numbers 1 to 100 and the corresponding halves.
- Add several numbers.
- Use known number facts and place value for mental addition and subtraction.
- Use doubling or halving starting from known facts, eg double/halve any two-digit number by doubling/halving the tens first
- **Know by heart multiplication facts up to 10 × 10.**
- Derive quickly division facts corresponding to tables up to 10 × 10.
- **Multiply and divide any positive integer up to 10 000 by 10 or 100 and understand the effect.**
- **Round any integer up to 10 000 to the nearest 10, 100 or 1000.**

Units	Days	Topics	Objectives
1	3	Place value, ordering and rounding	Use the vocabulary of comparing and ordering numbers, including symbols such as <, >, =. Give one or more numbers lying between two given numbers. Order a set of integers less than 1 million. **Order a given set of positive and negative integers** (eg on a number line, on a temperature scale). Caluculate a temperature rise or fall across 0°c.
		Using a calculator	Develop calculator skills and use a calculator effectively.
2–3	10	Understanding × and ÷	Begin to use brackets.
		Mental calculation strategies (× and÷)	Use factors (eg 8 × 12 = 8 × 4 × 3). Use closely related facts (eg multiply by 19 or 21 by multiplying by 20 and adjusting; develop the ×12 table from ×10 and ×2 tables). Partition (eg 47 × 6 = (40 × 6) + (7 × 6)).
		Pencil and paper procedures (× and ÷)	**Extend written methods to: short division of HTU by U** (with integer remainder)
		Problems involving 'real life', money and measures	**Use all four operations to solve simple word problems involving numbers and quantities** based on 'real life', money and measures (including time), using one or more steps, including making simple conversions of pounds to foreign currency and finding simple percentages.
		Making decisions	Choose and use appropriate number operations to solve problems, and appropriate ways of calculating: mental, mental with jottings, written methods, calculator.
		Checking results of calculations	Check with inverse operation when using a calculator.
4	5	Fractions, decimals and percentages, ratio and proportion	Order a set of fractions such as 2, 2³/4, 1³/4, 2¹/2, 1¹/2, and position them on a number line. **Relate fractions to division** and use division to find simple fractions, including tenths and hundredths, of numbers and quantities (eg 3/4 of 12, 1/10 of 50, 1/100 of £3). Order a set of numbers or measurements with same number of decimal places. **Round a number with one or two decimal places to the nearest integer.**
		Using a calculator	Develop calculator skills and use a calculator effectively.
5	8	Shape and space	Visualise 3-D shapes from 2-D drawings and identify different nets for an open cube. Recognise positions and directions, **recognise perpendicular and parallel lines.** Understand and use angle measure in degrees. Identify, estimate and order acute and obtuse angles. Use a protractor to measure and draw acute and obtuse angles to the nearest 5°. Calculate angles in a straight line.
		Reasoning and generalising about numbers or shapes	Solve mathematical problems or puzzles, recognise and explain patterns and relationships, generalise and predict.
6	2	Assess and review	

EVERY DAY: Practise and develop oral and mental skills (eg counting, mental strategies, rapid recall of + and – facts)

- Read and write whole numbers up to at least 10 000 in figures and words, and know what each digit represents.
- Recognise and extend number sequences formed by counting from any number in steps of constant size, extending beyond zero when counting back.
- Round any integer up to 10 000 to the nearest 10, 100 or 1000.
- Develop further the relationship between addition and subtraction.
- Use known number facts and place value for mental addition and subtraction.
- Know by heart multiplication facts for up to 10 × 10.
- Derive quickly division facts corresponding to tables up to 10 × 10.
- Derive quickly doubles of all whole numbers to 50, and the corresponding halves.
- Use known facts and place value to multiply and divide mentally.
- Use doubling or halving starting from known facts. For example: double/halve any two-digit numbers by doubling/halving the tens first.
- **Order a given set of positive and negative integers** (eg on a number line, on a temperature scale).
- Use, read and write standard metric units.
- **Use all four operations to solve simple word problems involving numbers and quantities** based on 'real-life', money and measures (**including time**), using one or more steps.

Units	Days	Topics	Objectives
7–8	10	Measures	**Understand area measured in square centimetres (cm²).** **Understand and use the formula in words 'length and breadth' for the area of rectangle.** Use, read and write standard metric units (km, m, cm, mm, kg, g, l, ml) including their abbreviations, and relationships between them. Convert larger to smaller units of mass (eg km to m, m to cm or mm, kg to g, l to ml). Suggest suitable units and measuring equipment to estimate or measure length, mass or capacity. Record estimates and readings from scales to suitable degree of accuracy.
		Making decisions	Choose and use appropriate number operations to solve problems and appropriate ways of calculating: mental, mental with jottings, written methods, calculator.
		Handling data	Solve a problem by representing and interpreting data in tables, charts, graphs and diagrams, including those generated by computer, for example: bar line charts, vertical axis labelled in 2s, 5s, 10s, 20s or 100s, first where intermediate points have no meaning (eg scores on a dice rolled 50 times), then where they may have meaning (eg room temperature over time).
9–10	10	Mental calculation strategies (+ and –)	Identify near doubles eg 1.5 + 1.6. Add or subtract the nearest multiple of 10 or 100 then adjust. Develop further the relationship between addition and subtraction.
		Pencil and paper procedures (+ and –)	Use informal pencil and paper methods to support, record or explain additions and subtractions. **Extend written methods to: column addition/ subtraction of addition two integers less than 10 000;** addition of more than two integers less than 10 000; addition or subtraction of a pair of decimal fractions, both with one or both with two decimal places (eg £29.78 + £53.34).
		Problems involving 'real life', money and measures	**Use all four operations to solve simple word problems involving numbers and quantities** based on 'real life' money and measures (including time) using one or more steps, including making simple conversions of pounds to foreign currency and finding simple percentages.
		Making decisions	Choose and use appropriate number operations to solve problems, and appropriate ways of calculating: mental, mental with jottings, written methods, calculator.
		Checking results of calculations	Check the sum of several numbers by adding in the reverse order. Check with an equivalent calculation.
11	5	Properties of numbers and number sequences	Recognise multiples of 6, 7, 8, 9 up to the 10th multiple. Recognise and extend number sequences formed by counting from any number in steps of a constant size, extend beyond zero when counting back. For example: count on in steps of 25 to 1000, and then back ; count on or back in steps of 0.1, 0.2, 0.3 ... Know and apply tests of divisibility of 2, 4, 5, 10 or 100.
		Reasoning and generalising about numbers or shapes	Make and investigate a general statement about familiar numbers, by finding examples that satisfy it. Suggest extensions, asking 'What if...?'
13	2	Assess and review	

Positive and negative ordering

In this unit children have to use their knowledge of place value to order both positive and negative numbers and use the symbols < and >.

LEARNING OBJECTIVES

	Topics	Starter	Main teaching activity
Lesson 1	Place value, ordering and rounding Using a calculator	● Read and write whole numbers in figures and words, and know what each digit represents. ● **Multiply and divide any positive integer up to 10 000 by 10 or 100 and understand the effect** (eg 9900 ÷ 10, 737 ÷ 10, 2060 ÷ 100).	● Use the vocabulary of comparing and ordering numbers, including symbols such as <, >, =. ● Order a set of integers less than 1 million. ● Develop calculator skills and use a calculator effectively.
Lesson 2	Place value, ordering and rounding	As for Lesson 1, plus: ● Round any integer up to 10 000 to the nearest 10, 100 or 1000.	● Use the vocabulary of comparing and ordering numbers, including symbols such as <, >, =. ● Order a set of integers less than 1 million.
Lesson 3	Place value, ordering and rounding Using a calculator	● **Multiply and divide any positive integer up to 10 000 by 10 or 100 and understand the effect** (eg 9900 ÷ 10, 737 ÷ 10, 2060 ÷ 100).	● **Order a given set of positive and negative integers** (eg on a number line, on a temperature scale). ● Develop calculator skills and use a calculator effectively.

Lessons overview

Preparation
For Lesson 2, make a set of four '<' and four '>' symbols on blank playing cards. For Lesson 3, make some of the digit cards show negative numbers by writing '–' in front of the digit.

Learning objectives
Starter
● Read and write whole numbers in figures and words and know what each digit represents.
● Multiply and divide any positive integer up to 10 000 by 10 or 100 and understand the effect (eg 9900 ÷ 10, 737 ÷ 10, 2060 ÷ 100).
Main teaching activities
● Use the vocabulary of comparing and ordering numbers, including symbols such as <, >, =.
● Order a set of integers less than 1 million.
● Order a given set of positive and negative integers (eg on a number line, on a temperature scale).
● Develop calculator skills and use a calculator effectively.

Vocabulary
compare, order, size, ascending/descending order, positive, negative, above/below zero, minus, integer, halfway between

You will need
Photocopiable pages
'Greater or smaller?', see page 87, one for each child; 'Weather around the world', see page 88, one for each child.

CD pages
'Place value arrow cards' and '0–9 digit cards', for teacher's/LSA's use (see General resources, Autumn term). 'Greater or smaller?' and 'Weather around the world', less able and more able versions (see Spring term, Unit 1).

Equipment
Individual whiteboards or paper and pencils; Blu-Tack; dice; calculators.

Lesson ①

Starter

Ask the children: *Think of the number 3. Multiply it by 10. What does it become? Now multiply it by 10 again… and again.* Ask the children to suggest another way we could have got from 3 to 3 000 (such as 3 × 1 000 or 3 × 100 × 10). Show how the number 3 grew to 3 000 using arrow cards. Ask the children to notice how the place value moved up one space each time the number was multiplied by 10. Repeat the process, starting at 5; then 0.4 or 0.03; then 1.6 or 0.17. Each time, ask the children to record the number pattern.

Main teaching activities

Whole class: Select four digits randomly from the digit card pack. Display them on the board using Blu-Tack. Ask the children to rearrange these digits into the smallest number possible. Write this up on the board. Now ask the children to rearrange the digits to make the largest number they can. Draw a blank number line on the board and write these two numbers at either end. Now ask the children to round each number to the nearest 100, then estimate the difference between them and work out the midpoint. Difference is 9 500 − 1 400 = 8 100. Half of this is 8 100 ÷ 2 = 4 050. So midpoint is 1 400 + 4 050 = 5 450. Mark this on the number line.

Now ask the children to use a calculator to follow this process and find the exact midpoint of the original numbers. Explain that it would be incorrect to simply halve the difference, because this would give only the midpoint of the difference without taking account of the starting number. Mark the exact midpoint on the original number line.

Individual work: Ask the children to repeat this activity, drawing their own number lines with a ruler. Ask them to estimate the difference by rounding and so find the approximate midpoint, then check using a calculator and add the exact midpoint to the number line.

Differentiation

Less able: The children can use three-digit or even two-digit numbers until their confidence in finding the difference and the midpoint grows.
More able: Extend the exercise to using five-digit numbers and attempting to find the quarter-point and three-quarter point by halving and halving again.

Plenary & assessment

Draw a number line on the board with 5 921 at one end and 6 844 at the other. Say:
- *Tell me a number between these integers.* (Write it on the line.)
- *Which integer is it nearer to? How do you know?*
- *What do you estimate is the midpoint? How did you work that out?*

Repeat this with another pair of four-digit integers.

Discuss the importance of considering the most significant digit first when ordering numbers. Write 6 473, 6 492 and 6 880 on the board. Ask the children to order these, the smallest first. *Which digits were most important when you decided the order?* Repeat this for other four-digit sets.

Lesson ②

Starter

Repeat the Starter from Lesson 1, but this time dividing repeatedly by 10. Start with 10 000, then 9 000. Now try 8 750 and 7 945, going on to at least one decimal place.

Main teaching activities

Whole class: Write up on the board the symbols =, < and >. Invite children to explain what these mean. Remind them that the smaller number always goes at the sharp end. Write some number sentences such as: 726 > 290; 3542 < 4687; 0.23 > 0.12.

Explain that these symbols can be useful when ordering numbers. Ask for a volunteer to write the numbers 256, 187, 387, 342 and 196 in ascending order, using the 'smaller than' symbol cards (stuck in place with Blu-Tack). Ask another child to rearrange these numbers in descending order, using the 'greater than' symbol cards. Now ask for a third child to use the integers and a mixture of symbol cards to write an accurate number sentence (for example, 256 > 187 < 387 > 342).

Paired work: Distribute the 'Greater or smaller?' activity sheet, explaining that the children have to generate numbers using dice and order them using the < and > symbols.

Differentiation

Less able: Provide the version of 'Greater or smaller?' with two- and three-digit numbers.
More able: Provide the version with four- and five-digit numbers.

Plenary & assessment

Write some pairs of numbers on the board. Invite children to write symbols between them. Include some negative numbers and some numbers that are equal. For example: 256 < 456; 3809 > 3807; 12 084 > 12 083; 0.3 > 0.03; 3.4 = 3.40; 1.77 < 1.78; –6 < 6; 8 > –2; –1 < 0; 112 = 112.0. Ask the child as he or she completes each example: *What part of the number are you using to help you decide which number is larger? Is it the same digit in every example? What must we consider when we are looking at negative numbers?* Discuss the fact that the minus sign in front of a negative number tells us that we are counting back from zero – the bigger the number size, the further below zero it is.

Write up some pairs of negative numbers to order using symbol cards.

Lesson

Starter

Give each child a whiteboard or paper and pencil. Ask the children to write a two-digit number, apply a rule you will tell them and pass it on. Say: *Multiply by 10; add 10; divide by 100; add 100; divide by 10.* Record the operations on the board so the children can check their calculations. Ask: *How big a number have you got? Who has a decimal number?* Check that the numbers are all in the same range.

Main teaching activities

Whole class: Draw a number line from –10 to +10. Display your prepared positive and negative digit cards, including zero. Ask the children to estimate each card's place on the line. Discuss the minus sign as meaning an amount less than zero or a distance from zero. The larger the number, the further from zero. Link this to temperatures below zero. *Which is colder, –1°C or –10°C?* (–10°C.)

Now ask the children to calculate differences in temperature. For example, *What is the difference between –6°C and 2°C?* You cannot take the 2 from the –6 because 2 is the bigger number. It is better to count on from –6°C to zero and then on to 2°C (making a difference of 8°C). Repeat with some more examples.

Individual work: Distribute the 'Weather around the world' activity sheet. The children have to place temperatures on the number line and calculate some differences.

Differentiation

Less able: Provide the version of the activity sheet with numbers closer to zero.
More able: Provide the version with more challenging differences to calculate.

Plenary & assessment

Write on the board a list of 12 random positive and negative integers within the range –20 to +20. Ask the children to say the coldest temperature (the lowest number), the next coldest and so on. Say: *Tell me two numbers that fall between 0 and –6; –8 and –15; –4 and –11.* For each answer, ask: *Which temperature is warmer?* Ask the children to calculate the differences. Remind them that counting on from the 'coldest' to the 'warmest' is the best method.

Draw a vertical number line and mark on zero to help the children with counting through zero. Ask: *Tell me the difference between –3 and –8; 4 and –3; 8 and –15.* Pose word problems such as: *If the temperature is –5°C at 02:00 and rises by 8 degrees by midday, what is the temperature then?* Invite children to pose similar questions to the class.

Name		Date	

Greater or smaller?

Throw a dice to make two 3-digit numbers.

Write them on either side of the < or > symbol, in the correct places. Do this five times. An example has been done for you.

Numbers thrown		Numbers thrown	
421 and 648	648 > 421		>
	<		<
	<		>

Now use the dice to make some 4-digit numbers and do the same thing.

Numbers thrown		Numbers thrown	
1275 and 8546	1275 < 8546		>
	>		<
	<		>

Write these numbers in ascending order, using the < symbol:

365   974   655   356   394

_____

Write these numbers in descending order, using the > symbol:

4675   7564   4665   7655   4567

_____

Write the < and > symbols into these number sentences so that they make sense.

834 _____ 945 _____ 756 _____ 757 _____ 576

2978 _____ 6457 _____ 2899 _____ 2795 _____ 2784

3967 _____ 4756 _____ 3987 _____ 3776 _____ 3765 _____ 3766

Name	Date

Weather around the world

°C

Here is a table of minimum temperatures, taken one November day all around the world.

Label the number line with arrows and the name of each place.

City	Min. temp. (°C)	City	Min. temp. (°C)
London	2	Washington	3
Reykjavik	−17	St Petersburg	−12
Moscow	−13	Oslo	−6
Copenhagen	−1	Barcelona	7
Paris	4	St Moritz	−5

What are the differences in temperature between...

London and Oslo? _____

Reykjavik and Paris? _____

St Petersburg and Oslo? _____

Washington and St Moritz? _____

Copenhagen and St Petersburg? _____

Which is the coldest place? _____

Which is the warmest place? _____

What is the temperature difference between these two places? _____

Number line values: 15, 14, 13, 12, 11, 10, 9, 8, 7, 6, 5, 4, 3, 2, 1, 0, −1, −2, −3, −4, −5, −6, −7, −8, −9, −0, −11, −12, −13, −14, −15, −16, −17, −18, −19, −20

Factors, brackets and partitioning for multiplication

This unit builds on previous work to introduce alternative methods for multiplying, given the knowledge that a set of numbers may be multiplied in any order. It uses the knowledge of partitioning numbers in order to use the grid method for written multiplication, leading onto, as appropriate to standard method.

LEARNING OBJECTIVES

	Topics	Starter	Main teaching activity
Lesson 1	Understanding multiplication and division Mental calculation strategies ($\times$ and $\div$) Checking results of calculations	● Continue to derive quickly all two-digit pairs that total 100 (eg 43 + 57).	● Begin to use brackets. ● Use factors (eg $8 \times 12 = 8 \times 4 \times 3$). ● Check with the inverse operation when using a calculator.
Lesson 2		As for Lesson 1.	As for Lesson 1.
Lesson 3	Mental calculation strategies ($\times$ and $\div$)	● Use doubling or halving starting from known facts. For example: double/halve any two-digit number by doubling/halving the tens first.	● Use closely related facts (eg multiply by 19 or 21 by multiplying by 20 and adjusting; develop the $\times 12$ table from $\times 10$ and $\times 2$ tables).
Lesson 4	Mental calculation strategies ($\times$ and $\div$)	● **Know by heart all multiplication facts up to 10×10.**	● Partition (eg $47 \times 6 = (40 \times 6) + (7 \times 6)$).
Lesson 5	Mental calculation strategies ($\times$ and $\div$) Pencil and paper procedures ($\times$ and $\div$)	As for Lesson 4.	● Partition (eg $47 \times 6 = (40 \times 6) + (7 \times 6)$). ● **Extend written methods to short division of HTU by U** (with integer remainder).

Lessons   overview

Learning objectives

Starter
● Continue to derive quickly all two-digit pairs that total 100 (eg 43 + 57).
● Use doubling or halving starting from known facts. For example: double/halve any two-digit number by doubling/halving the tens first.

Main teaching activities
● Begin to use brackets.
● Use factors (eg $8 \times 12 = 8 \times 4 \times 3$).
● Check with the inverse operation when using a calculator.
● Use closely related facts (eg multiply by 19 or 21 by multiplying by 20 and adjusting; develop the $\times 12$ table from $\times 10$ and $\times 2$ tables).

Vocabulary
double, halve, factor, inverse, approximately, multiple

You will need

CD pages
'Number cards 10–90', for teacher's/LSA's use (see General resources, Autumn term).

Equipment
Individual whiteboards and pens or paper and pencils.

Lesson ①

Starter

Distribute all the two-digit cards 10–90 between groups of children, who place them face up on their tables. One group call out one of their numbers, and the group with the corresponding number to make 100 hold it up. They keep the pair of cards and call a new number. The game continues until all the numbers are paired.

Main teaching activities

Whole class: Revise factors. Ask: *If 3 and 4 are factors of 12, what are the others?* (1 and 12; 2 and 6.) *Name the factors of 50.* (1 and 50; 2 and 25; 5 and 10.) Explain that we can use our knowledge of factors to multiply bigger numbers. For example: $50 \times 6 = 5 \times 10 \times 6$ or $(5 \times 6) \times 10$ or $(10 \times 6) \times 5$ or $(5 \times 10) \times 6$. Write all the variations on the board and ask for volunteers to come and calculate them, demonstrating that factors can be multiplied in any order. Explain that we can rearrange the factors to choose the easiest calculation, and that brackets make the order of multiplication clearer.

Repeat the process to solve 60×7 using factors. Ask: *What factors could I use to help me?*
Individual work: Provide each child with multiplication problems using multiples of 5 or 10 (eg 60×5) for one of the multiples. Explain that the children will be using factors to multiply multiples of 5 and 10. Ask them to explore possible arrangements of factors and choose the simplest order for calculation. Encourage them to write down a variety of arrangements and not just multiply the first order they think of.

Differentiation

Less able: Provide simplified questions with only multiples of 10 to be factorised, eg 50×5.
More able: Provide a version with multiples of 2, 5 and 10 to be factorised, eg 14×5.

Plenary & assessment

Ask: *What are factors? How can they help us multiply?* (They break down a larger number into more manageable 'chunks'.) Ask the more able group: *Were all the numbers you tried to multiply easier when you used factors?* Write an example on the board and explain that the first factorisation may not simplify the calculation enough: the numbers may need to be further broken down. For example: $25 \times 18 = (5 \times 5) \times (2 \times 9) = (5 \times 5) \times (2 \times 3 \times 3)$. This gives $(5 \times 2) \times (5 \times 9) = 10 \times 45 = 450$. The important thing is to know the times tables!

Lesson ②

Starter

Repeat the starter from Lesson 1. This time, time how long it takes to match up all the cards. Record this time and try to beat it in the future.

Main teaching activities

Whole class: Follow on from Lesson 1. Explain that today, the children are going to use factors to multiply any numbers less than 100. They may have to factorise numbers more than once in order to find a manageable calculation. Ask the class to find factors to help solve 32×15, using brackets to keep the calculation order clear. For example: $(16 \times 2) \times (3 \times 5) = (8 \times 4) \times (3 \times 5)$ or $(2 \times 4) \times (3 \times 5) \times 4$. Discuss which combination would be easiest to multiply. Demonstrate multiplying the different combinations, and emphasise that the factors may be multiplied in any order.

It may be easier to use multiples of 10 than multiples of 5, so $(16 \times 5) \times (3 \times 2) = (8 \times 5) \times (3 \times 4) = 40 \times 12 = 480$. Or $(4 \times 5) \times 3 \times 4 \times 2 = 20 \times 3 \times 4 \times 2 = 480$. Repeat this process for several more examples.

Individual work: Provide a sheet of multiplication problems with different factors for one multiple.

Differentiation

Less able: Provide a version with simple multiples of 2, 5 and 10.
More able: Provide a version with more challenging numbers that require further factorisation.

Plenary & assessment

Write the following calculations on the board: 17×23; 19×9; 12×24. Ask the children: *Which of these calculations is the easiest to break into factors? Are some numbers less helpful to factorise than others? Why?* Discuss why prime numbers and square numbers offer a limited choice of factors. Remind the children that larger numbers may have factors that need to be simplified further. Ask for a volunteer to factorise and work out 15×48. Encourage a method such as: $15 \times 48 = (3 \times 5) \times (6 \times 8) = (15 \times 4) \times 6 \times 2 = 60 \times 6 \times 2 = 360 \times 2 = 720$. Repeat with several more examples.

Lesson 3

Starter

Play 'Doubling around the room', with the groups passing on a number and doubling it each time. When you call 'change', change from doubling to halving. Start with 8, 16, 32… 'change'… Repeat, starting from 3 or 4; then from 7 or 11.

Main teaching activities

Whole class: Explain that the children are going to explore multiplying by numbers close to multiples of 10, such as 19 or 21. Say: *We can use what we know about place value and factors to help us multiply by multiples of 10. For example…* Demonstrate that $15 \times 20 = (15 \times 2) \times 10 = 30 \times 10 = 300$. *We can use this skill to multiply a number like 19 or 21 by rounding it to 20, then adjusting the answer by adding or subtracting the missing amount.* Demonstrate that:

$$15 \times 21 = ((15 \times 2) \times 10) + 15 = 300 + 15 = 315$$

and $15 \times 19 = ((15 \times 2) \times 10) - 15 = 300 - 15 = 285$

Repeat using 18×21; 18×19; 24×19; 24×21. Emphasise the importance of the final adjustment: *Is it one more "lot of", or one less?*

Individual work: Ask the children to solve problems of near multiples of 10, using the method they have learnt.

Differentiation

Less able: Provide simpler problems using single-digit numbers to be multiplied by 19 or 21.
More able: Provide a more challenging version using numbers to be multiplied by a variety of near multiples of 10 (such as 29 and 31).

Plenary & assessment

Write up 23×31 on the board. Ask: *Which of these numbers is the near multiple of 10? Would you try to round both of the numbers?* Agree that it is only practical to round and adjust using one multiple, as using both would lead to confusion. Ask for a volunteer to come and demonstrate how they worked it out, talking through their method: $23 \times 3 \times 10 = 69 \times 10 = 690 +$ the extra 'one lot of' $23 = 713$.

Now ask, *If we can do this with near multiples of 10, is it possible to do it with near multiples of 100?* Ask for a volunteer to work out 13×201 on the board: $13 \times 201 = (13 \times 2) \times 100 = 2600 +$ one extra $13 = 2613$. Use several more examples to consolidate these ideas.

Lessons overview

Equipment
Individual whiteboards and pens or paper and pencils.

Preparation
For Lesson 4, write on an OHP or board three 3-digit × 1-digit multiplication problems (see below). Sort out from your number cards a card for each child that is a times table answer (12, 20, 32…), discarding numbers that do not fall within the 10 × 10 times tables.

Learning objectives
Starter
● **Know by heart all multiplication facts up to 10 × 10.**
Main teaching activities
● Partition (eg 47 × 6 = (40 × 6) + (7 × 6)).
● **Extend written methods to short division of HTU by U** (with integer remainder).

Vocabulary
partition, remainder

You will need
Photocopiable pages
'Multiplying matters', see page 94, one for each child.

CD pages
'Number cards 10–90' (see General resources, Autumn term). 'Multiplying matters', less able and more able versions (see Spring term, Unit 2).

Lesson

Starter
Give each child a number card (see 'Preparation') with the answer to a known times table fact. Arrange the children in a circle, holding their card in front of them for the others to see. Start one child saying a times table fact the answer to which another child is holding. That child should call out the answer, say another multiplication fact and then sit down. Continue until everyone is sitting. Time the activity.

Main teaching activities
Whole class: Revise partitioning and the grid method of multiplying (see Term 1 Unit 4 Lesson 2). Ask children to solve the problems you have written. Three examples are shown below. Remind the children to estimate the answer first, so they know its approximate size.

X	H	T	U
			8
30			
4			

X	H	T	U
			9
40			
7			

X	Th	H	T	U
				5
100				
20				
3				

If a group of your children are very confident with the grid method, you could make them your focus group for this session and teach them vertical multiplication, starting with the most significant digit. The progression you adopt will depend on your individual school calculating policy.

H	T	U
1	2	4
X		6
6	0	0
1	2	0
	2	4
7	4	4

Start with the most significant digit: the 100. Remind the children that they are multiplying 20 × 6, not 2 × 6. Add using the largest number first: 600… 700… 720… 744.

Individual work: Ask the children to solve multiplication problems of three-digit numbers by one-digit numbers, using the multiplication method that each child is most comfortable with.

Differentiation
Less able: Provide a version of multiplication problems with T U × U problems only.
More able: Provide a version with more demanding numbers. Ask the children to use the vertical multiplication method throughout.

Plenary & assessment
Ask for two volunteers, one who is confident with the grid method and one who is confident with the vertical method, and ask them to find 206 × 4. Discuss what needs to be recorded when you

multiply 0 tens by 4 (0). Demonstrate that both methods work. Ask: *How could we check the answer?* (Use the inverse operation, division.) Demonstrate the use of a calculator to divide the answer by 4.

Write up the calculation below and ask the children: *Is this correct? How do you know? Can you estimate what size the answer should be? Will the actual answer be bigger or smaller than that? Can you correct the errors in this calculation? What advice would you offer this person to help them avoid errors in the future?*

```
      3 1 6
    ×   5
    1 5 0 0    Correct
          5    Incorrect place value
       3 0
    1 8 0 5    Poorly placed, inviting incorrect
```

Lesson

Starter

Repeat the Starter from Lesson 4. Time the activity. Have the children improved their time?

Main teaching activities

Whole class: Write the calculation 215×6 on the board. Ask for two volunteers to solve it in different ways. Check by using the inverse operation. Revise the 'chunking' method of division. (See Term 1 Unit 3, Lesson 3.)

```
H T U
1 1 5        3 ) 2 4
  ×   4         4 1 r 1
4 6 0
    2
```

If you have a group who are confident with 'chunking' division, you could teach them short division or standard vertical multiplication with carrying: Provide a number of examples for the children to attempt. Talk them through each stage:
● Multiply the units first ($5 \times 4 = 20$). You cannot put 20 in the units column, so record the 0 and carry the 2 to be included with the tens.
● Multiply the tens ($1 \times 4 = 4$ plus the carried over $2 = 6$).
● Multiply the hundreds.

Ask: *What do you think is the most common mistake made when multiplying like this? Why is it important to carry across? What happens if you forget to count it in?*

When doing short division, think of the numbers as separate digits: the 1 is worth 100, but can be treated as a single digit. Your careful placing of the numbers will give the correct place value.
● Divide, starting with the most significant digit (the 1 hundred). $1 \div 3$ is impossible.
● Move the 1 across to join the tens. Now you have $12 \div 3 = 4$. Record the 4 in the tens place.
● Move across to divide the units: $4 \div 3 = 1$ remainder 1.

Ask: *What is the most common error made in short division? Why can you not afford to forget any numbers that you could not divide? What is the value of the 1 in this calculation?*

Repeat using a number of examples.

Individual work: Ask the children to complete the 'Multiplication matters' activity sheet, using their chosen method. They should check their answers using division.

Differentiation

Less able: Provide the version of 'Multiplication matters' with T U × U problems only.
More able: Provide the version that includes word problems. Ask the children to use standard vertical multiplication, and to use standard short division for checking.

Plenary

Ask for three volunteers to find 107×6 using different methods, explaining each step. Discuss and correct any discrepancies. Ask for a fourth volunteer to check the agreed answer using division, explaining each step. Ask:
● *Where do you think mistakes are most often made in each of these methods? What effect does this have on the answer?*
● *How can you quickly find the approximate size that the answer should be? What do you do first when estimating?*
● *Could you suggest any helpful tips for someone who is calculating using your chosen method?*

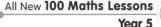

Name	Date

Multiplying matters

1. Do an inverse calculation to check your answers.

Check $50 \times 3 = 150$ with $150 \div 3 = 50$

312×3 423×3

_____   _____

352×5 371×6

_____   _____

263×7 216×9

_____   _____

2. There were 181 people at a meeting. The next week there were 3 times as many people. How many people were at the second meeting?

_____

3. Fred has 215 stamps in his collection; his brother has 4 times as many. How many stamps does his brother own?

_____

4. I have £18.34 in my money box. Dad says that if I work hard, I will have tripled this by Christmas. How much money will I have then?

_____

Written methods of division

Children use their knowledge of inverse operations to learn short division of HTU by a single digit.

LEARNING OBJECTIVES

	Topics	Starter	Main teaching activity
Lesson 1	Pencil and paper procedures (× and ÷)	● **Know by heart all multiplication facts up to 10 × 10.** ● Continue to derive quickly division facts corresponding to tables up to 10 × 10.	● **Extend written methods to short division of HTU by U** (with integer remainder).
Lesson 2	Pencil and paper procedures (× and ÷) Checking results	● **Know by heart all multiplication facts up to 10 × 10.**	As for Lesson 1, plus: ● Check with the inverse operation when using a calculator. ● Estimate by approximating (round to nearest 10 or 100), then check result.
Lesson 3	Problems involving 'real life', money and measures	As for Lesson 2.	● **Use all four operations to solve simple word problems involving numbers and quantities** based on 'real life', money and measures, using one or more steps.
Lesson 4	Problems involving 'real life', money and measures Making decisions	● Continue to derive quickly division facts corresponding to tables up to 10 × 10.	As for Lesson 3, plus: ● Choose and use appropriate number operations to solve problems, and ways of calculating: mental, mental with jottings, written methods, calculator.
Lesson 5		● Read and write whole numbers in figures and words, and know what each digit represents.	As for Lesson 4.

Lessons   overview

Preparation
For Lesson 2, draw an incomplete grid of multiples on the board as shown below.

Learning objectives
Starter
● **Know by heart all multiplication facts up to 10 × 10.**
● Continue to derive quickly division facts corresponding to tables up to 10 × 10.
Main teaching activities
● **Extend written methods to short division of HTU by U** (with integer remainder).
● Check with the inverse operation when using a calculator.

Vocabulary
product, multiplied by, times, divided by, equal groups of, group in pairs/threes… tens, one/two/three each, approximate, estimate, round to the nearest ten/hundred

	×3	×30	×300
6	18	180	1800
4			
7			

You will need
CD pages
'0–9 digit cards', a set for each child; 'Multiplication square', where needed for support (see General resources, Autumn term).

Equipment
Calculators.

Lesson ①

Starter

Play 'Factor facts'. Give each child a set of digit cards 0–9. Call out a number such as 12, 10, 16, 64, 21, 36… The children hold up all the factors of that number below 10.

Main teaching activities

Whole class: For progression in multiplication and division, refer to your own school calculating policy.

Introduce short division of HTU by U. Explain that we already know many TU ÷ U facts from the times tables, but having a written method is useful for bigger numbers. Short division assumes that the child is confident with place value. Work through an example such as 3)369 = 123. Explain that we divide into each digit separately: instead of writing 300 ÷ 3 = 100, we only need to consider the 3 as a digit, then put the answer in the correct place value position.

Once the children have grasped this idea, move on to dividing into digits that leave a remainder to be 'transferred along':

```
        1
3) 1 2 8
   0 4 2 r2
```

It is not possible to divide 1 by 3 using only whole numbers, so we can mark the place value with a 0 and transfer the 1 hundred across to the tens, so now we have 12 ÷ 3 = 4 and then 8 ÷ 3 = 2 remainder 2.

Repeat using 3)246 and 5)642. Emphasise that the remainders must be passed on to the next digit: they cannot be left behind or ignored. For example, discuss 3)172. Ask: *What should I put in the hundreds column? If I cannot divide 1 by 3 using whole numbers, what shall I do with the 1 hundred I have not used? Where should I put it so it can be divided? What value have I got in the tens column now? Can I divide it by 3? How much is the remainder? Where shall I put it so it can be divided? How many units are there now to be divided by 3?*

Individual work:

Provide a variety of division questions. Ask the children to use the examples to practise short division.

Differentiation

Less able: Provide some division questions that divide exactly with no remainders to transfer, just a few remainders at the end. Provide copies of the 'Multiplication square' to support division.
More able: Provide a variety of division sums and word problems with more challenging divisors.

Plenary & assessment

Write this calculation on the board and work through it with the children, asking: *What should I record for the tens column? Why is it important to place the 0 there? What should I do with the 2 tens that have not yet been divided? How many units are there now to be divided by 4?*

```
   H T U
4) 4 2 6
   1 0 6 r2
```

Next, write up a number of examples with incorrect answers (three examples are shown below). Ask for individuals to come and explain where the calculations have gone wrong and why. Ask: *Is this correct? How do you know? How can we put it right? Can you think of some helpful hints to stop other people making the same mistakes?* Design and display a 'Division Health Warning', using the children's suggestions.

```
5)275        6)709        4)572
 011          101 r3       118
```

Lesson

Starter

Invite two children to complete the prepared grid and explain their thinking as they do so. They should observe that the digits remain the same but move up a place value, and a zero fills the space to 'hold' or 'mark' the place value. As they work, ask the rest of the class: *What do you notice about the place value? What is the job of the zero? How is the number of zeros in the multiple related to the number of zeros in the answer?* Continue the grid horizontally, using other numbers (such as 70 and 900) to multiply by.

Main teaching activities

Whole class: Continue with short division from Lesson 1. Encourage the children to round and estimate first in order to predict the size of the answer. This may help them to spot errors in their own calculations. For example, 5)138 is approximately $150 \div 5 = 30$ (the exact answer is 27 r3). Demonstrate how to check the answer with the inverse operation, using a calculator. Key in $27 \times 5 = 135$ and then add on the remainder to make 138. (NB Until the children understand remainders as fractions or decimals, they cannot put the exact answer into their calculators. This 'short cut' method serves as a check.)

Individual work: Provide further HTU ÷ U questions. Ask the children to round and estimate first, then calculate using short division, then check using the inverse operation.

Differentiation

Less able: Provide children with simpler TU ÷ U questions. Provide copies of the 'Multiplication square' to support division.

More able: Provide this group with division questions using more challenging divisors, such as 7, 8 and 9, rounding, estimating and checking as before.

Plenary & assessment

Write the incorrect calculation 4)398 = 22 on the board. Ask: *Look at the answer to this calculation. Is it the right size? How can rounding and estimating help you to spot an error in a calculation? Where has the person made the mistake? Can you put it right?* Provide several more division calculations for the children to estimate the answers, such as: $486 \div 5$; $147 \div 5$; $266 \div 6$; $621 \div 3$. Ask for volunteers to come and solve these. Ask: *What would you round this number to so that the answer is easy to estimate?*

Lessons   overview

Preparation

Prepare an OHT as shown below. For Lesson 3, copy and laminate the 'Four operations vocabulary' cards and stick the multiplication and division cards randomly on the board. For Lesson 4, write the two-step problem (see 'Main teaching activities') on the board. For Lesson 5, write the numbers 3, 6, 30, 5 and 8 on the board.

1. 128 sweets are shared by 4 children. How many sweets do they have each?		
×/÷	Number question	Estimate
÷	128 ÷ 4 =	120 ÷ 4 = 30
Calculation	4)128	
128 ÷ 4 = 32	32	

Learning objectives

Starter
- **Know by heart all multiplication facts up to 10 × 10.**
- Continue to derive quickly division facts corresponding to tables up to 10 × 10.
- Read and write whole numbers in figures and words, and know what each digit represents.

Main teaching activities
- **Use all four operations to solve simple word problems involving numbers and quantities** based on 'real life', money and measures, using one or more steps.
- Choose and use appropriate number operations to solve problems, and ways of calculating: mental, mental with jottings, written methods, calculator.

Vocabulary

See vocabulary list for Lessons 1 and 2.

You will need

Photocopiable pages
'Multiply or divide?', see page 100, one for each child and 'Word problem frame', see page 101, one for each child.

CD pages
'Four operations vocabulary cards', for teacher's/LSA's use (see General resources). 'Multiply or divide?' and 'Word problem frame', less able and more able versions (see Spring term, Unit 3).

Equipment
Calculators, an OHP.

Lesson ③

Starter

Play 'Multiplication challenge'. All the children stand in a circle. One child challenges another with a quick-fire times table question. The second child either answers immediately or sits down. If the answer given is correct, the challenger sits down and the second child becomes the new challenger. If there is no answer or an incorrect answer, the rest of the class call out the answer and the challenger asks another child a new question. The last child standing is the winner. You could produce a 'handicap' system to level up the abilities: ask some groups about the 2, 5 and 10 times tables and others about the 7, 8 and 9 times tables.

Main teaching activities

Whole class: Explain that this lesson is about the language of multiplication and division, and the clues we can look for when we try to solve a word problem. Indicate the vocabulary cards stuck randomly to the board. Ask the children to help you to sort these into lists, one for multiplication and one for division.

Individual work: Distribute the 'Multiply or divide?' activity sheet. Explain that for each question, the children need to underline the key word or phrase that gives a clue to the operation needed, then circle the important numbers. Warn them that sometimes questions contain redundant information that has no bearing on the calculation needed. Ask the children to label each question with '×' or '÷', convert the words to a calculation and find the answer. Demonstrate using an example from the sheet with the OHT, which sets out the stages of solving a word problem. Please note that that answers are not only the methods of working out. The children could use mental or short division, for instance.

Differentiation

Less able: Provide the version of 'Multiply or divide?' with simpler numbers.
More able: Provide the version in which the problems include redundant information.

Plenary & assessment

Start by discussing what clues the children looked for to help them decide which operation to use for each question. Invite them to share their ideas, and scribe some of the best ones onto a 'Helpful hints for solving word problems' sheet for display. Ask: *What words suggest division… multiplication to you? Are there any other hints you might look for?* (For example, the relative sizes of the numbers.)

Ask for volunteers to demonstrate some of the trickier questions they tackled, using your prepared OHT and talking through their ideas. They should underline the key words in the question, identify the number question and demonstrate the calculation. Discuss any misconceptions that arise.

Lesson ④

Starter

Play 'Division challenge'. This is the same as 'Multiplication challenge' in Lesson 3, but the children ask division questions based on times tables facts. As before, a 'handicap' system may be operated.

Main teaching activities

Whole class: Indicate this question written on the board.

A chocolate factory makes 246 chocolates per day. These are packed into gift boxes of 6 chocolates. How many boxes can the factory produce each day?
The factory is open 5 days a week. How many boxes can it produce each week?

6)246
041 boxes per day

Explain that this is a two-step problem. To answer the second question, you need to have answered the first question. Look for clues such as *into gift boxes of 6* – putting a large number into lots of 6 must indicate a division. The numbers involved are big enough to require a written short division method.

Now we can solve the second step. 41 boxes are made in one day, so how many are made in 5 days? This indicates a TU × U question. Most children should be able to do this mentally or by using jottings: $41 \times 5 = (40 \times 5) + 5 = 205$. A few may need to use the grid method. The answer is 205 boxes of chocolates each week. Remind the children that a word question requires words in the answer, not just a number.

Individual work: Distribute the 'Word problem frame' activity sheet. Go through the questions, discussing the operations and calculating methods needed. Talk through the example on the sheet. Explain that the children need to identify the operation and method needed, isolate the number question and then estimate and calculate the answer.

Differentiation
Less able: Provide the version of 'Word problem frame' with multiples from 2 to 6.
More able: Provide the version with two-step problems. Encourage the children to use a range of methods, including standard written multiplication and short division.

Plenary & assessment
As in Lesson 3, use the prepared OHT to help the children talk through their methods as they demonstrate how they solved some of the problems. Ask: *Roughly what answer do you expect to get? How did you make this estimate? Do you expect your answer to be greater or less than your estimate? Why? Talk me through your method of solving the problem. What were the clues that helped you decide which operation to use?*

Lesson ⑤

Starter
Ask a child to provide a three-digit number. Indicate the numbers 3, 6, 30, 5 and 8 written on the board. Ask the children to use only these numbers and any or all of the four operations to get as close as possible to the three-digit number. Less able children could use calculators. Ask the child with the closest answer to explain his or her calculation, so that everyone can try it. Repeat, asking for a new three-digit number.

Main teaching activities
Whole class: Use this session to 'troubleshoot' difficulties with solving multiplication and division word problems.
Individual work: Provide some mixed × and ÷ questions including word problems. Work with individual children, looking for errors in the choice of operation or the layout of the calculation, uncertain place value and answers that are far wide of the estimates.

Differentiation
Less able: Provide × and ÷ questions.
More able: Provides some challenging mixed × and ÷ problems including word problems.

Plenary & assessment
As in Lessons 3 and 4. Ask for volunteers to demonstrate and talk through their decisions and calculations, using the OHT frame. Repeat the questions from the previous plenary.

Name	Date

Multiply or divide?

For these questions, you need to:

● underline the key words or phrases that will help you to decide whether the problem is a multiplication (**M**) or a division (**D**)

● circle the important numbers

● write the number question

● round and estimate, then calculate the answer.

---

1. 128 sweets are shared by 4 children. How many sweets do they have each?

×/÷	Number sentence	Estimate
÷	128 ÷ 4 =32	120 ÷ 4 = 30

Calculation

$$4\overline{)\ 128}$$
$$32$$

128 ÷ 4 = 32

---

2. 4 boys have 18 football stickers each. How many do they have altogether?

×/÷	Number sentence	Estimate

Calculation

---

3. Find the product of 14 and 9.

×/÷	Number sentence	Estimate

Calculation

---

4. 985 Multilink cubes were divided between 6 classes. How many did they have each?

×/÷	Number sentence	Estimate

Calculation

---

5. How many stars will Jay get if 415 stars are divided between the 6 people at his table?

×/÷	Number sentence	Estimate

Calculation

---

6. In the hall, there are 6 rows of 13 chairs. How many chairs are there altogether?

×/÷	Number sentence	Estimate

Calculation

Name	Date

Word problem frame

Use this framework to help you solve the word problems below.

An example has been done for you.

Jayne has 24 socks to sort into pairs. How many pairs of socks will she have?		
×/÷: ÷	Number question: $24 \div 2 =$	Estimate: $20 \div 2 = 10$
Method: Mental calculation		
Calculation: $24 \div 2 = 12$		

1. In a car park, there are 320 wheels.
Assuming that each car has 4 wheels, how many cars are parked in the car park?

×/÷:	Number question:	Estimate:
Method:		
Calculation:		

2. There are 12 pencils in a box. A school buys 24 boxes of pencils.
How many pencils is that altogether?

×/÷:	Number question:	Estimate:
Method:		
Calculation:		

3. Penny has 22 white mice. She keeps them 4 to a cage. How many cages does she need?

×/÷:	Number question:	Estimate:
Method:		
Calculation:		

Relating fractions to division

In this unit, children are taught to order mixed number fractions and how to find fractions of numbers by using division. They are also shown how to use a calculator to convert fractions into their decimal equivalents.

LEARNING OBJECTIVES

		Topics	Starter	Main teaching activity
Lesson	1	Fractions, decimals and percentages, ratio and proportion	● Derive quickly all pairs of multiples of 50 with a total of 1000 (eg 350 + 650).	● Order a set of fractions such as 2, 2¾, 1¾, 2½, 1½, and position them on a number line.
Lesson	2		● Recognise and extend number sequences formed by counting from any number in steps of constant size, extending beyond zero when counting back. For example: count on in steps from 25 to 1000, and then back.	● **Relate fractions to division,** and use division to find simple fractions, including tenths and hundredths, of numbers and quantities (eg ¾ of 12, 1/10 of 50, 1/100 of £3).
Lesson	3	Using a calculator	As for Lesson 2.	As for Lesson 2, plus: ● Develop calculator skills and use a calculator effectively.
Lesson	4	Fractions, decimals and percentages, ratio and proportion Using a calculator	● Order a set of fractions such as 2, 2¾, 1¾, 2½, 1½, and position them on a number line.	● **Round a number with one or two decimal places to the nearest integer.** ● Develop calculator skills and use a calculator effectively.
Lesson	5	Fractions, decimals and percentages, ratio and proportion	● Derive quickly all pairs of multiples of 50 with a total of 1000 (eg 350 + 650).	● Order a set of numbers or measurements with the same number of decimal places.

Lessons   overview

Preparation
For Lesson 3, provide a chart for children to fill in decimal and fraction equivalents, eg ½ = 0.5. For Lesson 4, draw a number line 0–1 with the fractions 0.5, 0.8, 0.25, 0.3, 0.75, *incorrectly* positioned along it. For Lesson 5, draw three similar stick men (not full-size, and only roughly to scale) labelled '1.69m', '1.77m', and '1.67m'.

Learning objectives
Starter
● Derive quickly all pairs of multiples of 50 with a total of 1000 (eg 350 + 650).
● Recognise and extend number sequences formed by counting from any number in steps of constant size, extending beyond zero when counting back. For example: count on in steps from 25 to 1000, and then back.
● Order a set of fractions such as 2, 2¾, 1¾, 2½, 1½, and position them on a number line.
Main teaching activities
● Order a set of fractions such as 2, 2¾, 1¾, 2½, 1½, and position them on a number line.
● **Relate fractions to division,** and use division to find simple fractions, including tenths and hundredths, of numbers and quantities (eg ¾ of 12, 1/10 of 50, 1/100 of £3).
● **Round a number with one or two decimal places to the nearest integer.**
● Order a set of numbers or measurements with the same number of decimal places.
● Develop calculator skills and use a calculator effectively.

Vocabulary
decimal fraction, decimal place, decimal point, numerator, denominator, equivalent, integer

You will need
Photocopiable pages
'Nearest and next', see page 107, and 'First and last', see page 108, one for each child.

CD pages
'Number fan cards 0–9', one for each child; 'Fractions, decimals and percentages' cards for teacher's/LSA's use (see General resources, Autumn term). 'Nearest and next' and 'First and last', less able and more able versions (see Spring term, Unit 4).

Equipment
Calculators; individual whiteboards and pens or paper and pencils.

Lesson

Starter

Explain that you want the children to think about pairs of multiples of 50 that add to make 1000, such as 450 and 550. Write a multiple of 50 on the board; the children use their number fans to show the matching number to make 1000. Repeat with other multiples of 50.

Main teaching activities

Whole class: Explain that this lesson is about ordering mixed numbers. Draw a number line labelled 0–5. Ask: *How can we mark different numbers and fractions on this line? Where on this number line would we place 2½? What about 3½? How would I know where to place 1¼ or 1¾?* Explain that we need some 'markers' to help us place numbers correctly on a line. In this instance, it would be helpful to mark the whole numbers 1–5 first. These in turn will enable us to find the 'half' numbers. Finally, we can mark in the quarters by halving each half. Demonstrate this on the number line, asking individuals to mark the numbers and fractions. Repeat with a number line from 10 to 20, asking the children to mark mixed numbers such as 13½, 15¼ and 17¾.

Individual work: Ask the children to draw a number line 10cm long on squared paper and label it 0–5, marking in the integers (whole numbers) every 2cm. Now ask them to label the line with the following: 1½, 3¼, 3¾, 2¼, 4½, 4¾, ½ , ¼ , 2½ , 3 1/8, 4 1/8.

Differentiation

Less able: The children could write in all the halves first (½, 1½, 2½…) and then the quarters (¼, 1¼, 2¼…) to encourage logical division of the lines. Ask them to mark the ¾ if you feel it is appropriate.
More able: Include more challenging fractions that require different divisions of the line, such as 1 1/3, 3 2/3, 4 1/8 and 4 3/8, to test the children's understanding of these divisions.

Plenary & assessment

Discuss how the children have placed mixed numbers on a number line by dividing up the line between each two successive integers into the appropriate fraction of a whole. Ask: *On a number line 0–1, where would you place 1/3? How would you divide up the line? What about finding 1/8?… 1/16?*

Discuss how repeated halving of the line can give quarters, eighths and sixteenths. In theory you could use this method to find 1/64, but in practice it would be difficult to do that on paper. Now discuss how it is possible to mark multiples of a fraction (such as ¾) on a number line. Ask: *Where should we place 3/8 or 2 3/16?* Invite volunteers to demonstrate this using a 0–5 number line on the board.

Lesson

Starter

Talk to the children about counting on and back in constant steps, such as 1, 2, 3, 4… or 2, 4, 6, 8… Ask the children to identify the steps you are counting in and to join in if they can. Say: *0, 0.1, 0.2, 0.3, 0.4…* Ask the class to count on as far as 2 and back again. Repeat, counting in steps of 0.2 from 0.8 to 4.0 and back. Count in steps of 0.5 from 0 to 10 and back, and from 4 to 14 and back. Ask: *What would happen if we counted back beyond zero in steps of 0.5? 0, −0.5, −1.0, −1.5…*

Main teaching activities

Whole class: Revise finding a simple fraction of a number. For example, we can find a half by dividing by 2, a quarter by dividing by 4 and so on. Ask the children to find a half of 18, 22, 24, 32. Ask: *What is a half of 7, 17, 23?* (3.5 or 3½ and so on.) Extend this process by asking the children to find one third of a number such as 12, 9, 18, 30. Ask: *If we can find 1/3 of a number, can anyone explain how we might find 2/3?* (Find 1/3 and double it.) *What is 2/3 of 15? 24? 36?* Repeat this process, finding ¼ and then ¾ of 32, 24, 40.

Individual work: Provide the children with questions that ask for simple and multiple fractions of numbers.

Differentiation

Less able: Provide questions which only ask for simple fractions (such as ½, 1/3, ¼) and multiple fractions using tenths only.

More able: Provide questions which ask for more complex fractions such as 3/8, 4/9 and 1 1/5.

Plenary & assessment

Write the number 5 on the board and ask the children to tell you some division facts that give this answer. Write these up around the number. Repeat for 2, 10 and 12. Encourage the children to use a wide range of times table facts. Ask: *How did you work this out?*

Now ask the children to tell you some fractions of numbers that give the answers above. Add these to the facts already recorded on the board. Discuss how fractions are closely related to division: the denominator is the divisor and the numerator is the multiple. Ask the children to tell you ¾ of 24, 2/3 of 9 and so on.

Lesson

Starter

Continue the starter from Lesson 2. Ask the children to identify the counting pattern and then count on and back. Count in steps of 0.2 from 0 to 3, and from 6 to 10. Count in steps of 0.25 from 0 to 5 and from 4 to –2.

Main teaching activities

Whole class: Give each child a calculator. Explain that a calculator can be very helpful for converting a fraction to its decimal equivalent. Discuss some familiar real-life examples of decimals, such as half of £1 (£0.50 = 50p) or temperatures such as 9.5°C.

Explain that a fraction such as ½ implies 1 ÷ 2. That is the numerator divided by the denominator. Ask the children to key this into their calculators and press =. They should be able to tell you that ½ = 0.5. Select the matching pair of fraction and decimal cards and fix them to the board. Explain that we can find all other decimal equivalents of fractions in the same way. Ask the children to find the decimal equivalents of 1/10 and ¼. Fix the matching pairs of cards to the board.

Now explain that some fractions have long and complicated decimal equivalents. Ask the children to key in 1/3. Explain that this number can be rounded to 0.33. Alternatively, the complete fraction can be shown as 0.33, using a dot to show the recurring digit (which would continue into infinity). Repeat for 1/7 and demonstrate that the decimal can be rounded to 0.14, but there is no single recurring digit.

Individual work: Ask the children to use their calculators to find the decimal equivalents of the fractions on a prepared chart of equivalent fractions and decimals. When they have finished, ask them to highlight with a small star the pairs they think will be useful to learn, and then to try to learn them.

Differentiation

Less able: The children may need some help to read the calculator display accurately and to round the numbers to two decimal places.

More able: Challenge the children to identify some more numbers as fractions or decimals and find their equivalents – for example, 2/3, 2/5 and 0.2.

Plenary & assessment

Ask the children to share their findings. Record their answers by displaying the pairs of equivalent fraction and decimal cards on the board. Ask: *Did anyone notice that some of the fractions had the same decimal equivalents? Can you explain why?* Draw two circles and dividing one into tenths and one into fifths to show that 2/10 is the same as 1/5. *Are there any other decimals that are equal to both a tenths fraction and a fifths fraction?* Discuss an example, such as 4/10 = 2/5 = 0.4. Explain that the numerator and denominator of 2/5 are both multiplied by 2 to give 4/10. Repeat this to show that 8/20 is another equivalent. Ask the children to check this with their calculators. Ask for a volunteer to suggest a rule for finding equivalents such as 2/10 = 0.2.

Lesson

Starter

Indicate the number line you have drawn on the board. Ask the children to look carefully at the fractions placed along it. *Are they correct? Why not?* Ask for volunteers to reposition them and explain how they decided where to place them.

Main teaching activities

Whole class: Ask the children to enter 0.6 into their calculators. Ask them: *How far is this from the next integer or whole number?* (0.4, because the next integer is 1.) Discuss the difference between the 'next integer' (which means that you are counting on) and the 'nearest integer' (which means that you need to round up or down, depending on whether the decimal fraction is larger or smaller than 0.5). Ask: *What would you add to 1.4 to reach the next integer?* Encourage the children to use their calculators. (The answer is 0.6, because the next integer is 2.) Repeat using 0.6, 1.8, 3.7 and so on, until everyone is comfortable with the term 'next integer'.

Individual work: Distribute the 'Nearest and next' activity sheet. Explain that some of these decimal numbers need rounding up to the *next* integer, and some need rounding up or down to the *nearest* integer.

Differentiation

Less able: Provide the version of 'Nearest and next' that includes number lines to assist counting.
More able: Provide the version that includes some numbers with two decimal places to be rounded.

Plenary & assessment

Explain that you are going to ask some questions. They may involve rounding up or down to the *nearest* integer, or counting on to the *next* integer. Discuss the difference. Ask:

- *Is 2.45 rounded to 2 or to 3? Why?*
- *I started with a number and rounded it to the nearest integer. The answer was 31. What number could I have started with? What is the smallest number I could have started with? How do you know?*
- *I started with a number and rounded it to the next whole number. The answer was 8. What could I have started with?*

Lesson ⑤

Starter

Remind the children of Lesson 1, when they made pairs of multiples of 50 that added to make 1000. Distribute whiteboards and pens, or paper and pencils, and ask groups of children to write as many such pairs as they can in 5 minutes. Compare their results at the end.

Main teaching activities

Whole class: Explain that this lesson is about ordering measures. Indicate the three labelled stick men on the board. Ask for a volunteer to order them from the shortest to the tallest. Ask the children how they can decide the order. (Look at successive decimal places: 1.7 > 1.6 from the first decimal place and 1.69 > 1.67 from the second decimal place.) Repeat by drawing three boxes labelled 2.34kg, 2.38kg and 2.32kg and asking the children to order them. Repeat with other measures.

Individual work: Distribute the 'First and last' activity sheet. Ask the children to order each set of measures, the smallest first, using their knowledge of decimal numbers.

Differentiation

Less able: Present the version of 'First and last' with measures that have to be ordered according to the first decimal place.

More able: Present the version where the second decimal place needs to be referred to in every case.

Plenary & assessment

Write '3.47kg' and '3.50kg' on the board. Ask: *What values, with the same number of decimal places, might be in between these two?* (3.48kg and 3.49kg.)

Revise with the children the rule that they apply when deciding whether a decimal number should be rounded up or down. Then ask: *On an aeroplane flight, my luggage must not exceed 30 kg. The mass of my suitcase was rounded to 22kg. What actual mass might it have been?* (Any value from 21.5kg to 22.49kg.) Discuss why the answer includes masses over 22kg. Repeat with other examples of measures or money.

Name	Date

Nearest and next

1. Round these numbers to the nearest integer.

1.4 ————▶ I   3.6 ————▶ _____   8.1 ————▶ _____

9.9 ————▶ _____   2.6 ————▶ _____   2.2 ————▶ _____

2. How much more would you need to add to reach the next integer?

2.4 + 0.6 = 3.0   7.2 +_____=_____

5.1 +_____= _____   3.8 +_____= _____

11.4 +_____= _____   7.8 +_____= _____

0.1 +_____= _____   3.4 +_____= _____

24.9 +_____= _____   9.7 +_____= _____

3. Circle the numbers that would be rounded to 2 as the nearest integer.
One has been done for you.

1.9   0.8   1.8   2.4   2.5   1.5   1.3

Circle the numbers that would be rounded to 10 as the nearest integer.

9.3   10.1   9.8   10.6   10.3   9.9   9.5   10.5

Circle the numbers that would be rounded to 1 as the nearest integer.

0.9   0.2   1.1   0.7   1.8   1.3   1.2   0.8   0.5

Name	Date

First and last

Write these measures in order of size, the smallest first.

 33.57kg    24.01kg   23.58kg

_____ _____ _____

 1.62m    1.63m    1.57m

_____ _____ _____

 2.59kg   3.10kg   3.67kg

_____ _____ _____

 47kg    0.98kg    1.31kg

_____ _____ _____

 1.22l   2.32l    1.31l

_____ _____ _____

 8.61cm    8.59cm   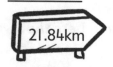 8.60cm

_____ _____ _____

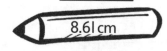 22.48km   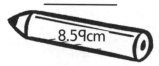 22.49km   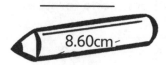 21.84km

_____ _____ _____

 32.61l    32.68l    31.69l

_____ _____ _____

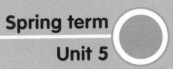

Solid shapes and measuring angles

In this unit children explore the vocabulary associated with solid shapes and investigate the nets of a cuboid. They then learn to use a protractor and calculate unknown angles.

LEARNING OBJECTIVES

	Topics	Starter	Main teaching activity
Lesson 1	Shape and space	● Recognise and extend number sequences formed by counting from any number in steps of constant size, extending beyond zero when counting back.	● Visualise 3-D shapes from 2-D drawings and identify different nets for an open cube.
Lesson 2		● Derive quickly decimals that total 1 (eg 0.2 + 0.8) or 10 (eg 6.2 + 3.8).	As for Lesson 1.
Lesson 3		As for Lesson 2.	● Understand and use angle measure in degrees.
Lesson 4		● **Round a number with one or two decimal places to the nearest integer.**	● Recognise positions and directions: **recognise perpendicular and parallel lines.** ● Understand and use angle measure in degrees.
Lesson 5		As for Lesson 4.	● Identify, estimate and order acute and obtuse angles. ● Use a protractor to measure and draw acute and obtuse angles to the nearest 5°.
Lesson 6		● Use doubling or halving, starting from known facts.	● Calculate angles in a straight line.
Lesson 7	Reasoning and generalising about numbers or shapes	As for Lesson 6.	● Solve mathematical problems or puzzles, recognise and explain patterns and relationships, generalise and predict.
Lesson 8		● **Know by heart all multiplication facts up to 10 × 10.**	● Solve mathematical problems or puzzles, recognise and explain patterns and relationships, generalise and predict.

Lessons overview

Preparation
Make nets of a square-based pyramid, a cuboid and a triangular-based prism using Clixi or Polydron.

Learning objectives

Starter
● Recognise and extend number sequences formed by counting from any number in steps of constant size, extending beyond zero when counting back.
● Derive quickly decimals that total 1 (eg 0.2 + 0.8) or 10 (eg 6.2 + 3.8).

Main teaching activities
● Visualise 3-D shapes from 2-D drawings.

Vocabulary
cube, cuboid, 3-D, three-dimensional, 2-D, two-dimensional, flat, prism, pyramid, face, side, line, edge, vertex, vertices

You will need

Photocopiable pages
'Match the nets', see page 116, one for each child.

CD pages
'Match the nets' less able and more able versions (see Spring term, Unit 5).

Equipment
Clixi or Polydron; a selection of 3-D shapes; a 1m counting stick; sticky labels or Post-It notes; calculators; card; felt pens; individual whiteboards and pens or paper and pencils.

Lesson

Starter
Ask the children to count on and back together from 0, 2 and 7 in steps of 0.1, 0.2 and 0.5, extending beyond zero (for example: 0, 0.5, 1.0, 1.5, 2.0, 2.5, 2.0, 1.5, 1.0, 0.5, 0, −0.5, −1.0, −1.5…) Now ask them to count around the room, changing the direction of the count when it crosses a pre-agreed number.

Main teaching activities
Whole class: Demonstrate what a cube looks like using Clixi or Polydron. Revise how many faces (6), vertices (8) and edges (12) it has. Open up the net of the cube. Explain that a net is the flat 2-D shape made when a 3-D shape is opened up. Ask: *Is this the only possible net? Can you visualise what another net of this cube might look like? Can you draw it?* As a volunteer draws his or her visualisation on the board, ask another child to build the net and fold it into a 3-D shape to check whether it creates a cube. Discuss possible rotations of this net. Repeat with other nets suggested by children.
Paired work: Ask the children to investigate and draw a variety of different nets to make an open cube, using Clixi to help. How many different ones can they find? Warn the children that some nets are just rotations of others. Most children should be able to find and draw 8–12 different nets.

Differentiation
Less able: Support the children's drawing and decision making. Discuss how rotated or inverted shapes are still the same shapes. Provide square templates to assist drawing.
More able: Ask the children to record the nets of successful open cubes and 'failed' nets that do not form an open cube. Ask them to explain, in the latter cases, why the shape would be incomplete.

Plenary & assessment
Use Clixi or Polydron to create and display the nets of a cuboid, a prism and a square-based pyramid. Ask the children to identify the solid shapes from their nets. Ask: *Are there any other ways of making nets for these shapes? Can you visualise and draw what the other nets might look like?*

Lesson

Starter

Play 'Pairs' with the children. You write a decimal number on the board; the children write the complementary decimal number to make 1.0 on their whiteboards and hold these up when you say *Show me*. Repeat several times.

Main teaching activities

Whole class: Display a variety of solid shapes: square-based pyramid, triangular-based pyramid, cuboid, prism and so on. Spend some time identifying and counting faces, vertices and edges. Ask the children whether any of these shapes would have an easily identifiable net. Why? (For example, the net for a square-based pyramid would contain a square and four triangles.)

Group work: Ask the children to investigate the shapes and try to draw nets for them without opening up the shapes, passing each shape from group to group. Ask them to complete the 'Match the nets' activity sheet, working individually to make the nets and match the correct nets to the solids.

Differentiation

Less able: Provide the version of 'Match the nets' with cubes and cuboids only.
More able: Provide the version that includes an octahedron (8-sided solid shape) and a decahedron (10-sided solid shape).

Plenary & assessment

Say: *Looking at our results, are there any generalisations we can make? For example, do shapes with more sides have a greater number of possible nets?* Share and record on the board the nets discovered by the children. Discuss the reflections and rotations of nets that the children have found. Draw a net of a cuboid and ask: *Can somebody visualise and draw this net rotated through 90°… through 180°?* Draw an incomplete net of a cube and ask: *What needs to be added to this to make it an accurate net of a cube? Can you draw it?*

Lessons   overview

Preparation
Draw some angles to measure on the OHP or board.

Learning objectives
Starter
- Derive quickly decimals that total 1 (eg 0.2 + 0.8) or 10 (eg 6.2 + 3.8).
- **Round a number with one or two decimal places to the nearest integer.**
- Use doubling or halving, starting from known facts.

Main teaching activities
- Understand and use angle measure in degrees.
- Recognise positions and directions: **recognise perpendicular and parallel lines.**
- Identify, estimate and order acute and obtuse angles.
- Use a protractor to measure and draw acute and obtuse angles to the nearest 5°.
- Calculate angles in a straight line.

Vocabulary
parallel, perpendicular, horizontal, vertical, diagonal, right angle, acute, obtuse, degree, straight line, protractor, angle measurer

You will need
Equipment
Protractors; an OHP with a protractor; rulers; a 1m counting stick; sticky labels or Post-It notes.

Lesson ③

Starter

Write a decimal number such as 6.3 on the board. Ask the children to identify the number that goes with this number to make 10, ie 3.7. Repeat with 2.3, 4.9, 7.1, 8.2, 6.8, 9.9, 1.7, 0.2. Encourage the children to think in terms of 'pairs to make 10'.

Main teaching activities

Whole class: Explain that a protractor is used to measure the degrees of turn about a point. Display a protractor on the OHP. Explain that the main divisions are in tens and then subdivided into fives, and each small line is worth one degree. Explain that the common semicircular protractors are for measuring between 0 and 180°, but a circular one is more useful for measuring up to 360°(a complete turn).

Explain that to measure an angle, you place the 'viewfinder' on the point of the angle and line up the straight line along the bottom of the protractor with one of the angle's lines. The inner and outer scales measure from zero from each end so that you can measure either a 'right-hand' or a 'left-hand' angle.

As an ICT link, you could use the *Becta* package (see the DfE training pack *Using ICT to support mathematics in primary schools*), which provides a demonstration protractor and many differentiated activities on angle measurement.

Individual work: Distribute a prepared sheet of different angles. Ask the children to measure the angles on the sheet accurately (to the nearest 1°).

Differentiation

Less able: Provide a sheet of simple angles and ask the children to measure to the nearest 5°.
More able: Provide a version with more demanding angles to measure, including some adjacent angles to make 180° on a straight line.

Plenary & assessment

Use an OHP to draw some angles. Ask for volunteers to come and measure them. Ask the children: *Is the protractor in the correct position? Which scale will we be using? Is the angle an exact measurement in line with the markings on the protractor? Which angle is it nearer? How big is the angle?* Check the children's measurements on the OHP. Discuss why there are minor variations (variable accuracy of lining up). Repeat using some different angles.

Lesson ④

Starter

Draw a number line labelled 5–6. Ask the children what number should be placed at the midpoint (5.5), then at ¼ and ¾ of the way along the line (5.25 and 5.75). Ask for volunteers to place 5.1, 5.95, 5.4 and so on, and to explain how they decided where to place each number.

Main teaching activities

Whole class: Draw a horizontal line on the OHP. Talk about its properties: it is **horizontal** (level with the horizon), the angles on a straight line equal 180°, it will go on to infinity and so on. Now draw a line at a 90° angle to the first one. Explain that any line at right angles with another line or surface is said to be **perpendicular** to it. In this case, the second line is **vertical** (at 90° to the horizon). Label the right angles on your diagram.

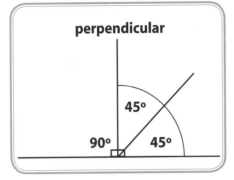

perpendicular

Now draw and label two 45° angles on the same diagram (see below). Ask the children how we know that these are 45°. (They are half of 90°.) Measure them with a protractor. Use these lines to demonstrate and discuss **acute** angles (less than 90°) and **obtuse** angles (more than 90°).

Individual work: Ask the children to draw and label their own perpendicular lines (one horizontal, one vertical) and use these to create acute and obtuse angles. Ask them to write a definition for each of these mathematical terms. Ask them to draw and label another five obtuse angles and five acute angles, using the corner of a ruler as a right-angle guide.

Differentiation

Less able: Work with a group, providing support with vocabulary.
More able: Expect more precise diagrams. Ask the children to make a list (with sketches) of acute and obtuse angles in the school environment.

Plenary & assessment

Draw several pairs of perpendicular lines on the board, using different orientations (so that there is not always a horizontal line). Ask:

● *What is the difference between a vertical line and a horizontal line?*
● *Perpendicular lines are very important for the building industry. Can you think why?*
● *Can somebody draw another line on this diagram that is parallel to one of the lines shown? Is it perpendicular to the other line?*
● *What do we mean by 'parallel'?* Write a class definition on a piece of card and display it. *How many parallel lines can you see in this room?*

Lesson ⑤

Starter

Use a 1m counting stick (with 10cm divisions) to count in steps of 0.1 from 0 to 1. Next, point to a place along the line (for example, 0.7) and ask the children to identify the decimal. Label it, using a sticky label, and then ask whether it would be rounded to 0 or 1. Ask the children to calculate how much more would need to be added to make 1. Repeat with more decimals.

Main teaching activities

Whole class: Draw two acute angles and two obtuse angles, jumbled up, on the board. Ask the children to identify which is which. Ask for four volunteers, one at a time, to come and measure the angles accurately with a protractor. Ask them to talk through what they are doing as they measure, saying which scale they intend to use (inside or outside) and why.
Individual work: Ask the children to use a ruler to draw a pattern of six lines that cross each other. Then they should choose at least four angles they think are acute and four they think are obtuse, measure them carefully with a protractor, then label them with the angle (in degrees) and the code 'O' or 'A'. Ask them to count up the numbers of acute and obtuse angles created in the pattern: are there more of one type of angle than the other?

Differentiation

Less able: Work with a group, providing support. Encourage the children to measure angles to the nearest 5°.
More able: Challenge the children to create a pattern of straight lines where all the angles are obtuse.

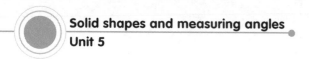
Plenary & assessment

Share examples of drawings, including the extension challenge. Discuss why a drawing with only obtuse angles is difficult to achieve. (Whenever shapes are joined together, acute angles tend to appear.) Ask: *Do you think it is possible to draw a quadrilateral with only obtuse angles?* (No, because the angles of a quadrilateral equal 360°, which is 4 × 90°. If you have two angles over 90°, then inevitably the other two must be acute.)

Lesson

Starter

Start with a known doubling fact, such as the double of 2, 6, 9 or 10, and double around the room, going from group to group. Then start with 100, 90, 120 or 70 and halve around the room. Include decimal numbers to two decimal places – for example, 70, 35, 17.5, 8.75.

Main teaching activities

Whole class: Ask for a volunteer to draw a horizontal line on the board or OHP. Then ask him or her to add a vertical line and a slanting line crossing the horizontal line at the same point (see figure below). Explain that we are going to investigate the angles along a straight line. They add up to 180° (half a complete turn), so the three angles in the diagram must add up to 180°. Ask for a second volunteer to measure the three angles and add them up. Repeat this several times with other volunteers. Now draw a similar set of three lines and ask a child to measure two of the angles, then calculate the last angle.

Individual work: Explain that the children are going to check the accuracy of their angle measuring. Ask them to create three angles on paper by drawing three straight lines (as above), then measure them as accurately as possible. Now ask them to add the angles together. Do they make 180°? If not, there has been an inaccurate measurement. Can they identify and correct it? Tell the children that they need to be accurate within at least 2° either way. When they have measured three angles that add up to 180°, ask them to label the angles on their diagram, and then to repeat the process several times with different angles.

Differentiation

Less able: The children may need support when measuring. They could use calculators to find the totals.

More able: Challenge the children to create three angles as before, measure two of them and predict the third by subtracting from 180°. Then they should extend the slanted line down below the horizontal line, and use it as a new base line of 180° to calculate the new angles created.

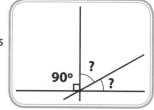

Plenary & assessment

Compare the children's results. Discuss the variations in the angle totals (such as 178°–182°) as indicating the margin of error. Talk about why this might happen: lining up the protractor, thickness of pencil lines. Emphasise that angles on a straight line always add up to 180°.

Draw a horizontal line with two lines extending from it, as before. Ask for a volunteer to measure the angles. Extend one of the lines down below the horizontal, thus creating two more angles. Ask the children to use their knowledge of angles in a straight line to calculate the new angles without measuring. Are there any other patterns that the children can observe here? (Opposite angles are equal.) Explain that in this way we can calculate angles within a whole turn (360°).

Lesson 7 overview

Learning objectives

Starter
- Use doubling or halving, starting from known facts.
- **Know by heart all multiplication facts up to 10 × 10.**

Main teaching activities
- Solve mathematical problems or puzzles, recognise and explain patterns and relationships, generalise and predict.

Vocabulary
See vocabulary list for Lessons 3–6.

You will need

Photocopiable pages
'What's the angle?', see page 117, one for each child.

CD pages
'What's the angle?', less able and more able versions (see Spring term, Unit 5).

Equipment
Calculators; A4 sheets of card; felt pens.

Lesson 7

Starter

Explain that the children are going to double decimal numbers. Start with a familiar example such as double 2.5 = 5. Ask the children to double 7.5, 9.5, 11.5, 15.5. Ask: *Why do these numbers always double to a whole number?* Ask the class what happens when we double ¼ or 0.25. For example, double 2.25 = 4.5, which can be doubled again to make 9. Repeat with starting points of 3.25, 1.25, 8.25 and so on to build confidence and familiarity.

Main teaching activities

Whole class: Draw two crossed lines. Label one of the angles as 110° (for example). Ask the children to use their knowledge of angles to find the other three angles. You might recap facts such as *the angles in a straight line equal 180°* and *the angles in a complete turn add up to 360°*. Also remind the children that opposite angles are equal. Talk the children through finding the missing three angles. Put in the opposite angle first, then count on to 180° to find the angle along the straight line.

Individual work: Distribute the 'What's the angle?' activity sheet. Ask the children to use their knowledge to find the missing angles. Explain that they should show in their writing how they calculated the angles.

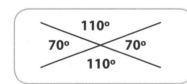

Differentiation

Less able: Provide the version of 'What's the angle' where the children only have to find a missing angle on a straight line. They could use a calculator to work out the answers.

More able: Provide the version that includes finding a missing angles in a triangle. (The three internal angles of a triangle add up to 180°.)

Plenary & assessment

Compare the children's results. Distribute A4 sheets of card and felt pens; ask each group to write a different 'angle fact' that they have learnt and draw a diagram to show it. For example, they might write 'The angles in a triangle total 180°' and draw a triangle with the angles labelled. Ask the children: *What is the least amount of information you need to calculate a 'missing' angle? If I didn't have a protractor, how could I identify a right angle? If a straight line is crossed by two lines that are both perpendicular to it, what are the angles?*

Name

Date

Match the nets

Use Clixi or Polydron to make these nets.

Fold each net to make a 3-D shape. Tick the diagram if it makes a complete solid shape. Put a cross by it if it doesn't.

Label each correct net with the name of the 3-D shape it makes.

■SCHOLASTIC
photocopiable

Name	Date

What's the angle?

Find the missing angles in each diagram.

Do not measure them: just use your knowledge of angles along a straight line or in a complete turn to help you work out the answers.

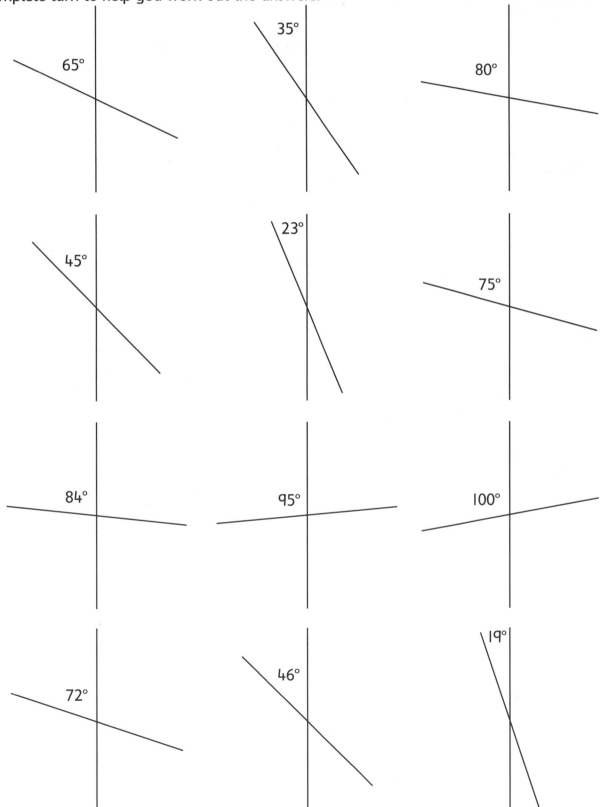

Spring Term
Unit 7

Area

In this unit children are taught the formula 'length x breadth' to find area and are given a number of problems related to area, including composite shapes.

LEARNING OBJECTIVES

		Topics	Starter	Main teaching activity
Lesson	1	Measures	● **Multiply or divide any positive integer up to 10 000 by 10 or 100 and understand the effect** (eg 9900 ÷ 10, 737 ÷ 10, 2060 ÷ 100).	● **Understand area measured in square centimetres (cm²).**
Lesson	2		● **Order a given set of positive and negative integers** (eg on a number line, on a temperature scale).	● **Understand and use the formula in words 'length × breadth' for the area of a rectangle.**
Lesson	3		As for Lesson 2.	● **Understand and use the formula in words 'length × breadth' for the area of a rectangle.** ● Use, read and write standard metric units (km, m, cm, mm, kg, g, l, ml), including their abbreviations, and relationships between them. Convert larger to smaller units (eg km to m, m to cm or mm, kg to g, l to ml).
Lesson	4		● Use, read and write standard metric units (km, m, cm, mm, kg, g, l, ml), including their abbreviations, and relationships between them. Convert larger to smaller units (eg km to m, m to cm or mm, kg to g, l to ml).	● Suggest suitable units and measuring equipment to estimate or measure length, mass or capacity.
Lesson	5	Measures Making decisions	As for Lesson 4.	● Record estimates and readings from scales to a suitable degree of accuracy. ● Choose and use appropriate number operations to solve problems, and appropriate ways of calculating: mental, mental with jottings, written methods, calculator.

Lessons   overview

Preparation
Make the sets of cards from the general resource sheets. For Lesson 1, make a decimal point card; make an OHT of a rectangle and another polygon, marked in square centimetres. For Lesson 2, draw a –10 to 10 number line and place the digit cards randomly along it. For Lesson 5, display the equivalent measures cards randomly on the board; write an area question (see 'Main teaching activities') on the board.

Learning objectives
Starter
● **Multiply or divide any positive integer up to 10 000 by 10 or 100 and understand the effect** (eg 9 900 ÷ 10 737 ÷ 10, 2 060 ÷ 100).
● **Order a given set of positive and negative integers** (eg on a number line, on a temperature scale).
● Use, read and write standard metric units (km, m, cm, mm, kg, g, l, ml), including their abbreviations, and relationships between them. Convert larger to smaller units (eg km to m, m to cm or mm, kg to g, l to ml).
Main teaching activities
● Understand area measured in square centimetres (cm²)
● Understand and use the formula in words 'length × breadth' for the area of a rectangle.
● Use, read and write standard metric units (km, m, cm, mm, kg, g, l, ml), including their abbreviations, and relationships between them. Convert larger to smaller units (eg km to m, m to cm or mm, kg to g, l to ml).
● Suggest suitable units and measuring equipment to estimate or measure length, mass or capacity.
● Choose and use appropriate number operations to solve problems and appropriate ways of calculating.
● Record estimates and readings from scales to a suitable degree of accuracy.

Vocabulary
area, covers, surface, square centimetre (cm²), square metre (m²), square millimetre (mm²), length, width, breadth, long, longer, longest, short, high, low, tall, height, depth, ruler, metre stick, tape measure

You will need
Photocopiable pages
'Count the area', see page 123, one for each child; 'Calculate the area', see page 124, one for each child.

CD pages
'0–9 digit cards', a set for teacher's/LSA's use; 'Negative number cards (–1 to –20)' and 'Equivalent measures cards', both a set for teacher's/LSA's use (see General resources). 'Count the area' more able version and 'Calculate the area', less able and more able versions (see Spring term, Unit 7).

Equipment
1cm squared paper; individual whiteboards or paper and pencils.

Lesson

Starter
Play 'Place value shuffle'. Use the digit cards 0–9 and a decimal point card to create a two-digit whole number such as 79. Ask two children to hold up these cards, then ask the rest of the class to predict where these digits would move to if 79 were multiplied by 100. Ask: *What should we put in the 'spaces' left when the digits 'shuffle' up the place value?* (Zeros to hold the place value: 7 900.) Repeat using different numbers such as 8.2 and 168. Include dividing by 10 or 100.

Main teaching activities
Whole class: Show the children your OHT of a rectangle divided up into cm². Explain that the squares cover the 2-D space on the page enclosed by the rectangle. This is known as the **area** of the rectangle. By counting the squares, we can calculate how much area the rectangle covers. Count the squares altogether and record as A = ____ cm². Explain that area is measured in square centimetres or cm² because the rectangle can be measured in two ways: length and breadth (width). A line in one direction is measured in cm, but an area is covered by square centimetres. 1cm² is a square 1cm long and 1cm wide.
Repeat this, using the other polygon on your OHT.

Individual work: Distribute the 'Count the area' activity sheet. Explain that these are 2-D shapes divided into square centimetres. Ask the children to find the area that each shape covers by counting the squares.

Differentiation

Less able: Provide additional support. It may help the children to keep count of the squares if they tick off or colour each square.

More able: Provide also the version of 'Count the area' with composite shapes, and with half-squares to count.

Plenary & assessment

Using squared paper, shade a rectangle 6cm by 7cm. Ask:

● *What unit do we use to measure area? Can you explain why area is measured in **square** centimetres?*

● *What is the area of this shape? How do you know? By counting the squares? Can anybody suggest a quicker way to find the number of squares?* (Multiplying the number of squares across by the number down. So 6cm × 7cm = 42cm².)

Draw several more squares and rectangles on squared paper. For each one, ask the children to supply a number sentence that gives the area.

Lesson ②

Starter

Indicate the number line on the board with digits placed along it at random. Ask the children whether the digits are correctly placed. Ask them to place each digit correctly by adding or subtracting. For example, if −3 is placed where 0 should be, then move −3 to the left by three places. Carry on until all the digits are in the correct places.

Main teaching activities

Whole class: Remind the children of how they found areas by counting square centimetres in Lesson 1. Explain that for squares and rectangles, the area can be calculated as length × breadth. Draw a rectangle and label the sides 2cm and 6cm. Apply the formula: area = 2cm × 6cm = 12cm². Check your answer by asking the children to count the squares. Repeat using a number of different squares and rectangles.

Individual work: Ask the children to draw some squares and rectangles on 1cm squared paper (using the printed lines), then measure the sides and apply the length × breadth formula to find the area. They should record the area, then check it by counting the squares.

Differentiation

Less able: If the children find the calculation difficult, they can find the area by counting the squares. They may also need assistance to draw the shapes accurately.

More able: The children could be encouraged to draw composite shapes made up of two or more different squares or rectangles joined together, find the area of each section and then add them to find the total area.

Plenary & assessment

Check the understanding of how to calculate area by drawing and labelling several rectangles and asking the children to find the area of each. Draw a composite shape such as an 'L' shape, and ask: *How can we find the area if the shape is not a rectangle?* (If it has straight sides, we may be able to divide it into squares and rectangles.) Demonstrate that the 'L' shape is made up of two rectangles. Find the area of each rectangle, then add them together. Repeat with another composite shape.

Lesson ③

Starter

Make a human number line. Give a positive or negative digit card to each of eight children and ask them to stand in a line. Ask the rest of the class to reorder the children, from the smallest to the largest number, by giving them instructions such as 'Jane, move three places to your left.'

Main teaching activities

Whole class: Draw a rectangle on the board and explain that this represents a field. Label the sides as 4m and 3m. Ask the children to find the area (12m²). Now label the sides 4m and 320cm. Ask the children whether they can see a difficulty with finding this area (there are mixed units). Explain that combining two different units means that the calculation will be incorrect, so we need to make sure that both sides are measured in the same unit: either 4m × 3.2m or 400cm × 320cm. Remind the children that they can partition to help them multiply decimals or multiples of 100. In this case, 4 × 3 = 12 and 4 × 0.2 = 0.8, so area = 12.8m². Alternatively, 400 × 300 = 120 000 and 400 × 20 = 8000, so area = 128 000cm². (This value would have to be divided by 100 to convert it back to m².)
    Repeat this, using other mixed units such as cm and mm or km and m.
Individual work: Distribute the 'Calculate the area' activity sheet. Ask the children to look very carefully at the units of measurement, and to convert each pair of lengths to the same unit before finding the area of each shape.

Differentiation

Less able: Provide the version of 'Calculate the area' where the units do not need to be standardised.
More able: Provide the version that involves finding the areas of composite shapes as well as converting units.

Plenary & assessment

Draw a rectangle with the sides labelled 2.3m and 300cm. Write in the middle: 'Area = 6.9cm'. Ask: *Is this area correct? Why not? How can we put it right? What tips would you give to someone who wanted to find the area of this shape?*
    Draw a rectangle and label its area as 12m². Ask: *What lengths might the sides be? Is there more than one possible answer? Why?* List all the possible answers. Repeat with another rectangle with the area 18cm² and a square with the area 16cm².

Lesson ④

Starter

Revise converting units of measure by asking: How many millilitres in a litre?… metres in a kilometre?…grams in a kilogram?…centimetres in a metre? Ask questions such as: *How many grams are there in 1.5kg? 2 000m is equal to how many km? How many metres are equivalent to 300cm?*

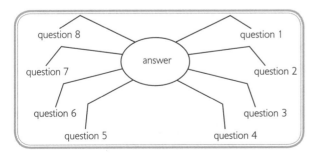

Main teaching activities

Whole class: Ask the children to think about the area of the classroom floor, their living room and bathroom floors, and the playground. Ask: *What units would it be measured in? How would you measure it?* Ask the children to estimate each area.
    Now ask: *If the answer is 24cm², what could the question be?* Take suggestions (such as 'What is the area of a rectangle with the sides measuring 2cm and 12cm?') and record some

on the board. Repeat with: *If the answer is 1.5l, what could the question be?* Write the answer in the centre of a spidergram (see figure on left) and record a variety of questions. As a class, generate more questions and answers on a measures theme.

Paired work: The children can work in pairs to generate another three answers each, then swap and write eight possible questions to match each answer.

Differentiation

Less able: Provide answers (such as 25cm, 12cm², 3 litres, 32m², 1500g, 1000ml) for this group to match with questions.

More able: Ask this group to suggest two-step questions. For example, if the answer is 4.2m², the question could be: 'If one of the sides of a rectangle is 0.7m and the other is 600cm, convert them to a common unit and find the area.'

Plenary & assessment

Write on the board: 64.2cm × 5. Ask the children to imagine that they work in a DIY store, and this is a problem they need to solve. Ask them to note down a possible scenario that requires this calculation. Share some ideas and record them for a display. Ask: *Is there another way this answer could have been reached? Could you change your question to make a two-step problem?* For example: 'I am making 5 bookshelves for my bedroom. Each shelf has to be 64.2cm long to fit into an alcove. How much wood will I need to buy? If wood costs £5 a metre, how much will I need to spend?

Repeat using (£20 + £17) × 5. Ask the children to write a two-step problem and explain how they would solve it.

Lesson

Starter

Indicate the randomly displayed weights and measures cards on the board. Ask individual children to find matching pairs such as 1.5l =1500ml.

Main teaching activities

Whole class: Repeat the initial whole-class activity from Lesson 4, but focus on smaller areas in the classroom such as the cover of an exercise book, the cover of an atlas and a lunchbox lid.

Write the following problem on the board. *A farmer has a field 6m long and 9m wide. What is its total area? He then buys a smaller square field adjoining the first one, with a side length of 4m. What is the total area of the farmer's land?* Ask a child to visualise and draw the two adjoining fields (with a shared boundary line), and to label the sides of

$$6m \times 9m = 54m^2$$
$$4m \times 4m = \underline{16m^2}$$
$$\text{total area} = 70m^2$$

each field. Remind them that the l × b formula only works for squares and rectangles, so the areas of the two fields need to be calculated separately and then added together:

Group and individual work: Ask the children, working in pairs, to measure the dimensions and calculate the areas of the classroom objects discussed in the whole-class session. Ask: *How did you work out the area? Was it close to your original estimate? What units does the area have?* Ask them to write the calculation as an l × b sum.

Differentiation

Less able: Provide shapes which have whole cm measurements. Children can find the areas of them, using the straightforward l × b formula.

More able: Ask children to estimate and measure composite shapes such as the area of carpet in the classroom.

Plenary & assessment

Recap on the children's understanding of area. Ask: *How can I find the area of a rectangle? What is the formula or rule that we use?* Now draw a shape consisting of a joined square and rectangle. Ask: *How can we find the area of this shape? Why can it not be solved using one calculation?*

| Name | Date |

Count the area

Find the area of each rectangle or square by counting the square centimetres.

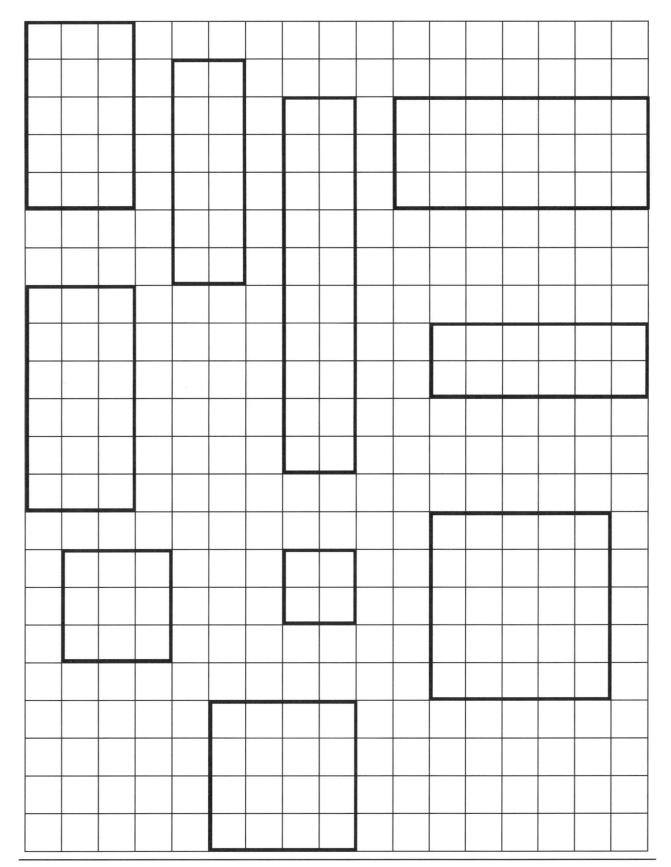

Name   Date

Calculate the area

Calculate the area of each shape.

Warning! Look carefully at the units of measurement.

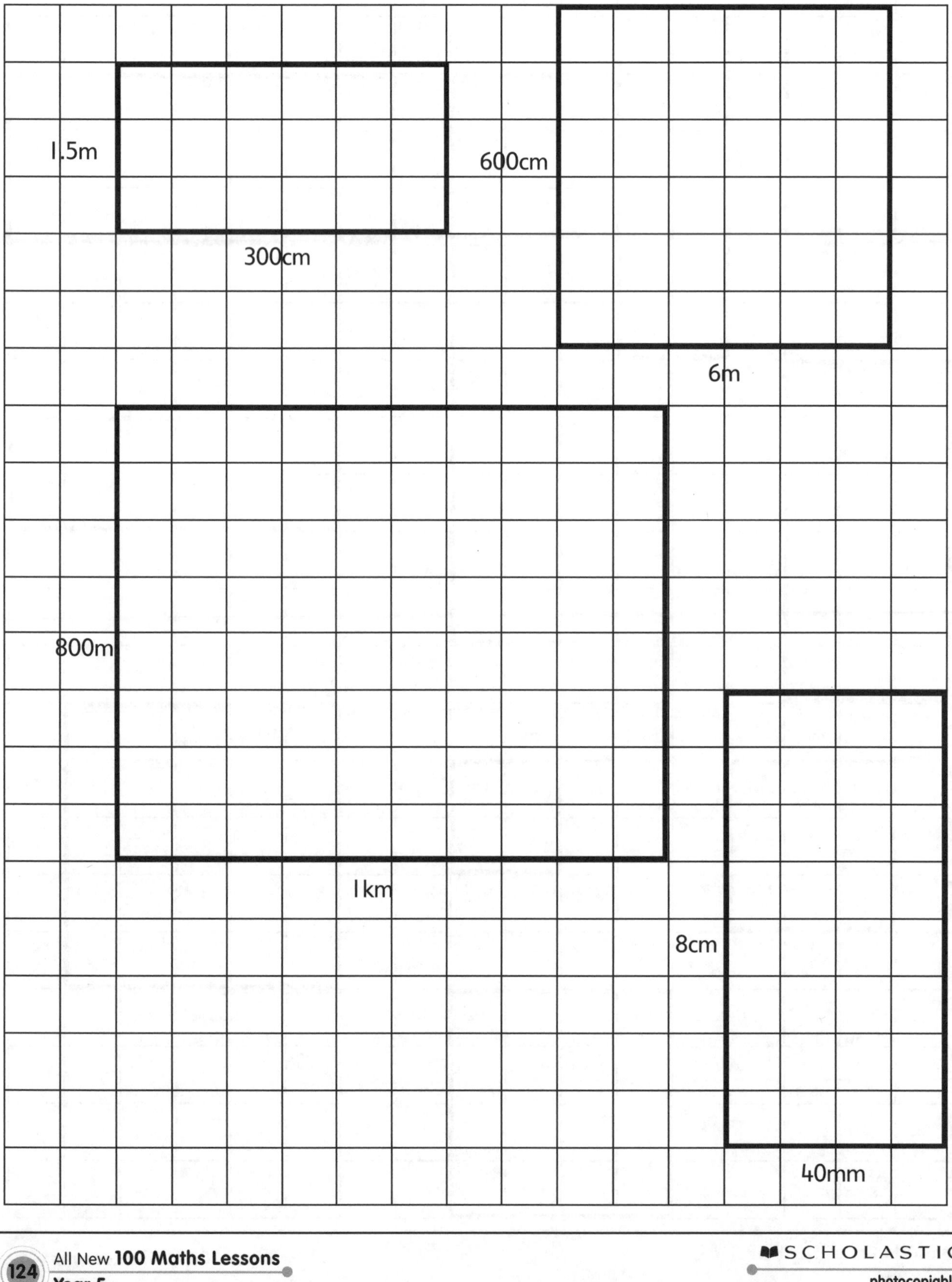

1.5m

300cm

600cm

6m

800m

1km

8cm

40mm

◾SCHOLASTIC
photocopiable

Handling data

This unit gives children opportunities to collect data to provide information relevant to their individual school situation. They then have to present their data in an appropriate graph or chart and present the information to others.

LEARNING OBJECTIVES

	Topics	Starter	Main teaching activity
Lesson 1	Handling data	● Derive quickly all two-digit pairs that total 100 (eg 43 + 57).	● Solve a problem by representing and interpreting data in tables, charts, graphs and diagrams, including those generated by computer, for example: bar line charts, vertical axis labelled in 2s, 5s, 10s, 20s or 100s, first where intermediate points have no meaning (eg scores on a dice rolled 50 times), then where they may have meaning (eg room temperature over time).
Lesson 2		As for Lesson 1.	As for Lesson 1.
Lesson 3		● **Round a number with one or two decimal places to the nearest integer.**	As for Lesson 1.
Lesson 4		● **Multiply and divide any positive integer up to 10 000 by 10 or 100 and understand the effect** (eg 9900 ÷ 10, 737 ÷ 10, 2060 ÷ 100).	As for Lesson 1.
Lesson 5		● Read and write whole numbers in figures and words, and know what each digit represents.	As for Lesson 1.

Lessons   overview

Preparation
For Lesson 1, prepare a 1–100 number line; also provide an example of a bar chart, a comparative bar chart and a line graph, one of which has no title or labels. For Lesson 5, write the calculations (see 'Starter') in words on the board.

Learning objectives
Starter
● Derive quickly all two-digit pairs that total 100 (eg 43 + 57).
● **Round a number with one or two decimal places to the nearest integer.**
● **Multiply and divide any positive integer up to 10 000 by 10 or 100 and understand the effect** (eg 9 900 ÷ 10, 737 ÷ 10, 2060 ÷ 100).
● Read and write whole numbers in figures and words, and know what each digit represents.
Main teaching activities
● Solve a problem by representing and interpreting data in tables, charts, graphs and diagrams, including those generated by computer, for example: bar line charts, vertical axis labelled in 2s, 5s, 10s, 20s or 100s, first where intermediate points have no meaning (eg scores on a dice rolled 50 times), then where they may have meaning (eg room temperature over time).

Vocabulary
count, tally, sort, vote, survey, database, line graph, represent, bar chart, bar line chart, comparative bar chart, frequency table, mode, range, median, maximum/minimum value, outcome

You will need
Photocopiable pages
'Every picture tells a story', see page 130, one for each child.

CD pages
'Number fan cards 0–9', one for each child; a set of 'Number cards 1–100', a set for teacher's/LSA's use (see General resources, Autumn term). 'Every picture tells a story', less able version (see Spring term, Unit 8).

Equipment
Rough paper and pencils; squared or graph paper; large sheets of paper or card.

Lesson ①

Starter

Ask a child to pick a number card (1–100) and place it as accurately as possible on your prepared 1–100 number line, then use the number line to find its partner to make 100 by counting on (for example: '43 add 7 makes 50 and another 50 makes 100. So the pair to make 100 are 43 and 57.' Repeat with other numbers. Then ask the children to recall pairs to make 100 without counting on the number line. Repeat several times, then ask: *Which pairs can you recall at once? Which pairs are more difficult?*

Main teaching activities

Whole class: Explain that this week of activities is all about graphs and how they represent information in a visual form that others can extract information from easily. Revise with the children the types of graph most appropriate for different kinds of data. Ask: *If I wanted to compare the number of visitors to a shopping centre on different days of the week, what sort of graph would be most appropriate? Can you suggest other kinds of information that might be shown on a bar chart or a bar line graph? How would my graph look different if I wanted to compare the numbers of boys and girls who visited the centre on each day?*

Remind the children that sometimes bar charts can be used to compare two sets of data. In this example, we could draw two bars in different colours for each day, comparing the numbers of male and female visitors. This is called a **comparative bar chart**, and it extends the number of different factors that can be presented.

Now display a line graph and ask: *What do we call this type of graph? What kind of information is displayed on a line graph? Why is it not a suitable way of displaying a comparison – for example, of shoe sizes?*

Display a graph of any type, without a title or any labels. Discuss how graphs need titles and labels to tell the reader what was being measured or compared. Ask the children to guess what your unlabelled graph might be showing. Can they suggest a title and suitable labels for the axes?

Individual work: Distribute the 'Every picture tells a story' activity sheet. Explain that this page shows some graphs, but somebody forgot to write the titles and label the axes. Remind the children that all graphs 'tell a story'. Ask them to think about what each graph might represent, and to label and title it accordingly.

Differentiation

Less able: Provide the version of the activity sheet with the labels and titles provided in a jumbled-up order for the children to relate to the appropriate graphs.

More able: Ask the children to generate an 'unlabelled graph' of their own for a friend to label. They should decide what the labels should be before they draw the graph.

Plenary & assessment

Ask what the graphs on the activity sheet might represent. Suggestions might include: visitors to a library; noise in a dining hall; rainfall in two different places. Ask: *Who might use this graph? Why do people represent information on a graph instead of writing it?* Explain that graphs tell people things, and often more useful information can be presented in a single graph than could be explained in several pages of writing. However, graphs give no information at all if they do not have appropriate titles and labels.

Lesson ②

Starter

Show the children a 1–100 number card and ask them to show you the matching number to make 100 with their number fans.

Main teaching activities

Whole class: Explain that the rest of the week's activities are going to involve collecting information, creating a database and presenting the data graphically. Each group will collect data to find the answer to a question. If possible, it should be a question of practical use and interest to people in, or connected with, the school. Discuss what questions the groups might wish to ask, and what information they will need to collect. Suggestions might include:

- 'What are the most/least popular dishes served for school lunch?'
- 'What PE equipment is used in the school?' (This could be divided into indoor and outdoor equipment to make the data collection more manageable.)
- 'Which computer program do we spend the most time working with?' This could be applied to the computer suite or the classroom computers. A log could be kept next to the computer, and times and programs entered for a day or a week.

There are many possible surveys related to the school. Emphasise that they must be manageable in terms of data collection and the time available. Discuss how the children intend to collect the data – they can't stand in one place all day logging data. Encourage them to produce a tally chart for efficient data collection.

Paired/group work: Ask each pair or group to plan an investigation posing a question which can be solved by collecting and displaying data.

Differentiation

Less able: Guide the children towards a simple comparison of data, such as the numbers of different balls used for PE, netball, tennis and so on.

More able: Guide the children towards making a comparative line graph. For example, they could carry out a time audit to compare the amount of computer use in the computer suite, in a classroom and in the office each hour over a day.

Plenary & assessment

Check the groups' progress, and discuss the manageability of their projects with them. Ask each group to report to the class what data they are going to collect, how they intend to represent the information and who they think will find it useful.

Lesson ③

For the starter, ask the children to write (on paper) a number with two decimal places between 1 and 2 (such as 1.26). Now ask groups or the whole class to sort their numbers according to whether they would be rounded up to 2 or down to 1. Ask the children to suggest a rule for this. (1.5 or above is rounded up to 2.)

In the main teaching activity, let the groups or pairs carry out the data collection they planned in Lesson 2. This may be ongoing if collection is to take place over a day. Decide which groups or pairs need more support, or can be guided towards a more challenging investigation. Use the plenary to check the children's progress and iron out any difficulties. Ask: *How are you going to turn the data into a graph? What type of graph will it be?*

Lesson ④

Starter
Select some examples of the decimal numbers written in Lesson 3. Hold them up and ask the children to multiply or divide each number by 10 or 100. Record their answers on the board. Revise the effect of these operations: the digits remain the same but move up one or two places, and the 'spaces' are filled by 0 to hold the place value. Revise the effect of dividing by 10 or 100: the digits move down one or two places. If the digits move beyond the decimal point, the number becomes a decimal.

Main teaching activities
Whole class: Before the children go on to create their graphs, either by hand or with a computer program such as *Number Box* or *Excel*, they need to establish a viable and manageable scale for the x and y axes. For children counting items of PE equipment, a y-axis scale in ones might be used. For children investigating the use of a computer, a time scale on the x axis of 09:00–15:00 in steps of 15 or 30 minutes might be used. The necessary scale will depend on the data collected and the size of the sample. Remind the children that the graph must fit on one page, and that changing the scale can make the data look very different.
Paired/group work: The children should create a graph to represent their data.

Differentiation
Less able: It may help the children to have the scale of the graph provided for them.
More able: The children should be able to create a comparative line graph on a computer, if one is available. They might like to experiment with changing the scales on the y axis to manipulate the 'look' of their graph. This can be linked to the Year 5 QCA unit for ICT 'Introduction to databases'.

Plenary & assessment
Establish that all the children are well on the way to creating a graph. Display some of the graphs that have been manipulated to 'look different' by using different scales. Discuss the effect. *Why would anyone want to do this?*

Lesson ⑤

Starter

Indicate the calculations shown below, written (in words) on the board. Ask the children what language clues are in each one to suggest what type of calculation is needed. Ask the children to find the answers and explain their methods.

> *Find the total of eighty-one and sixty-eight.*
> *What is the product of 25 and 3?*
> *Subtract seventeen from fifty.*
> *How many grams are there in two and a half kilograms?*

Main teaching activity

Whole class: Explain that the children now have a visual image of their data, and they can use this to inform or persuade other people. Model an example: *This graph clearly shows…* or *From this graph we can draw the conclusion…*

Revise the idea of the mode: the 'most popular' option or highest bar in a bar chart. Teach the idea of the median: the middle number in a range when the numbers are written in order of increasing size. For example, scores of 3, 6, 4, 2, 1, 8, 9 can be written in size order: 1, 2, 3, 4, 6, 8, 9. The median is the middle number or bar – in this case, 4. Explain that if the number of numbers or bars is even, the median is calculated by adding the two middle values and dividing by 2.

Paired/group work: Ask each group to create a presentation based on their findings. This should include a statement beginning 'Our graph shows…' and an outline of the process, including the planning, a tally chart, details of any problems, the graph and a conclusion. Their presentations will also be used in a display, and perhaps used to inform the relevant person in the school – for example, the kitchen staff might like to know which dishes are most popular, or the PE staff might find an equipment audit helpful.

Encourage the children to think of any suggestions that might follow from their findings. For example: *Our graph shows that we need to buy more tennis balls before next summer.* Or: *Perhaps we could persuade the kitchen not to cook cabbage, because our graph shows that nobody likes it.*

Differentiation

Less able: The children should make simple statements based on their graph, such as 'The most popular food is…'
More able: The children should be able to look at further implications of their findings. For example: 'We found out that there are 3 fully inflated basketballs. We need to inflate the others or buy new ones, since this is not enough for a class lesson.'

Plenary & assessment

Use this time to reflect on the process, and for the groups to present and persuade using their graphs. Ask questions such as:

● *How would your data be different if you had monitored the use of the computer over a longer period of time?*
● *How would your graph be different if you had asked the whole school about their food choices? How would you have changed the scale of the graph?*

Name   Date

Every picture tells a story

Using your imagination and your knowledge of graphs, think about what each of these graphs might be showing. Label the axes of each graph and give the graph a title.

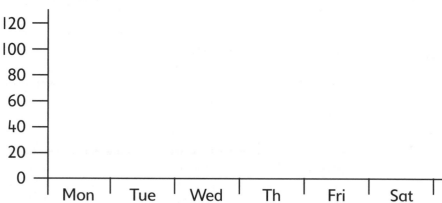

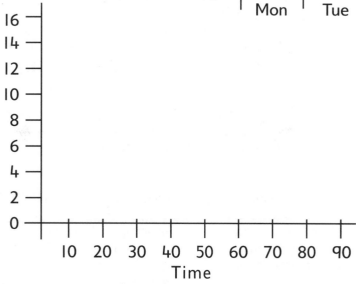

A graph to show contrasting temperatures in _____ and _____

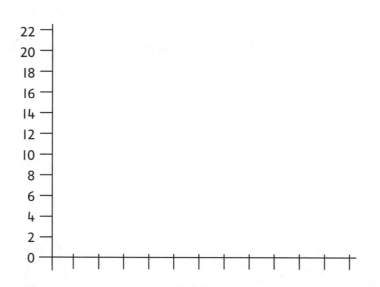

Adding and subtraction

In this unit, children are shown strategies for making seemingly tricky calculations simpler, for example rounding and adjusting numbers to be added together. This then leads on to formal written addition and subtraction to solve problems.

LEARNING OBJECTIVES

		Topics	Starter	Main teaching activity
Lesson	1	Mental calculation strategies (+ and −)	● Know addition and subtraction facts for all numbers to 20 (Year 4 revision).	● Add or subtract the nearest multiple of 10 or 100, then adjust. ● Develop further the relationship between addition and subtraction.
Lesson	2	Mental calculation strategies (+ and −Pencil and paper procedures (+ and −)	As for Lesson 1.	● Identify near doubles, such as 1.5 + 1.6. ● Use informal paper and pencil methods to support, record or explain additions and subtractions.
Lesson	3	Pencil and paper procedures (+ and −)	● Use doubling or halving, starting from known facts. For example: double/halve any two-digit number by doubling/halving the tens first.	● **Extend written methods to column addition/subtraction of two integers less than 10 000.**
Lesson	4	Pencil and paper procedures (+ and −)	● **Use all four operations to solve simple word problems involving numbers and quantities** based on 'real life', money and measures **(including time)**, using one or more steps.	● Extend written methods to: addition of more than two integers less than 10 000; addition or subtraction of a pair of decimal fractions, both with one or both with two decimal places (eg £29.78 + £53.34).
Lesson	5	Pencil and paper procedures (+ and −)	As for Lesson 4.	As for Lesson 3.

Lessons overview

Preparation
For Lesson 4, write the word problems (see 'Starter') on the board.

Learning objectives
Starter
● Know addition and subtraction facts for all numbers to 20 (Year 4 revision).
● Use doubling or halving, starting from known facts. For example: double/halve any two-digit number by doubling/halving the tens first.
● **Use all four operations to solve simple word problems involving numbers and quantities** based on 'real life', money and measures **(including time)**, using one or more steps.
Main teaching activities
● Add or subtract the nearest multiple of 10 or 100, then adjust.
● Develop further the relationship between addition and subtraction.
● Identify near doubles, such as 1.5 + 1.6.
● Use informal paper and pencil methods to support, record or explain additions and subtractions.
● **Extend written methods to: column addition/subtraction of two integers less than 10 000;** addition of more than two integers less than 10 000; addition or subtraction of a pair of decimal fractions, both with one or both with two decimal places (eg £29.78 + 53.34).

Vocabulary
add, addition, more, plus, increase, double, near double, subtract, take away, minus, decrease

You will need
Photocopiable pages
'Written methods for addition', see page 136, one for each child; 'Written methods for subtraction', see page 137, one for each child.

CD pages
'Number fan cards 0–9', one for each child (see General resources, Autumn term). 'Written methods for addition' and 'Written methods for subtraction', less able and more able versions (see Spring term, Unit 9).

Equipment
Dice.

Lesson ①

Starter

Draw a Venn diagram of two overlapping set rings on the board, labelling one ring '24' and the other '18'. Ask the children to supply number facts to fit into the diagram, such as $6 \times 4 = 24$ or $12 + 6 = 18$. Ask the children whether any number facts will fit into the intersection. (No.) Repeat using two different numbers.

Main teaching activities

Whole class: Explain that today's activity is about using familiar number facts and adjusting them in order to calculate with more difficult numbers. Remind the children how they multiplied by 19 or 21 (see Term 2 Unit 2, Lesson 3). This time, they are going to add and subtract near multiples of 10 or 100. Ask: *Can you round 49 to the nearest 10?* (50.) Explain that as 50 is easier to add than 49, we can add 49 quickly by rounding and adjusting. For example: $49 + 114$ is 1 short of $50 + 114 = 164$. So the answer is $164 - 1 = 163$.

Demonstrate how this can help with subtracting. $204 - 57$ is 4 over $200 - 57 = 143$. So the answer is $143 + 4 = 147$. Repeat with several examples of addition and subtraction to make sure the children know which way to adjust the answer after rounding up or down. For example: $39 + 46$; $156 + 206$; $49 - 23$; $203 - 189$. Remind the children that informal jottings can help us to keep track, especially when rounding and adjusting.

Individual work: Distribute a sheet of adding and subtracting near multiples of 10 and 100. The children can use this to practise addition and subtraction by rounding and adjusting near multiples of 10 or 100.

Differentiation

Less able: Provide a version of problems with only two-digit numbers.
More able: Provide a version with more challenging addition and subtraction problems, requiring informal jottings.

Plenary & assessment

Write '$1003 - 69$' on the board. Ask for a volunteer to come and work it out: $1003 - 69$ is $(3 + 1)$ less than $1000 - 70 = 930$ so answer is $930 + 4 = 934$.

Ask: *How can this method help us to calculate money?* (We can round to the nearest £1 or £10). Ask the children: *I have £29.58 and my aunt has sent me £15. How much do I have now?* (£29.58 is 42p short of $£30 + 15 = £45$ so answer is $£45 - £0.42 = £44.58$.)

Lesson ②

Starter

Repeat the Venn diagram activity from Lesson 1, labelling one ring 'multiples of 6' and the other 'multiples of 8'. This time there will be numbers in the section where the two rings overlap. Discuss why. Repeat with rings labelled 'even numbers' and 'multiples of 3'. Ask the children to predict the numbers in the overlap.

Main teaching activities

Whole class: Write '$35 + 37$' on the board. Ask the children to suggest ways of calculating this. Hopefully someone will notice that these numbers are near doubles. Explain that we can use this fact to double and adjust: $35 + 35 = 70$ so the answer is $70 + 2 = 72$.

Encourage the children to use informal jotting to track their use of near doubles. Explain that they can use the same method to find near doubles of decimal numbers, such as $3.5 + 3.7$. The digits are the same as double 35, but the decimal place needs to be kept to arrive at the correct place value answer: $3.5 + 3.5 = 7.0$ so answer is $7.0 + 0.2 = 7.2$.

Repeat with other near doubles generated by throwing two or three dice. Throw one dice to generate the tens number for both parts of the sum, then throw two dice for the units numbers. So if we throw a 5 followed by a 3 and a 4, the sum generated is 53 + 54. Three dice could be used to generate pairs of three-digit numbers or decimal numbers.

Paired work: The children can use dice to generate near doubles to add, including one-place decimals. They should record using informal jottings.

Differentiation

Less able: The children can use two dice to create two-digit numbers or one-place decimals as appropriate.

More able: The children can use three dice to create three-digit numbers or two-place decimals.

Plenary & assessment

Write some two-digit numbers such as 65, 27, 33, 38, 29, 17, 32, 35 on the board. Ask: *Can all these numbers be doubled easily? Which ones are more difficult? Which ones do you know straight away? Why do some numbers greater than 50 start to cause difficulty when we are doubling? How could doubling help me to solve this problem: 24 × 4?* Ask the children to use repeated doubling to multiply other two-digit numbers by 4.

Lesson

Starter

Following on from the plenary in Lesson 2, look at multiplying by 4. Demonstrate that 16 × 4 is 16 doubled twice; double 16 = 32 and double 32 = 64. Repeat using different numbers. Ask: *Can we use a similar method for dividing by 4?* (Yes: halving and halving again.) Demonstrate that 52 ÷ 4 is 52 halved twice; half 52 = 26 and half 26 = 13. Repeat using 64 ÷ 4; 72 ÷ 4; 68 ÷ 4. The children can use their number fans to show the answers. Now try 26 ÷ 4 = 26; halved twice = half 13 = 6.5.

Main teaching activities

Whole class: Revise column addition (see Term 1 Unit 11). It is probable that some children will be using the expanded method, adding the most significant digit first, and some will be using the

	H T U		H T U		H T U
	1 4 3		2 1 6		3 8 6
+	1 3 2	+	1 4 8	+	1 4 4

standard compact method and 'carrying' digits. (You will need to refer to your school calculation policy to plan the development of various methods.) The most important thing is that each child should have a reliable and accurate written method of addition that they can use with confidence.

Ask for volunteers to solve these problems using their chosen method. Each time, also demonstrate the standard written method, emphasising the 'carried' digit.

Individual work: Distribute the 'Written methods for addition' activity sheet for the children to work through using their chosen method. You may wish to use this time to focus on a group who are ready to move from the expanded method to a more compact one.

Differentiation

Less able: The children can complete the version of the activity sheet with simpler three-digit addition problems, using the expanded written method.

More able: The children can complete the version with four-digit numbers, including decimals.

Plenary & assessment

It may be useful to go through some of the problems from the sheet, asking individuals to demonstrate and talk through their method on the board. Ask: *Can a written calculation be used for adding more than two numbers?* (Both methods will work for adding multiple numbers, though the standard compact method can accommodate larger 'carried' digits more easily.) Ask for a confident volunteer to demonstrate how they would add three HTU numbers:

```
    1 2 1
    2 3 4
  + 1 9 7
    5 5 2
    1 1
```

Lesson ④

Starter

Indicate the word problems shown below, written on the board. Ask the children to solve them and use their number fans to show the answer. Discuss the operations and methods the children have used.

> 1. A man cycles 5 miles to work and the same on his return. He works 5 days a week. How far does he cycle each week?
> 2. Joe has collected 45 football stickers. He buys 19 more. How many stickers does he have in total?
> 3. Felicity decides that she has far too many hair clips, and gives half of them to her sister. If she started with 52 hairclips, how many does Felicity have left?
> 4. Fruity chews are sold in bags of 84. Each bag has equal numbers of the 4 different flavours. How many of each flavour are there?

Main teaching activities

Whole class: Explain to the children that they are going to carry on adding more than two numbers. Look at a shopping list on the board, such as the one on the right. Demonstrate this calculation, using the compact method. Encourage the children to look for numbers to 'make 10' when adding a large column of figures. Emphasise that the units add up to 22 – that is, 2 in the

crisps	64p
sweets	26p
carrots	39p
a banana +	43p
	172p = £1.72
	2

units and 2 tens (to be added to the tens column). Repeat this using decimal numbers, as on the left.

Highlight the fact that the decimal points must always stay aligned, one under the other, in all the column numbers including the answer.

apples	£1.54	
squash	£1.29	Keep the place
a chicken	£3.99	value by
biscuits +	0.65	including 0
	£7.47	pounds.
	2 2	

Individual work: Ask the children to create some shopping list sums with three or four numbers. Ask them to record the items and the prices. Encourage careful presentation to make sure that place value is handled correctly.

Differentiation

Less able: The children can use a version of the shopping list with items priced in multiples of 5p to simplify addition. They can use the expanded method of addition.

More able: The children can use a version with more difficult numbers. Encourage them to try longer additions.

Plenary & assessment

Ask the children to devise a class rule for helping someone add a long list of prices. They should suggest: line up the decimal points; keep the place value correct; 'carry over' any extra digits to the next place value and record them beneath the sum; remember to add any 'extras' to the next column. Record this as a class 'brainstorm' on a large sheet of paper to be displayed in the classroom for future reference.

Lesson ⑤

Starter

Ask the children to think of word problems involving mental calculations, such as: 'I picked 28 plums from my aunt's tree. She gave me half of them to take home. How many plums did I have?' Take suggestions. Write good examples on the board and ask the class to solve them, explaining their methods.

Main teaching activity

Whole class: Revise column subtraction, using both the expanded method and the standard compact method with decomposition. (See Term 1 Unit 11.) Ask for two volunteers to come and calculate the following using their preferred method (one child using each method):

Individual work: Distribute the 'Written methods for subtraction' activity sheet. Explain that

```
              100        130
  H  T  U
  2  3  9  =  200  +  30  +  9
 -1  4  6  =  100  +  40  +  6
 ────────    ─────────────────
     9  3      0  +  90  +  3
```

```
  H   T   U
  2¹  ¹3  9
 -1   4   6
 ───────────
      9   3
```

these are all subtraction questions to be solved by using a written method. While the children are working on the sheet, you might choose to focus on a group who are ready to move on to the standard compact method.

Differentiation

Less able: Provide the version of the activity sheet with simplified two-digit and three-digit numbers. The children should use the expanded method.
More able: Provide the version with more demanding problems. Expect the children to use the standard compact method.

Plenary & assessment

Write the following incorrect calculation on the board. Ask the children to look at it carefully and decide where the person has made a mistake. Then ask: *Can you correct this calculation?* (The person has taken each smaller digit from the larger digit instead of taking the bottom number from the top. The answer should be 389.) *What tips would you give someone to help them with column subtraction?*

```
                          400   100  12
  H T U
  5 6 2 =            500 + 60 +2
 -1 7 3 =            100 + 70 +3
 ────────           ─────────────
  3 3 9 =            300 + 30 + 9
```

Repeat using a different incorrect calculation where the mistake is in the redistribution of the numbers. For example:

```
  H T U
  4 7 2
 -1 8 4
 ───────
  3 1 2
```

Name	Date

Written methods for addition

Use a written method to answer these questions.

1. 134 + 231

_____

2. 442 + 169

_____

3. H T U
   3 1 4
+ 2 9 1

_____

4. H T U
   2 8 8
+ 1 7 4

_____

5. H T U
   2 0 8
+ 3 0 4

_____

6. Lee had 127 game cards. His brother gave him another 158. What was the total number of cards that Lee had?

_____

7. Anya scored 149 in her first game and 216 in the next game. What was her total score?

_____

Name   Date

Written methods for subtraction

Use a written method to answer these questions.

1. 2 3 8
   – 1 2 5
   _____

   _____

2. 4 7 1
   – 3 4 6
   _____

   _____

3. 3 1 1
   – 2 0 1
   _____

   _____

4. 6 8 4
   – 1 7 9
   _____

   _____

5. Jim has 122 CDs. He sells 36 of them at a sale. How many does he keep?

_____

6. Ailish has £48.62 in her purse. She spends £26.91. How much does she have left?

_____

7. 641 – 318

_____

8. 702 – 249

_____

9. 806 – 419

_____

Written addition and subtraction

This unit offers further opportunities to practise written addition and subtraction in a 'real life' context, using money.

LEARNING OBJECTIVES

	Topics	Starter	Main teaching activity
Lesson 1	Pencil and paper procedures (+ and −)	● Order a set of fractions such as 2, 2 ¾, 1¾, 2½, 1½.	● **Extend written methods to: column addition/subtraction of two integers less than 10 000;** addition or subtraction of a pair of decimal fractions, both with one or both with two decimal places (eg £29.78 + £53.34).
Lesson 2	Problems involving 'real life', money and measures	As for Lesson 1.	● **Use all four operations to solve simple word problems involving numbers and quantities** based on 'real life' money and measures **(including time),** using one or more steps.
Lesson 3	Problems involving 'real life' and money Checking results of calculations Making decisions	● Use, read and write standard metric units (km, m, cm, mm, kg, g, l, ml, l), including their abbreviations, and relationships between them. Convert larger to smaller units (eg km to m, m to cm or mm, kg to g, l to ml).	● **Use all four operations to solve simple word problems involving numbers and quantities** based on 'real life' money and measures **(including time),** using one or more steps. ● Check the sum of several numbers by adding in the reverse order. ● Choose and use appropriate number operations to solve problems, and appropriate ways of calculating: mental, mental with jottings, written methods, calculator.
Lesson 4		As for Lesson 3.	As for Lesson 3.
Lesson 5		As for Lesson 3.	As for Lesson 3.

Lesson ① overview

Learning objectives
Starter
● Order a set of fractions such as 2, 2 ¾, 1¾, 2½, 1½.
Main teaching activities
● **Extend written methods to: column addition/subtraction of two integers less than 10 000;** addition or subtraction of a pair of decimal fractions, both with one, or both with two decimal places (eg £29.78 + £53.34).

Vocabulary
See Unit 9.

You will need
Equipment
Paper and pencils or individual whiteboards.

Lesson

Starter
The children work in groups of six. Ask them each to write down a fraction between 6 and 7 (such as 6 1/3). Ask the group to order their fractions, the smallest first. Ask: *How do you know which is bigger, 1/5 or 1/8?* (The larger the denominator, the smaller the fraction.) Ask each group to read out their list for the class to check. Correct any errors.

Main teaching activities
Whole class: Continue the work on column subtraction from Unit 9. You may choose to work with children experiencing difficulties, or with those ready to move on to the standard method of written subtraction.

With the class, revise the various strategies available for solving subtraction problems: counting on, counting on using a number line or informal jottings, the expanded method of written calculation and the standard compact method. Discuss briefly when each method might be appropriate (for example, counting on for time or small money differences; a written method for large differences).

Individual work: Provide a variety of subtraction word problems. Remind the children that they can choose from a number of subtraction strategies to solve these word problems.

Differentiation
Less able: Provide some simplified subtraction word problems where the calculations can be managed using counting on methods.

More able: Provide word problems with more demanding calculations and some two-step problems.

Plenary & assessment
Write a time problem on the board (such as: 'Westweekers' starts 19.15, ends 20.35). Ask: *Is it appropriate to do a written subtraction calculation with this problem? Which method did you use?* Ask for a volunteer to demonstrate how to find the answer by counting on, using informal jottings to keep track of the hours and minutes. Ask: *Which sort of question definitely needed a written column subtraction? Which are mental calculations?*

Write '156 – 93' on the board. Say: *Think of a word problem that could be solved by using this calculation. What method would you use to solve it?* Take a few suggestions for word problems. Ask for volunteers to solve the problems in their chosen way. Repeat with 1373 – 894.

Lessons   overview

Learning objectives
Starters
● Use, read and write standard metric units (km, m, cm, mm, kg, g, l, ml, l), including their abbreviations, and relationships between them. Convert larger to smaller units (eg km to m, m to cm or mm, kg to g, l to ml).

Main teaching activities
● **Use all four operations to solve simple word problems involving numbers and quantities** based on 'real life' money and measures **(including time)**, using one or more steps.
● Check the sum of several numbers by adding in the reverse order.
● Choose and use appropriate number operations to solve problems, and appropriate ways of calculating: mental, mental with jottings, written methods, calculator.

Vocabulary
sign, operation, symbol, method, strategy, jotting, answer, how much?…, how many?…, change, calculate, calculation

You will need
Photocopiable pages
'Sid's Snowy Sports shop', see page 143, one for each child and 'All new 100 Maths Theme Park', see page 144, one per child.

CD pages
'Sid's Snowy Sports shop', less able version (see Spring term, Unit 10).

Equipment
Paper and pencils.

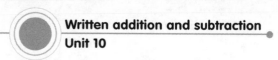

Lesson ②

Starter

Continue the work on ordering fractions from Lesson 1. Each group of six children can order the fractions belonging to another group. Work with the whole class to order all of the fractions. Discuss equivalent fractions as they arise (for example, 6 6/9 = 6 2/3).

Main teaching activities

Whole class: Explain that today's activities will include adding more than two items. Revise how to do this, including 'carrying' (see Term 2 Unit 9, Lesson 4). Remind the children of familiar addition strategies, such as looking for opportunities to make 10 or using near doubles. Also demonstrate how we can check an addition by adding the numbers in a different order, perhaps adding the most significant digits first (as in the expanded method).

Individual work: Distribute the 'Sid's Snowy Sports shop' activity sheet. Ask the children to calculate the given shopping bills from the price list. The last question is relatively 'open'.

Differentiation

Less able: Provide a version of the activity sheet with a simplified price list.
More able: Encourage the children to use the standard compact method for their calculations, and to check their answers by adding in a different order (using informal jottings).

Plenary & assessment

Write a list of three of the items from Sid's Snowy Sports shop on the board. Ask: *Why is it inadvisable to try to add more than two of these numbers mentally? What advice would you give to someone who is adding a list of numbers, especially decimal numbers such as amounts of money?* Make a class checklist of suggestions. This should include: line up the place values exactly; write the carried-over number below the calculation, but in the correct place value space; look for easy addition strategies; check with an alternative calculation.

Share some of the children's answers to the activity sheet. Ask the children to use the class checklist to find out where they have made errors, and to correct some of the calculations together on the board. Use this to establish any problem areas.

Lesson ③

Starter

Explore capacity equivalents by asking questions such as: How many millilitres in a litre? How many millilitres make 3.5 litres… 6.8 litres… 5.2 litres… 4.9 litres? Convert these amounts into litres: 4500ml… 1300ml… 550ml… 250ml. The children volunteer answers by raising their hands.

Main teaching activities

Whole class: Explain that today's activity continues with the theme of Sid's Snowy Sports Shop, but involves problems with more than one step. For example: *If I buy my nephew a pair of skates, socks, gloves and a hat, how much change will I get from £100?* Work through this problem together, pointing out that the first step is to work out how much was spent and the second step is to subtract that from £100. Ask for volunteers to work through the steps on the board. Ask: *Do we need written subtraction to work out the change?* Help the children to see that it is easier to count on to £100, since this is a relatively small difference.

Individual work:. Set a budget and ask the children to calculate the change for five sets of two items, using the price list on 'Sid's Snowy Sports shop'.

Differentiation

Less able: The children should use a version of the price list (see Lesson 2) with more manageable numbers.

More able: See Lesson 2. Offer an additional challenge: *Imagine you have £200 to spend on sports equipment. You cannot go over this limit. Try to spend as much money as possible. What is the **smallest** amount of change you could receive?*

Plenary & assessment

Ask the class: *What is an inverse operation? How can using the inverse operation help us to check this work?* Remind the children that the inverse is the opposite of a given operation, reversing the effect – for example, adding after subtracting or multiplying after dividing. This is helpful for checking an answer: for example, we can check a subtraction by adding back the answer and the lower number to get the higher number. Demonstrate this, using some of the sports shop examples. Ask one child to provide a back-up by checking these examples on the board, using the expanded method of addition with informal jottings.

Lesson 4

Starter

Explore equivalent measures by asking such questions as: Which is heavier, 3.2kg or 2300g?… 3.5kg or 3400g?… 6kg or 600g? Remind the children how many grams are in a kilogram. Ask: How many grams are in ½ or ¼ or ¾ of a kilogram? Convert these masses to kilograms: 2350g, 4170g, 2381g.

Main teaching activities

Whole class: Explain to the children that during the next two days, they are going to use all of their problem-solving, addition and subtraction skills. They have to use the information on the 'All New 100 Maths Theme Park' sheet to plan a seven-day holiday for two people. They will need to plan visits and activities over the seven days, and everything spent must be kept as a running budget. Their holiday spending money is €1000 for the week, and this must pay for everything including fares, drinks, food and so on.

Model an example that might represent Day 1, such as:

Visit to All new 100 Maths Theme Park
Entry fees 2 × €11.00 = €22.00
Tricky Tractors 2 × 1.50 = €3.00
Wacky Walrus 2 × 2.00 = €4.00
Sky Rider 2 × 3.00 = €6.00
Ice cream 2 × 1.00 = €2.00
Creepy Cinema 2 × 7.00 = €14.00

Total for the day = €61.00
Money left over: €1000 – €61 = €939

Paired work: Ask the children to use the theme park holiday tariff on the 'All New 100 Maths Theme Park' activity sheet to plan holiday activities for two people for 7 days, keeping within the €1000 overall budget. Allow the children to work in pairs at their own pace. Some may manage only a few days' planning; others may complete the week.

Differentiation

Less able: The children can use a prepared supplementary planning sheet as a framework for planning activities and calculating costs, and use a calculator to keep track of their budgeting.

More able: Differentiate the activity by outcome. Look for more adventurous choices.

Plenary & assessment

Use this time to check the children's progress and troubleshoot difficulties. Remind the children that there are two people and everything has to be paid for per person, so some doubling will be needed.

Ask: *What method are you using to keep track of your running total?* Some children may prefer to draw a number line and count on each day's spending; others will be subtracting as they go, using the compact written method. Ask: *If I spent €379 in the first two days, how much will I have left for the rest of the week?* Ask for a volunteer to demonstrate each method of finding the answer, as shown below.

Lesson ⑤

Starter

Ask various questions about equivalent measures of length, such as: How far in metres is 1.75km?… 3.7km? How far in kilometres is 3295m… 500m? How many centimetres are there in a metre? How many millimetres are equivalent to 250cm?… 385cm?… 1514cm? What unit of measurement would you use to measure the distance from here to France… the length of your pencil?

Main teaching activities

Continue from Lesson 4. Allow the children to add to the tariff list with their own ideas of holiday fun. An extension challenge, for children who have finished the main task, might be to plan an alternative day out: the budget is €100, and all expenses must be fully accounted for. They can invent places to visit and think of likely costs.

Differentiation

Less able: Provide a modelled supplementary planning sheet with the activity sheet as a framework for planning activities and calculating costs. Children can use a calculator to keep track of their budgeting.
More able: Differentiate the activity by outcome. Look for more adventurous choices. The children should move on to the extension activity.

Plenary & assessment

Ask questions to assess the children's ability in computation, estimation and decision-making. *What skills have you employed to solve this problem?* (The children should be able to identify decision-making, doubling, adding, subtracting and so on.) *How did you decide which part to do first? Did you plan how much to spend each day? How did you calculate the cost of that excursion? Which operation did you use? Did anybody run out of money?*

Name	Date

Sid's Snowy Sports shop

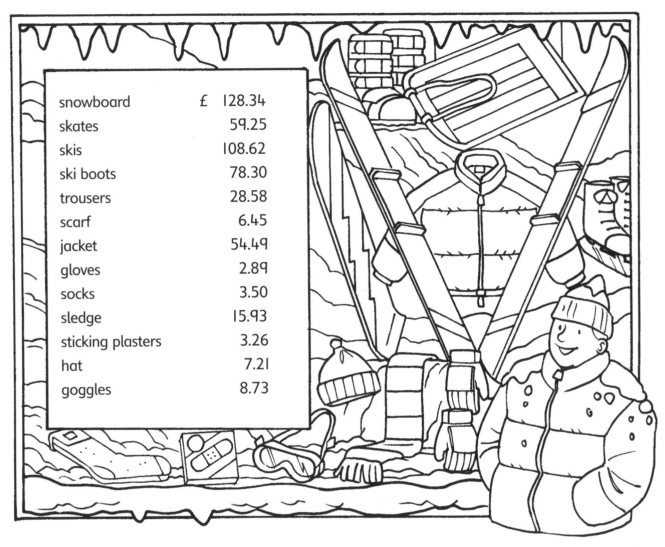

snowboard	£ 128.34
skates	59.25
skis	108.62
ski boots	78.30
trousers	28.58
scarf	6.45
jacket	54.49
gloves	2.89
socks	3.50
sledge	15.93
sticking plasters	3.26
hat	7.21
goggles	8.73

On another sheet of paper, use Sid's price list to calculate the cost of...

a. skates and socks _____

b. ski boots, socks and trousers _____

c. hat, scarf and gloves _____

d. jacket, trousers, hat, scarf and gloves _____

e. sledge and sticking plasters _____

f. snowboard, goggles, hat and gloves _____

g. everything I might need for skiing _____

Name	Date

All new 100 Maths Theme Park

THEME PARK ACTIVITIES

	€
Entry fee per person	16.00
Tricky Tractors	1.50
Wacky Walrus	4.00
Skyrider	3.00
Creepy Cinema	7.00
Numbskull Ride	3.80
Ice rink	6.50
Banana Boat	4.50

SNACKS AND DRINKS

	€
Ice cream	1.00
Fizzy orange	1.25
Cola	1.50
Hot dog	2.50
Burger	1.80
Veggie burger	1.60
Fruit juice	2.10
Doughnut	0.50
Coffee/Tea	1.00
Chips	1.20
Picnic	13.00 per person

DAY TRIPS

€ 2.00 per person for each km travelled

Sea	12km
Forest	30km
Mountains	35km
Diamond caves	48km
Pool	2km
Film set	3km
Play area	1km
Crazy golf	4km

ENTRY FEE PER PERSON

	€
Swimming pool	7.00
Crazy golf	3.50
Film set	18.00
Play area	4.00
Diamond caves	17.50
Ski lift (mountains)	12.50
Pedal boats (sea)	11.25
Water skiing (sea)	38.50
Paragliding (sea)	29.50

Number patterns, observations about number and generalisations

Children are given the opportunity to investigate numbers and to make generalisations about them. They have the opportunity to play a number of games to reinforce their understanding of number patterns and the vocabulary associated with number.

LEARNING OBJECTIVES

	Topics	Starter	Main teaching activity
Lesson 1	Reasoning and generalising about numbers	● **Know by heart all multiplication facts up to 10 × 10.**	● Make and investigate a general statement about familiar numbers by finding examples that satisfy it. ● Suggest extensions, asking 'What if…?'
Lesson 2	Properties of numbers and number sequences	As for Lesson 1.	● Know and apply tests of divisibility of 2, 4, 5, 10 or 100.
Lesson 3	Properties of numbers and number sequences	As for Lesson 1.	● Recognise and extend number sequences formed by counting from any number in steps of a constant size, extending beyond zero when counting back. For example: count on in steps of 25 to 1000, and then back; count on or back in steps of 0.1, 0.2, 0.3…
Lesson 4	Properties of numbers and number sequences	● Continue to derive quickly division facts corresponding to tables up to 10 × 10.	● Recognise multiples of 6, 7, 8, 9 up to the 10th multiple.
Lesson 5	Properties of numbers and number sequences	As for Lesson 4.	● Recognise multiples of 6, 7, 8, 9 up to the 10th multiple. ● Know and apply tests of divisibility of 2, 4, 5 or 10.

Lesson overview

Preparation
Draw a table on the board with the headings:

× 2	× 5	× 10	× 100

Learning objectives
Starter
● **Know by heart all multiplication facts up to 10 × 10.**
Main teaching activities
● Make and investigate a general statement about familiar numbers by finding examples that satisfy it.
● Suggest extensions, asking 'What if…?'

Vocabulary
multiple of, rule, generalisation, pattern

You will need:
CD pages
'Number fan cards', one for each child (see General resources, Autumn term).

Equipment
Calculators.

Lesson

Starter

Ask the children random multiplication fact questions (up to 10 × 10). They can work in pairs to display the answers with their number fans when you say *Show me*.

Main teaching activities

Whole class: Indicate the table headings you have drawn on the board. Invite the children to recall everything that they know about multiples of 2, 5, 10 and 100 (for example: 'All multiples of 2 are even numbers'; 'All multiples of 10 end in a zero') and write them in the table.

Now explain that the children are going to investigate multiples of 4. Are there any patterns in the multiples of 4? Can they write a generalisation or a rule about multiples of 4? Begin by asking the children to recall the multiples of 4. Record them on the board together: 4, 8, 12… 40, 44, 48.

Paired work: Ask the children to work in pairs to investigate multiples of 4 and make some general statements about them (such as 'All multiples of 4 are even'). They should record their observations and then test them by generating higher multiples of 4 using a calculator, such as 16 × 4 or 42 × 4. Are the observations true for all cases?

Differentiation

Less able: The children may need adult support in order to make observations and generalisations about multiples of 4.

More able: Expect a higher level of thinking from this group. For example, they may spot or recall the link with the 2× table (halves of the 4× table) or the 8× table (doubles).

Plenary & assessment

Make a record of the children's observations on the board. Most children should be able to tell you that all multiples of 4 are even and that the units digit follows a pattern of 0, 4, 8, 2, 6 which repeats. Ask the children to find a sequence of higher multiples (such as 22, 23 and 24 times 4) to test whether the second generalisation is true. From what the children have found out, ask: *Can anyone make a prediction about multiples of 40 or multiples of 8?*

Lessons   overview

Preparation

For Lesson 2, copy and cut out enough sets of cards from 'Multiples snap' for each group of four in the class. For Lesson 3, write three or four number patterns (see 'Main teaching activities') for the children to recognise and continue.

Learning objectives

Starter

● **Know by heart all multiplication facts up to 10 × 10.**
● Continue to derive quickly division facts corresponding to tables up to 10 × 10.

Main teaching activities

● Know and apply tests of divisibility of 2, 4, 5, 10 or 100.
● Recognise and extend number sequences formed by counting from any number in steps of a constant size, extending beyond zero when counting back. For example: count on in steps of 25 to 1000, and then back; count on or back in steps of 0.1, 0.2, 0.3…
● Recognise multiples of 6, 7, 8, 9 up to the 10th multiple

Vocabulary

next, consecutive, sequence, predict, pattern, relationship, divisible (by), divisibility, factor, square number

You will need

Photocopiable pages

'Multiples snap', see page 150, a set of cards for each group and 'Multiples bingo', see page 151, a set of cards for each group.

CD pages

'Number cards 1–10' (see General resources, Autumn term), one card for each group.

Equipment

Dice (one for each pair) labelled 2, 3, 4, 5, blank, blank; individual whiteboards or paper and pencils; coloured counters; dice (one for each pair) labelled 6, 7, 8, 9, blank, blank; coloured pencils.

Lesson 2

Starter

Repeat the starter from Lesson 1. Then reverse the activity by asking the children (in pairs) to show you two factors of a given multiple, using their number fans. For example, if you say *42*, the children could hold up 7 and 6 on their number fans.

Main teaching activities

Whole class: Refer to the work on multiples of 2, 4, 5 and 10 from Lesson 1. Ask: *What is 30 divisible by?* (6, 5, 15, 2, 1, 30.) These are the **factors** of 30. *Think of a number that is divisible by 4 and 2.* (Any multiple of 4 is also divisible by 2. Likewise any multiple of 8 is divisible by both 4 and 2.)
Group work: Play 'Multiples snap' in groups of four. Distribute the cards from the activity sheet. Explain that this game will help the children to practise knowledge of divisibility, and also to test the generalisations they made in Lesson 1 for multiples of 2, 4, 5 and 10.

The cards are shuffled and shared out evenly among the group. Each player in turn places a card face upwards on the discard pile. This continues until two numbers from the same times table appear consecutively. The first player to say 'Snap!', and then to say what both numbers are divisible by, wins the whole of the discard pile. The first player to gain all the cards wins. For instance, if 25 and 50 are turned over consecutively, the common factor or divisor is 5 (or 25).

Differentiation

Less able: The children could be asked to look for specific devisors – for example, to look for numbers that are divisible by 2 or 5.
More able: On completion of the game, the children could use blank cards to create their own number cards, including numbers divisible by 9 (or higher numbers outside the 10 × 10 times table) to add to the game.

Plenary & assessment

Discuss how we can tell whether a number is divisible by 4. Ask: *Which of your observations about multiples of 4 help us with divisibility? Which ones don't? What about numbers that are divisible by 9? What observations can you make?* (The digits of the 9 times table add up to 9, so they are easy to spot. For example, 18 → 1 + 8 = 9.)

Lesson 3

Starter

Play a multiplication challenge game. The children stand in a circle, and one child starts by calling out another child's name and a multiplication fact question (such as '7 times 6'). That child must reply quickly and correctly or sit down. If they answer correctly, they can call another name and multiplication question. The winners are those still standing after approximately 5 minutes of playing the game.

Main teaching activities

Whole class: Indicate these number patterns, written on the board.

105, 90, 75, 60, ____, ____, ____   4.7, 4.5, 4.3, 4.1, 3.9, ____, ____, ____

2.0, 1.5, 1.0, 0.5, ____, ____, ____

Discuss the patterns and how to continue them. State a rule for each one, such as: 'This pattern is decreasing by 15 each time.'

Paired work: On squared paper, each pair create a number pattern wordsearch using a run of four numbers in the same number pattern, eg 4, 8, 12, 16. These may run vertically, horizontally or diagonally. On completion, swap with another pair and solve the puzzle

Differentiation
Less able: With adult support, create simplified patterns of only 2, 5 and 10s.
More able: Aim to create more complex patterns, eg negative or decimal numbers.

Plenary & assessment
Check that everyone has found all the number patterns and written in the missing numbers. Ask: *Do all number patterns have to be made by adding or subtracting? What is the pattern here: 1.0, 0.1, 0.01, 0.001… or 3, 0.03, 0.0003… Can you state a rule?'*
      Give each pair a small whiteboard or paper and pencil and ask them to create a number pattern that uses division or multiplication. In turn, each pair can hold up their pattern for the rest of the children to continue and state a rule for.

Lesson ④

Starter
Play a divisibility game. Give each group a number card: 2, 4, 5 or 10. Call out numbers that are divisible by at least one of those numbers. The group who have a correct 'divisibility card' should stand up. Discuss why more than one group stands up for some numbers. Call out 16, 15, 30, 40, 18, 35, 20, 12, 100, 50 and 120. At the end, find out whether anyone remembers which numbers everyone stood up for.

Main teaching activities
Whole class: Distribute the 'Multiples Bingo' activity sheet. Explain that today's activity is an opportunity to practise remembering multiples of 6, 7, 8 and 9. Ask the children to tell you some examples of multiples of each to get them started. Record them on the board as shown in the illustration. Ask: *Are there any observations you can make about multiples of 6, 7, 8 or 9?* (For example, 'Multiples of 8 are all even numbers' or 'The digits of a multiple of 9 add up to 9').

```
6×   36, 12, 42, 18, 30
7×   49, 42, 14, 28, 35
```

Paired work: Give each pair of children a copy of the 'Multiples bingo' game sheet. Explain that the grid contains some multiples of 6, 7, 8 and 9 all jumbled up. The children will need a dice marked with these numbers and two blank faces, and a different coloured pencil each. Go through the rules as described on the sheet. The children take turns to roll the dice and colour a multiple of the number rolled. If they roll a blank, or if there is no appropriate multiple left, they miss a turn. The winner is the player with more squares coloured at the end.

Differentiation
Less able: The children could give an answer based on estimation or mental calculation, and then use a calculator to check by dividing.
More able: Pairs within a more able group can play against the clock. Which pair can complete the grid accurately in the fastest time?

Plenary & assessment
Ask for four volunteers to write the multiples of 6, 7, 8 and 9 (up to 10 × each) in order on the board. Ask: *Did you observe any other patterns or generalisations that might help you to recognise numbers that are divisible by 6, 7, 8 or 9?* Take suggestions. These might include the fact that all multiples of 6 or 8 are even, or that the multiples of 6 or 8 follow a pattern with their unit numbers (for example, **6, 12, 18, 24, 30, 36, 42, 48, 54, 60**). With the multiples of 7, you just have to know them!

Lesson

Starter

Play 'Division Lotto' as in Term 1 Unit 2, Lesson 4. Shuffle a pack of several sets of number cards 2–10 and give six cards to each group of children. Call out a division fact question (such as *24 ÷ 6*). Any group holding the answer turns that card face down. The first group to turn all its cards face down and shout 'Lotto' wins.

Main teaching activities

Whole class: Ask the children to listen carefully to your description of a mystery number, then raise their hands to offer the answer. They must be sure of their answer, not just guessing. Say each question twice.

● *I am thinking of a number that is an even number. It is a multiple of 10. Its digits add up to the name of the times table it belongs to. Its factors include 5 and 18.* (90)

● *This is an odd number. It is a multiple of 7. It is a square number. What is it?* (49)

● *I am thinking of an even number that appears in four different times tables in a 10 × 10 grid. Half of this number is an even number. 6 is one of this number's factors.* (24)

Paired work: Ask the children to make up some clues to a mystery number of their own to test on a partner. They can use a multiplication square to help them think of clues. Ask them to make sure that there is only one correct answer to their puzzle.

Differentiation

Less able: It may help some children if you suggest the numbers that they might write clues for. Some numbers have more 'properties' than others. Suggest 6, 15, 4, 25 and so on.

More able: The children should be able to think of clues involving square numbers, factors and so on.

Plenary & assessment

Share some examples of good mystery number puzzles and ask the rest of the class to solve them. The children should not try to guess the number until they have heard all the clues. Ask: *Which numbers are more difficult to write clues for?* (For example, square numbers have too small a field of clues and so are easy to guess.) *Could you have guessed any of the numbers from just one clue? How? Was the clue too specific?* (For example, 'This number has factors including 2 and 7'.)

Multiples snap

A game for 4 players.

Cut out these playing cards and use them to play 'Multiples snap'.

25	42	8	12	20
14	15	28	18	32
60	52	35	26	44
13	5	24	38	17
60	52	35	26	44
22	36			
50	10			
48	30			
9	6			
75	21			
45	55	34	8	100

Name	Date

Multiples bingo

A game for 2 players.

You need:

- a dice labelled 6, 7, 8 and 9 with two blank faces
- a colouring pencil each.

Throw the dice and colour a multiple of the number thrown.
If you throw a blank or there are no multiples of the number
you have thrown left, you miss a turn.

The winner is the player with more multiples coloured at the end.

9	49	40	42	18
14	36	6	48	21
7	81	35	90	63
64	24	32	56	45
42	56	72	28	70
80	36	12	27	30
24	63	48	54	16

EVERY DAY: Practise and develop oral and mental skills (eg counting, mental strategies, rapid recall of + and – facts)

- Use known number facts and place value for mental addition and subtraction.
- Read and write whole numbers in figures and words and know what each digit represents.
- **Multiply and divide any positive integer up to 10000 by 10 or 100 and understand the effect (eg 9900 ÷ 10, 737 ÷ 10, 2060 ÷ 100).**
- Round any integer up to 10 000 to the nearest 10 or 100, or 1000.
- **Order a given set of positive and negative integers (eg on a number line, on a temperature scale).**
- Know and apply tests of divisibility by 2, 4, 5, 10 or 100.
- Order a set of fractions such as 2, 2¾, 1¾, 2½, 1½, and position them on a number line.
- **Round a number with one or two decimal places to the nearest integer.**
- **Relate fractions to their decimal representations: that is, recognise the equivalence between decimal and fraction forms of one half, one quarter, three quarters… and tenths and hundredths (eg 7/10 = 0.7, 27/100 = 0.27).**
- Derive quickly or continue to derive quickly all two-digit pairs that total 100 (e.g.43 + 57).
- Derive quickly or continue to derive quickly decimals that total 1 (eg 0.2 + 0.8) or 10 (eg 6.2 + 3.8).
- Derive quickly or continue to derive quickly all pairs of multiples of 50 with a total of 1000 (eg 350 + 650).
- **Use doubling or halving starting from known facts. For example: to multiply two-digit numbers by 4, double, then double again.**
- **Know by heart all multiplication facts up to 10 × 10.**
- Derive quickly or continue to derive quickly division facts corresponding to tables up to 10 × 10.
- Partition (eg 47 × 6 = (40 × 6) + (7 × 6)).

Units	Days	Topics	Objectives
1	3	Place value, ordering, and rounding	Use vocabulary of estimation and approximation. Make and justify estimates of large numbers and estimate simple proportions, such as one third, seven tenths. Round any integer up to 10 000 to the nearest 10, 100 or 1000. Calculate a temperature rise or fall across 0°C.
		Using a calculator	Develop calculator skills and use a calculator effectively.
2–3	10	Understanding × and ÷	Begin to express a quotient as a fraction, or as a decimal when dividing a whole number by 2, 4, 5, or 10 or when dividing £ and pence. Round up or down after division, depending on the context.
		Mental calculation strategies (× and ÷)	Use relationship between multiplication and division. Use known facts and place value to multiply and divide mentally.
		Pencil and paper procedures (× and ÷)	**Extend written methods to: long multiplication of TU by TU.**
		Problems involving 'real life', money and measures	**Use all four operations to solve simple word problems involving numbers and quantities** based on 'real life' money and measures **(including time)**, using one or more steps, including making simple conversions of pounds to foreign currency and finding simple percentages.
		Making decisions	Choose and use appropriate number operations to solve problems, and appropriate ways of calculating: mental, mental with jottings, written methods, calculator.
		Checking results	Check results with an equivalent calculation.
4–5	10	Fractions, decimals and percentages	**Relate fractions to their decimal representations:** that is, recognise the equivalence between the decimal and fraction forms of one half, one quarter, three quarters… and tenths and hundredths (eg 7/10 = 0.7, 27/100 = 0.27). Begin to understand percentage as the number of parts in every 100, and find simple percentages of small whole-number quantities (eg 25% of £8).
		Ratio and proportion	Solve simple problems using ideas of ratio and proportion ('one for every…' and 'one in every…').
6	8	Handling data	Solve a problem by representing and interpreting data in tables, charts, graphs and diagrams, including those generated by a computer, for example: bar line charts, vertical axis labelled in 2s, 5s, 10s, 20s, or 100s, first where intermediate points have no meaning (eg scores on a dice rolled 50 times), then where they may have meaning (eg room temperature over time). Find the mode of a set of data.
		Using a calculator	Develop calculator skills and use a calculator effectively.
7	2	Assess and review	

EVERY DAY: Practise and develop oral and mental skills (eg counting, mental strategies, rapid recall of + and – facts)

As for previous half term, and
- Order a set of numbers or measurements with the same number of decimal places.
- Begin to understand percentage as the number of parts in every 100, and find simple percentages of small whole number quantities (eg 25% of £8).
- Use factors (eg $8 \times 12 = 8 \times 4 \times 3$).
- **Use all four operations to solve simple word problems involving numbers and quantities based on 'real life' money and measures (including time) using one or more steps, including making simple conversions of pounds *foreign currency and finding simple percentages.***
- Use, read and write standard metric units (km, m, cm, mm, kg, g, l, ml) including their abbreviations and relationships between them.
- Convert larger to smaller units (eg km to m, m to cm or mm, kg to g, l to ml).

Units	Days	Topics	Objectives
8–10	15	Shape and space	Recognise reflective symmetry in regular polygons, for example, know that a square has four axis of symmetry and an equilateral triangle has three. Complete symmetrical patterns with two lines of symmetry at right angles (using squared paper or pegboard). Recognise where a shape will be after reflection in a mirror line parallel to one side (sides not all parallel or perpendicular to the mirror line). Recognise where shape will be after translation.
		Reasoning and generalising about numbers or shapes	Make and investigate a general statement about familiar numbers or shapes by finding examples that satisfy it.
		Measures	Use timetables. Use units of time; read the time on a 24-hour digital clock and use 24-hour notation, such as 19.53. Use, read and write standard metric units (km, m, cm, mm, kg, g, l, ml) including their abbreviations and relationships between them. Convert larger to smaller units (eg km to m, m to cm or mm, kg to g, l to ml). Know imperial units (mile, pint, gallon). Suggest suitable units and measuring equipment to estimate or measure length, mass or capacity. Record estimates and readings from scales to a suitable degree of accuracy.
		Problems involving 'real life', money and measures	**Use all four operations to solve simple word problems involving numbers and quantities** based on 'real life' money and measures (including time) using one or more steps, including making simple conversions of pounds to foreign currency and finding simple percentages.
		Making decisions	Choose and use appropriate number operations to solve problems, and appropriate ways of calculating: mental, mental with jottings, written methods, calculator.
11	5	Mental calculation strategies (+ and –)	Add several numbers (eg four or five single digit, or multiples of 10 such as 40 + 50 + 80). Use known number facts and place value for mental addition and subtraction (eg 470 + 380, 810 – 380, 7.4 + 9.8, 9.2 – 8.6).
		Pencil and paper procedures (+ and –)	**Extend written methods to:** **column addition/subtraction of more than two integers less than 10000,** addition or subtraction of a pair of decimal fractions, both with one or both with two decimal places (eg £29.78 + £53.34).
		Money and 'real life' problems	**Use all four operations to solve simple word problems involving numbers and quantities** based on 'real life', money and measures (**including time**) using one or more steps, including making simple conversions of pounds to foreign currency and finding simple percentages.
		Making decisions	Choose and use appropriate number operations to solve problems, and appropriate ways of calculating: mental, mental with jottings, written methods, calculator.
		Checking results	Use knowledge of sums and differences of odd or even numbers.
12	5	Properties of numbers and number sequences	Find all the pairs of factors of any number up to 100. Make general statements about odd or even numbers, including the outcome of sums and differences.
		Reasoning and generalising about numbers	Explain a generalised relationship (formula) in words.
13	2	Assess and review	Solve a problem by representing and interpreting data in tables, charts, graphs and diagrams, including those generated by a computer, for example: bar line charts, vertical axis labelled in 2s, 5s, 10s, 20s, or 100s, first where intermediate points have no meaning (eg scores on a dice rolled 50 times), then where they may have meaning (eg room temperature over time). Find the mode of a set of data. Develop calculator skills and use a calculator effectively.

Summer Term
Unit 1

Rounding numbers using a number line

This unit uses fractions of a number line to work out where to place a new number within that range. This is extended to include both positive and negative numbers.

LEARNING OBJECTIVES

	Topics	Starter	Main teaching activities
Lesson 1	Place value, ordering and rounding	● **Multiply and divide any positive integer up to 10 000 by 10 or 100 and understand the effect** (eg 9900 ÷ 10, 737 ÷ 10, 2060 ÷ 100).	● Use the vocabulary of estimation and approximation. ● Round any integer up to 10 000 to the nearest 10, 100 or 1000.
Lesson 2	Place value, ordering and rounding	● Round any integer up to 10 000 to the nearest 10, 100 or 1000.	● Make and justify estimates of large numbers, and estimate simple proportions such as one third, seven tenths.
Lesson 3	Place value, ordering and rounding Using a calculator	● Calculate a temperature rise or fall across 0°C.	● Calculate a temperature rise or fall across 0°C. ● Develop calculator skills and use a calculator effectively.

Lessons   overview

Preparation
For Lesson 2, prepare a chart on the board with the headings 'Nearest 10', 'Nearest 100' and 'Nearest 1000'. Also for Lesson 2, prepare a sheet with four number lines divided into tenths (ending with 100), fifths (ending with 200), thirds (ending with 120) and quarters (ending with 80). Label each line with a, b, c at appropriate points. For Lesson 3, draw a number line or thermometer showing –10°C to 10°C.

Learning objectives
Starter
● Multiply and divide any positive integer up to 10 000 by 10 or 100 and understand the effect (eg 9900 ÷ 10, 737 ÷ 10, 2060 ÷ 100).
● Round any integer up to 10 000 to the nearest 10, 100 or 1000.
● Calculate a temperature rise or fall across 0°C.
Main teaching activity
● Use the vocabulary of estimation and approximation.
● Round any integer up to 10 000 to the nearest 10, 100 or 1000.
● Make and justify estimates of large numbers, and estimate simple proportions such as one third, seven tenths.
● Calculate a temperature rise or fall across 0°C.
● Develop calculator skills and use a calculator effectively.

Vocabulary
rounding up/down, nearest, ascending/descending order, halfway between, estimate, nearest 10/100/1000, negative, positive, minus, below zero

You will need:
Photocopiable pages
'Rise and fall', see page 157, one copy for each child.

CD pages
'Number cards 1–100', for teacher's/LSA's reference; '0–9 digit cards', for each child (see General resources, Autumn term). 'Rise and fall', less able and more able versions (see Summer term Unit 1).

Equipment
Two whiteboards or large sheets of paper; marker pens.

Lesson ①

Starter

Invite three volunteers to stand at the board: one to multiply by 10, one by 100 and one by 1000. Pick a number card from the pack and ask the three children to record their answers. Ask the class: *Can you tell me a quick rule that they might use to multiply?* (Move the digits up in place value by the number of zeros in the multiple, using zeros to hold the place value.) Repeat multiplying then dividing by 10, 100 and 1000: 98 × 100 = 9800 ÷ 10 = 980.

Main teaching activities

Whole class: Draw a number line on the board and label the ends 2000 and 3000. Ask the children to estimate where 2347 might go. Discuss how we can round this number to the nearest 100, then find the halfway point (2500) and divide the rest of the line into 100s. We can then place the number more precisely by rounding it to the nearest 10 (2350) and repeating the process. Ask: *What fraction have we divided this line into?* (Tenths.) Discuss what fraction of the whole line comes before 2300 (3/10), and what comes after (7/10). Repeat for other examples, such as 3000 to 4000.
Paired work: The children can use digit cards to generate a four-digit number, then draw a number line 10cm long and mark the ends with whole thousands to fit the four-digit number thrown. Now mark the whole hundreds that border their number, then use rounding to help them divide the line into tenths (100 each), halves (500), quarters (250) in order to place their number as closely as possible.

Differentiation

Less able: The children can use a three-digit or even a two-digit number.
More able: The children can use a five-digit number, perhaps with one or two decimal places.

Plenary & assessment

Write the number 2571 on the board. Ask: What would 2571 become if I rounded it to the nearest 10?... 100?... 1000? Now write a decimal number such as 326.47. Ask: *Can you round this number to the nearest tenth? What is the nearest whole number? Can you tell me a rule for rounding?* (Round 5 and above up to the next place value.) Write this up for all to see.

Divide the class into two teams to play a rounding game. Give each team a whiteboard or large sheet of paper. Call one team the 'Round me ups' and the other the 'Round me downs'. One team writes a number to round up to the nearest tenth, ten, hundred or thousand, the other team a number to round down. Write a number such as 3600 and ask: *What number could be rounded up or down to the nearest 100 to give this answer?* The first team to hold up a correct answer gains a point. Repeat with other targets and multiples: *What number could be rounded to the nearest tenth to give 12?... to the nearest thousand to give 5000?*

Lesson ②

Starter

Indicate the chart you have prepared on the board. Generate four-digit numbers using digit cards and ask the children to round them according to the headings (for example, 7485 would be 7490 to the nearest 10, 7500 to the nearest 100 and 7000 to the nearest 1000). Repeat using different numbers, including one- and two-place decimals.

Main teaching activities

Whole class: Draw a 1–100 number line. Ask the children to estimate the number that is halfway along. Ask: *How did you work that out?* (By dividing 100 by 2.) Explain that using this principle and their knowledge of division facts, they are going to mark more fractions along the number line. Ask:

What number is 1/3 of the way along the line? (Approximately 33.) Repeat with ¼, ¾, 2/3 and so on. Draw a number line 1–50 and repeat the activity.

Individual work: Distribute your prepared sheet with divided number lines. Explain that these number lines have been divided into different fractions. The children have to identify the numbers marked on the lines, using their knowledge of fractions.

Differentiation

Less able: Present a version of the sheet that asks for simple fractions of numbers to 100.
More able: Present a version that asks for more difficult fractions of larger numbers.

Plenary & assessment

Draw a number line 20–60. Ask: *How can I find the halfway point of this line? Is it 30? Why not?* (Calculate the length of the line, divide it by 2, then add this to the lower number. In this case 60 − 20 = 40, 40 ÷ 2 = 20 and 20 + 20 = 40, so the midpoint is 40.) Repeat this process with various number lines such as 10 to 70, 20 to 100 and 15 to 105.

Lesson

Starter

Draw a −2 to 2 number line on the board. Ask: *What is the midpoint of this line?* (Zero.) Mark in zero, −1 and 1. Ask: *Where would you place 1.5? What about 0.25 or −1.5?* Discuss how to divide up the number line between whole numbers. Ask: *Where would you place −1.49?* Remind the children to count back from zero, and to place −1.49 just to the right of −1.5.

Main teaching activities

Whole class: Draw a vertical number line −10 to 10, like a thermometer. This can assist thinking about temperatures rising and falling. Ask questions such as:

● *The temperature was −2°C at 7am, but had risen by 4 degrees by 11 o'clock. What was the new temperature?*
● *The temperature fell from 7°C to −1°C. By how many degrees did it fall?*
● *The temperature rose from −4°C by 10 degrees. What was the new temperature?*

Teach the children to count from the start temperature through zero to the new temperature. Some children will add 10 degrees to −4°C and say the result is 14°C. Discuss why this is wrong: it does not take account of the negative number. Demonstrate how to enter a negative number into a calculator, and use it to check the temperature calculations. Emphasise that a negative number is less than zero.

Individual work: Distribute the 'Rise and fall' activity sheet. Ask the children to calculate the temperature differences and check them with a calculator.

Differentiation

Less able: Provide the version of 'Rise and fall' with the number line marked in ones from 10°C to −10°C.
More able: Provide the version with a scale from 20°C to −20°C.

Plenary & assessment

Share feedback of the children's work to assess their confidence in calculating with negative numbers. Then ask: *If it is −8°C in Helsinki and 2°C in London, what is the temperature difference?* (10°C) *Cairo is 33°C hotter than Oslo. In Oslo it is −3°C. What is the temperature in Cairo?* (30°C) *Can anyone suggest a rule for calculating temperature differences across 0°C?* (Count down to zero and on from there.)

Name	Date

Rise and fall

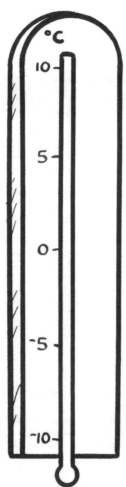

Use the number line above to help you calculate the following:

1. At 6am the temperature was –2°C. By midday, it had risen by 10 degrees. What was the temperature at midday? _____

2. The temperature has fallen from 10°C to –3°C. How far has it fallen _____

3. There is a difference in temperature of 12 degrees between the classroom and the playground. The classroom is warmer. It is at 9°C. How cold is the playground? _____

4. The daytime temperature is 6°C, but by evening it has fallen by 9 degrees. What is the temperature in the evening? _____

5. The temperature rises by 6 degrees from –6°C. What is the new temperature? _____

Using known multiplication facts for larger multiples and division

Children are encouraged to multiply and divide much bigger multiples of 10 or 100 using known times tables. They learn to express a remainder from a division calculation as a fraction and then convert this to a decimal fraction.

LEARNING OBJECTIVES

	Topics	Starter	Main teaching activities
Lesson 1	Mental calculation strategies (× and ÷)	● **Order a given set of positive and negative integers** (eg on a number line, on a temperature scale).	● Use the vocabulary of estimation and approximation. Use the relationship between multiplication and division. ● Use known facts and place value to multiply and divide mentally. ● Round any integer up to 10 000 to the nearest 10, 100 or 1000.
Lesson 2	Understanding multiplication and division	● Know and apply tests of divisibility by 2, 4, 5 or 10.	● Begin to express a quotient as a fraction, or as a decimal when dividing a whole number by 2, 4, 5 or 10, or when dividing £.p.
Lesson 3		● **Know by heart all multiplication facts up to 10 × 10.**	As for Lesson 2.
Lesson 4		● Continue to derive quickly division facts corresponding to tables up to 10 × 10.	As for Lesson 2.
Lesson 5	Understanding multiplication and division Problems involving money and measures	As for Lesson 4.	● Round up or down after division, depending on the context. ● **Use all four operations to solve simple word problems involving numbers and quantities** based on 'real life', money and measures.

Lessons overview

Preparation
For Lesson 2, prepare a grid of multiples of 2, 4, 5 and 10 and some dice labelled 2, 4, 5, 10, blank, blank. For Lesson 3, prepared short division questions with a known fraction/decimal answer, such as 105 ÷ 4 = 26 1/4 = 26.25. Also display a list of common fraction/decimal equivalents, such as 1/4 = 0.25, 1/2 = 0.5, etc. For Lesson 4, prepared short division questions which have less common decimal fraction remainders which require a calculator, such as 125 ÷ 3 = 41 r2 = 41 2/3 = 41.66.

Learning objectives
Starter
● Order a given set of positive and negative integers (eg on a number line, on a temperature scale).
● Know and apply tests of divisibility by 2, 4, 5 or 10.
● Know by heart all multiplication facts up to 10 × 10.
● Continue to derive quickly division facts corresponding to tables up to 10 × 10.
Main teaching activity
● Use the relationship between multiplication and division.
● Use known facts and place value to multiply and divide mentally.
● Begin to express a quotient as a fraction, or as a decimal when dividing a whole number by 2, 4, 5 or 10, or when dividing £.p.

Vocabulary
times, product, multiple, share, share equally, divided into, divisible by, remainder, factor, quotient, inverse

You will need:
CD pages
'Number fans', one for each child (see General resources, Autumn term).

Equipment
6-sided and 10-sided dice; coloured pens; calculators.

Lesson ①

Starter

Indicate the sets of numbers you have written on the board, and ask for volunteers to help you write them in order of increasing size. Remind the children to look carefully, since some sets contain both positive and negative numbers.

Main teaching activities

Whole class: Revise the idea of an inverse (opposite) operation – for example, division is the inverse of multiplication. Remind the children that they can do many two-digit calculations mentally, using their known multiplication facts and place value. For example, ask: *What is 60 × 8? Or 60 × 80? How did you calculate that? What knowledge did you use? Are there any other calculations that knowing 6 × 8 might help you to solve?* (For example, 12 × 8 or 6 × 16.)

Ask questions to elicit a variety of number facts related to 6 × 8, such as: *What number sentence could I make if I doubled each of the factors?… if I multiplied each factor by 100? What about using the inverse operation to create division facts: how are they related?* Display the related facts as a 'tree' diagram:

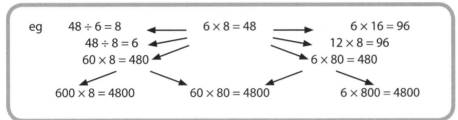

eg
$48 \div 6 = 8$ $6 \times 8 = 48$ $6 \times 16 = 96$
$48 \div 8 = 6$ $12 \times 8 = 96$
$60 \times 8 = 480$ $6 \times 80 = 480$
$600 \times 8 = 4800$ $60 \times 80 = 4800$ $6 \times 800 = 4800$

Individual work: Ask the children to create their own 'known facts' tree diagram, based on a known multiplication fact such as 8 × 3, 6 × 7 or 5 × 6. They should use a calculator to check their facts when they have finished.

Differentiation

Less able: The children can start with a simple table fact such as 2 × 3 or 4 × 2.
More able: The children can extend their tree diagram to a third or fourth layer, exploring numbers into the thousands.

Plenary & assessment

Write 400 × 800 on the board. Ask: *Can you calculate 400 × 800 mentally? How?* (By using a known fact and increasing the place value by four places.) *How did you know the approximate size of the answer?* (By the number of zeros in the question.) *What other number facts did 4 × 8 help you to find?* (Inverses and doubles, such as 40 × 80, 40 × 800, 32 000 ÷ 80.)

Now write the number 320 in the middle of the board. Invite the children to use their knowledge of numbers and place value to find number facts with this answer (such as 32 000 ÷ 100, 8 × 40, 80 × 4, 3.2 × 100).

Lesson ②

Starter

Display an A3 copy or OHT of a grid containing multiples of 2, 4, 5 and 10. Divide the class into two teams, each with a captain. The teams take turns to roll a 2, 4, 5, 10 dice. If they roll a blank they miss a turn. For each number they roll, the team captain has to cross out a related multiple (using a coloured pen). The first team to cross out four numbers in a row wins.

Main teaching activities

Whole class: Revise short division of a three-digit number by a single digit. Depending on your school calculation policy, some of your children may be confident with written short division and others may just be starting to use it. You may choose to use this lesson to focus on children who need extra help in this area.

Demonstrate a division such as 137 ÷ 3:

$$3) \overline{1\,{}^13{}^17}$$
$$4\,5{}^{r2}$$

Relate this method to the times table facts the children looked at in Lesson 1. Explain that the remainder can be expressed as a fraction – in this case, we have 2 left over out of the 3 that we were dividing by. This can be expressed as 2/3. So 137 ÷ 3 = 45 2/3. Repeat this demonstration with other examples, such as 129 ÷ 4, 208 ÷ 5, 211 ÷ 2.

Individual work: Explain that the children are going to practise short division by generating numbers (with a 2, 4, 5, 10 dice) to use as divisors. If the division has a remainder, this should be expressed as a fraction. For example, the children can generate a three-digit number (such as 533) by throwing one ordinary dice three times, then generate the divisor by throwing once the prepared dice, then work out the division (for example, 533 ÷ 4 = 133 remainder 1, which is 133 and ¼).

Differentiation

Less able: The children can use the prepared dice to generate numbers and divisors. They may need adult support with short division, and express leftovers as a remainder only.
More able: The children can use a ten-sided dice to generate higher numbers.

Plenary & assessment

Check the children's understanding of how remainders can be expressed as fractions by asking for volunteers to demonstrate these examples: 151 ÷ 2, 216 ÷ 5, 418 ÷ 10. Ask: *How do you know what the numerator will be? How do you know what the denominator will be?* (The numerator is the number remaining; the denominator is the divisor.)

$$151 \div 2 = 75\ r1 \rightarrow 75\frac{1}{2}$$
remainder
devisor

Draw the children's attention to 418 ÷ 10. Ask: *Did we need to use a calculator to solve this? What answer would we have got?* (41.8.) *What answer did we get when we used short division?* (41 8/10). *Can anybody spot a link between these two answers?* (8/10 is the same as 0.8.)

Lesson ③

Starter

Ask quick-fire multiplication questions such as: *8 × 7. How many 5s in 45? Three lots of 6. What is 5 squared?* The children work in pairs in order to be able to cooperate with answers with repeated digits such as 55 ÷ 5 = 11, using their number fans to show you the answer when you say *'Show me'*.

Main teaching activities

Whole class: Tell the children that today, they will continue to use short division and express the remainders as fractions – but they are also going to change the fractions into decimals. Explain that they already know some fraction and decimal equivalents, for example 1/10 = 0.1, 1/5 = 0.2, 8/10 = 0.8. Revise other known equivalents such as those of ¼, ¾, 1/3 and 2/3. Record these on the board for reference.

Individual work: Distribute the questions of short division. Explain that all of the questions will generate answers with fraction remainders, which the children should be able to convert to decimals using the equivalents listed on the board.

Differentiation

Less able: The children may still need adult support with short division. Provide a version of the activity sheet with TU ÷ U questions.
More able: Provide a version with ThHTU ÷ U questions.

Plenary & assessment

Explain to the children that we need a way to check our division calculations. Sometimes the inverse calculation is straightforward – for example, we can check $48 \div 6 = 8$ using $6 \times 8 = 48$. However, some calculations involving fractions might be difficult to check, especially if we want to use a calculator. Ask: *How could we check this calculation using a calculator?* Write on the board: $118 \div 4 = 29 \, 2/4 = 29\frac{1}{2}$. *What knowledge do we have to have that will help us to put this into the calculator?* (The knowledge of equivalent fractions and decimals.) $29\frac{1}{2} = 29.5$ and $29.5 \times 4 = 118$.

Revise known fraction/decimal equivalents such as $\frac{1}{2} = 0.5$ and $\frac{1}{4} = 0.25$. Use a calculator to demonstrate that $137 \div 3 = 45 \, 2/3 = 45.666666$. Write this as $45.6\dot{6}$.

Ask: *What does the dot above the last digit mean?* (A recurring number. The actual division goes on to infinity.) *Will this inverse be accurate? $45.67 \times 3 = 137.01$* (Not quite, because 45.66 is the original answer rounded to two decimal places.)

Ask the children to try the following calculations, using a calculator, and check which inverse operations give an accurate answer: $122 \div 7$; $131 \div 5$; $241 \div 8$; $126 \div 9$. Ask: *Why did some of these not give an exactly correct answer when reversed?* (Because the original answer had to be rounded up or down.)

Lesson

Starter

Ask quick-fire division questions with one-digit answers, such as: How many 6s in 42? $27 \div 9$? What is the square root of 81? The children use their number fans to show you the answer when you say 'Show me'.

Main teaching activities

Whole class: Explain that today, the children will continue to use short division and express the answer as a decimal. Point out that some fraction/decimal equivalents are difficult to remember. Ask: *What can we do if we get a fraction remainder where we don't know the decimal equivalent?* (Use a calculator.) Explain that any fraction can be changed into a decimal by dividing the numerator by the denominator. Key into the calculator: $3 \div 10 = 0.3$. Try with other known equivalents before trying unknown fractions such as 5/6 or 4/7. Explain that some recurring decimals, such as 4/7, have a recurring group of digits ($0.57142857\ldots$). These decimals can be rounded to two decimal places (0.57). So, for example, $281 \div 7 = 40 \, 1/7 = 40.14$. Remind the children that they cannot use the inverse operation for accurate checking if they have rounded an answer to two decimal places.
Individual work: Distribute the short division problems. Some of the answers may need rounding. Remind the children to use short division first, only using a calculator to determine an unknown decimal.

Differentiation

Less able: Provide similar division problems with TU ÷ U questions and simple or no remainders.
More able: Provide similar division problems with ThHTU ÷ U questions.

Plenary & assessment

Ask the children:
- *Which fractions created recurring decimals? What do we have to remember when we check these?*
- *Have you learnt any new equivalents that you think you will remember?*
- *What did you notice about 2/4 or 2/10?*

Provide each pair of children with a calculator. You call out a fraction or a decimal and the children use their calculator to find the equivalent. Fractions are easier: they can simply be keyed into the calculator. Finding a fraction for a given decimal is more a matter of trial and error. To earn a point, the children must give the correct answer and explain what they did to find it. Give extra points at your own discretion for clear explanations and reasoning. The pair with the highest number of points are deemed the 'winners'.

Lessons overview

Learning objectives

Starter
● Continue to derive quickly division facts corresponding to tables up to 10 × 10.

Main teaching activity
● Round up or down after division, depending on context.
● Use all four operations to solve simple word problems involving numbers and quantities based on 'real life', money and measures.

Vocabulary

times, product, multiple, share, share equally, divided into, divisible by, remainder, factor, quotient, inverse

You will need:

Photocopiable pages
'Division word problems', see page 163, one for each child.

CD pages
'0–9 digit cards', for teacher's/LSA's use (see General resources, Autumn term). 'Division word problems', less able and more able versions (see Summer term, Unit 2).

Equipment
Calculators.

Lesson

Starter

Play 'Fraction Division Lotto'. Distribute six different 0– 9 digit cards to each group of children. Call out fraction division questions such as *1/6 of 42*. The groups who have the answer card turn it face down. The first group to turn all its cards face down wins.

Main teaching activities

Explain that the children are going to apply their skills to solving word division problems that use money and measures. Remind them how to convert a word problem into a number sentence and then calculate the answer, perhaps generating a fraction or decimal remainder. For example, *Mrs Smith has 1945 centimetres of wood to make into four equal-length bookshelves. How long will each shelf be?*

$$\underline{0\ 4\ 8\ 6}\ \text{r1} = 486¼\text{cm or } 486.25\text{cm each}$$
$$4)1\ ^1 9\ ^3 4\ ^2 5$$

Individual work: Distribute the 'Division word problems' activity sheet. Ask the children to solve the word problems, using their division skills.

Differentiation

Less able: Provide the version of 'Division word problems' with simpler problems.
More able: Provide the version with two-step problems.

Plenary & assessment

Share some of the children's answers with the class and iron out any difficulties or misconceptions that occur. Then ask: *What is the practical reason for rounding long decimal numbers to two decimal places when we are talking about money or measures?* (We usually cannot measure to any more than two decimal places, and money is only available in two decimal places. *Why do we convert fractions of numbers into decimals for money and measures?* (¼ of 1cm or £1 doesn't mean much, and isn't easily measurable until converted to mm or pence by using the decimal form.

Ask: *Tell me a word problem that might use the calculation 204 ÷ 3.* This could be any practical problem Repeat with 274 ÷ 8. Now ask: *Tell me a division word problem that has the answer 12 or 25.* Go through the steps necessary to go backwards from an answer to a calculation and then to a word problem. This is useful for reinforcing the solving of word problems.

Name	Date

Division word problems

1. Aunt Joan sent £152 to be divided equally between me and my two sisters. How much did we receive each?

_____

2. In a marathon relay race, 6 people run a total of 159 miles. How far does each individual run?

_____

3. There are 209 litres of fuel to be shared between 5 vans. How much fuel will each van receive?

_____

4. I have 342cm of fabric to make 4 identical cushions. How much fabric can I use in each one?

_____

5. I use 1265g of flour to make 8 cakes. How much flour is used in each cake?

_____

Now make up some division word problems of your own.

Multiplication and division for word problems

The children revise standard written methods for multiplication and division and apply these in 'real life' problem-solving activities.

LEARNING OBJECTIVES

	Topics	Starter	Main teaching activities
Lesson 1	Pencil and paper procedures (× and ÷) Checking results of calculations	● Read and write whole numbers in figures and words, and know what each digit represents.	● **Extend written methods to long multiplication of TU by TU.** ● Check with an equivalent calculation.
Lesson 2	Pencil and paper procedures (× and ÷) Checking results of calculations	As for Lesson 1.	As for Lesson 1.
Lesson 3	Problems involving 'real life', money and measures	● Consolidate knowing by heart addition and subtraction facts for all numbers to 20. (Year 4 revision)	● **Use all four operations to solve simple word problems involving numbers and quantities based on 'real life', money and measures.**
Lesson 4	Making decisions	As for Lesson 3.	● Choose and use appropriate number operations to solve problems, and appropriate ways of calculating: mental, mental with jottings, written methods, calculator.
Lesson 5	Making decisions	● Continue to derive quickly all two-digit pairs that total 100 (eg 43 + 57).	As for Lesson 4.

Lessons overview

Preparation
Write on the board:
● for Lesson 1, some four-digit and five-digit numbers in digits
● for Lesson 2, some four-digit and five-digit numbers in words.
Prepare for Lesson 1, a sheet of HTU × TU multiplication problems.

Learning objectives
Starter
● Read and write whole numbers in figures and words, and know what each digit represents.
Main teaching activity
● Extend written methods to long multiplication of TU by TU.
● Check with an equivalent calculation.

Vocabulary
strategy, informal jotting, calculation

You will need:

Equipment
Dice, paper and pencils.

Lesson ①

Starter
Show the children some four-digit and five-digit numbers, such as 4368 and 52912. Highlight individual digits and ask the children the value of those digits.

Main teaching activities
Whole class: Revise short multiplication with the children. Emphasise that we start with the units. Depending on your calculation policy, some children may still be using the grid method where others are able to calculate:

```
  1 2 8
×     5
  6 4 0
  1 1
```

Practise a number of examples before moving on to a long multiplication problem such as 514 × 13. Estimate the answer first: 500 × 13 = 6500. Now demonstrate the written method:

```
    514
×    13
   1542    Start by multiplying by the 3 units.
 + 5140    Put in a zero to hold the place value for ×10.
   6000
    600    Add the most significant digit first.
     80
      2
   6682
```

Emphasise the importance of using a zero to hold the place value, and of adding in the 'moved up' digits carefully.

```
    314
×    12
    628
   3140  ◄——— The placeholder zero has the effect of multiplying
 + 3768         by a multiple of 10 not a unit.
```

Repeat for other examples.
Individual work: Ask the children to use long multiplication to answer the questions.

Differentiation
Less able: This group may be ready to move on to short vertical multiplication, using HTU × U questions.
More able: This group should be able to calculate answers with up to six figures, with ThHTU × TU questions.

Plenary & assessment
Write a question such as 37 × 14 on the board. Ask for a volunteer to calculate this using long multiplication, while you complete the same calculation using the grid method. Ask: *Which two numbers multiplied together make 370?* Ask the children to identify where 7 and then 30 are multiplied by 10. Now ask: *How would the answer be different if I worked out 14 × 37 – that is, put the number the other way round?'* (No difference.) Discuss the different layouts, explaining that the grid method allows you to see each whole-number answers whereas long multiplication relies on accurate place value recording and 'carrying' digits into the next place value. Repeat with other examples to make sure the children understand clearly.

Lesson ②

Starter
As for Lesson 1, but write the numbers up in words (for example: eight thousand, nine hundred and fifty-two). Ask for a volunteer to come and write each number in digits. Then ask: *How many more would I need to add to this number to make the next whole thousand? How many more would I need to add to make 10 000? Repeat with other word examples up to ten thousand.*

Main teaching activities
Whole class: Continue from Lesson 1. Work through some long multiplication examples, using decimals in real-life contexts such as money or length. For example: *I need to buy 15 lengths of material, each measuring 3.52m. What length should I buy in total?* Demonstrate how we can use partitioning to solve this:

3m × 15	= 45m
50cm × 15	= 750cm or 7.5m
2cm × 15	= 30cm or 0.3m
Total	= 52.8m

Now ask: *If each length costs £5.75, how much will I spend?* Ask for a volunteer to demonstrate how they would calculate this using long multiplication, and an additional volunteer to come and check it using partitioning or the grid method. Emphasise the importance of the decimal point being fixed in one place.

Repeat with another example, such as: *My uncle has bought 36 ornamental fish for his pond. Each fish cost £4.45. How much did it cost him to restock his fish pond?*

Individual work: Ask the children to generate decimal multiplication problems by throwing a dice. They can throw the dice three times to give numbers with one or two decimal places, then throw it a further two times to give the multiple. For example, they might throw the dice three times and score 6, 4 and 5. This gives them a decimal number of 6.45 or 64.5. Then they might throw a 2 and a 3, generating the calculation 64.5 × 23. The children should solve these problems using long multiplication.

Differentiation
Less able: The children can calculate TU × U multiplications.
More able: The children can throw the dice four times to generate a number with four digits and two decimal place numbers, then throw it twice more to generate a two-digit multiple.

Plenary & assessment
Show the children some examples (on the board) of long multiplications with mistakes in them, as shown below. Ask them: *Can you identify the mistakes, explain why they happened and say how they can be corrected?* Ask the children to start by estimating the answers.

3.26	£4.27	24.18
× 18	× 16	× 24
26₂.0₄8	24.22	96.72
3.2 6	42.70	48.36
29.3₁4	66.92	145.08
Forgot to allow for place value.	Forgot to add in carried digits.	Decimal point placed incorrectly.

Lessons   overview

Preparation

For Lesson 3, prepare a sheet of multiplication and division word problems. Write some word problems on the board (see 'Main teaching activities').

Learning objectives

Starter
● Consolidate knowing by heart addition and subtraction facts for all numbers to 20. (Year 4 revision)
● Continue to derive quickly all two-digit pairs that total 100 (eg 43 + 57).

Main teaching activity
● Use all four operations to solve simple word problems involving numbers and quantities based on 'real life', money and measures.
● Choose and use appropriate number operations to solve problems, and appropriate ways of calculating: mental, metal with jottings, written methods, calculator.

Vocabulary

pattern, puzzle, operation, symbol

You will need:

Photocopiable pages
'Ocean world', see page 169, one for each child.

CD pages
'Number cards 1–20 and 10–90' (see General resources, Autumn term), for teacher's/LSA's use; 'Four operations vocabulary' cards (see General resources, Spring term) for display and discussion by all. 'Ocean world', less able version (see Summer tem, Unit 3).

Equipment
Individual whiteboards and pens or paper and pencils.

Lesson

Starter

Ask for 20 volunteers to stand up and distribute the number cards 1–20. Ask one child to start with the number on his or her card and say an addition fact with an answer up to 20 – for example, 6 + 4 = 10. The child holding 10 must now say a new number fact up to 20 – for example, 10 + 7 = 17. The child holding 17 can make the number fact to reach 20: 17 + 3 = 20. The chain begins again with different children. The non-participating children must check each number fact for accuracy.

Main teaching activities

Whole class: Go through the 'Four operations' vocabulary cards in random order. Discuss words such as 'product', 'shared', 'times' and 'divide'. Indicate the word problems that you have written on the board. For example:
● *What is the product of 124 and 15?*
● *What does each person have if you share £169 between 7 people?*
● *How big is a field that measures 4.18m by 1.7m?*
● *Divide 20.47 by 5.*

Encourage the children to estimate the answer to each question. Now ask for volunteers to come and calculate some of the answers, talking through the methods they use.

Individual work: Distribute some further multiplication word problems. Explain that these problems contain a variety of multiplication and division problems, and that most (but not all) of them require a written method to solve them. Remind the children to estimate the answers first.

Differentiation

Less able: The children should attempt questions that focus on short multiplication, short division and simplified long multiplication.
More able: The children can attempt more challenging questions with four-digit numbers and higher multiples.

Plenary & assessment

Ask: *How do I know that 378 × 17 cannot be 642?* (A rough estimate, 380 × 15, would give us 5700. Ask for a volunteer to work through the example. Ask: *How do we estimate calculations with decimal numbers?* (Round up to the next whole number, so 27.85 would round up to 28.)

Distribute individual whiteboards and pens, and ask the children to estimate the following decimal calculations: 23.14 × 12; 34.67 × 15; 56.01 × 21; 65.25 × 13. Go through each example, asking individuals to explain how they arrived at their estimations.

Lesson 4

Starter

Repeat the starter for Lesson 3, this time extending the task in order that each child holds a number card 1 to 30+ (the number in class) – but do this at speed. How many chains of three number facts can the children complete in ten minutes?

Main teaching activities

Whole class: Compile a short list of five or six items available at a fast food outlet. Using this, pose 'real life' calculation problems. Ask the children to choose the items. Remind the children of how to set out money problems, aligning the decimal points for calculations.

Individual work: Distribute the 'Ocean World' activity sheet. Explain that the children need to use their problem-solving skills to discover the cheapest way for each of the three families to visit 'Ocean World'. They can choose between different ticket offers, and select one of the special offers. Point out that the solution may be different for different families. Ask: *Would the third special offer be a good idea for the Foyles?* (No, because they have no children.)

Differentiation

Less able: The children can use the version of 'Ocean World' with simplified prices.
More able: This group can use the more challenging version of 'Ocean World'.

Plenary & assessment

Invite the children to discuss the activity. Ask for volunteers to demonstrate their choices and calculations. Ask: *How did you decide to choose that option? What did you compare it with? What operations did you use to work out the price? How did you know which ones to use?*

Lesson 5

Starter

Distribute all the number cards 10–90 between different groups. Start with one random number, such as 17: the group with the corresponding number to make 100 hold it up, call out the number fact (17 + 83 = 100) and call out another of their numbers.

Main teaching activities

Continue with the discussion of the 'Ocean World' problems. Troubleshoot any difficulties with problem-solving and with written methods of multiplication and division.

Differentiation

As Lesson 4.

Plenary & assessment

Ask the children to consider the Jacksons. There is Mrs Jackson, Granny and Grandad, Annie (10) and Alan (15). The entrance fees are the same as shown on the 'Ocean World' activity sheet but senior citizens are given a £1 concession daily. Invite the children to calculate the best value daytime ticket. Compare choices and calculation methods.

Name	Date

Ocean world

Use the prices and special offers to calculate the cheapest way to spend a day at this water theme park, including a route planner and a guide book.

Entrance fees		The families
Day pass:		The Smiths: 2 adults and 2 children (aged 6 and 15).
Adult	£15.95	
Child (11–16 years)	£12.60	
Child (4–10 years)	£9.24	The Elliots: Mum and 4 children (aged 3, 7, 8 and 15).
Family ticket		
(2 adults, 2 children under 16)	£46.99	The Foyles: Mr and Mrs Foyle, no children.
Route planner	£2.80	
Guide book	£5.00	

Special offers

Youngest child free offer
Cannot be used with any other offer.

Free Commemorative Route Planner
Cannot be used with any other offer.

Children under 11 half price
Cannot be used with any other offer.

50% off guide book price
Cannot be used with any other offer.

The Smiths _____

The Elliots _____

The Foyles _____

Fractions, decimals and percentages

This unit helps children to link their knowledge of fractions and decimal equivalents to percentages and then to use this knowledge to solve 'real life' problems, using money.

LEARNING OBJECTIVES

	Topics	Starter	Main teaching activities
Lesson 1	Fractions, decimals and percentages	● Continue to derive quickly all two-digit pairs that total 100 (eg 43 + 57).	● Representations: that is, recognise the equivalence between the decimal and fraction forms of one half, one quarter, three quarters… and tenths and hundredths (eg $7/10 = 0.7, 27/100 = 0.27$).
Lesson 2		● Continue to derive quickly all pairs of multiples of 50 with a total of 1000 (eg 350 + 650).	As for Lesson 1.
Lesson 3		As for Lesson 2.	● Begin to understand percentage as the number of parts in every 100, and find simple percentages of small whole-number quantities (eg 25% of £8).
Lesson 4		● Use doubling or halving, starting from known facts.	As for Lesson 3.
Lesson 5		As for Lesson 4.	As for Lesson 3.

Lessons overview

Preparation
For each of Lessons 2 and 3, list ten multiples of 50 on the board. For Lesson 4, prepare a sheet of varied percentage problems using a range of percentages and different numbers.

Learning objectives
Starter
● Continue to derive quickly all two-digit pairs that total 100 (eg 43 + 57).
● Continue to derive quickly all pairs of multiples of 50 with a total of 1000 (eg 350 + 650).
● Use doubling or halving, starting from known facts.
Main teaching activity
● Relate fractions to their decimal representations: that is, recognise the equivalence between the decimal and fraction forms of one half, one quarter, three quarters… and tenths and hundredths (eg $7/10 = 0.7, 27/100 = 0.27$).
● Begin to understand percentage as the number of parts in every 100, and find simple percentages of small whole-number quantities (eg 25% of £8).

Vocabulary
equivalent, reduced to, cancel, one whole, tenth, hundredth, twentieth, in every, to every, as many as, percentage, per cent, %

You will need:
Photocopiable pages
'Sally's sports', see page 175, one for each child.

CD pages
'0–9 digit cards', for teacher's/LSA's use; 'Number cards 1–100', for teacher's/LSA's use; 'Fractions, decimals and percentages' cards, for teacher's/LSA's use; 'Blank 100 square', one for each child (see General resources, Autumn term). 'Sally's sports', less able and more able versions (see Summer term, Unit 4).

Equipment
Calculators; individual whiteboards and pens or paper and pencils; Blu-Tack.

Lesson

Starter

Play 'Pairs to 100'. Distribute the number cards 10–90 randomly among the children. Ask for one child to hold up a number card and call out its value. The child holding the number that adds to the first number to make 100 calls it out, then offers another number from his or her cards. This continues until all the pairs have been found. Once all a child's cards have been used, they must continue to follow the game, checking the accuracy of the pairs making 100.

Main teaching activities

Whole class: Write '7/10' on the board. Ask the children: *What does this mean? Is it more or less than 1? How would I write it as a decimal?* (0.7.) Repeat the questions for 7/100. Now write '70/100'. *How would I write this as a decimal?* (0.70 or 0.7.) Point out that 7/10 and 70/100 are equivalent. Explain this by saying: *I have two identical cakes. I cut one into 10 pieces and the other into 100 pieces. Which would be more: 7 of the 10 pieces or 70 of the 100 pieces?* (They are the same amount.) Ask the children to put both fractions into the calculator to check that they are equivalent. Demonstrate that the larger-numbered fraction can be divided by 10 to simplify it: 70/100 = 7/10 = 0.7.

Remind the children that the size of a fraction is determined by two things:
- how many pieces a whole (number, cake and so on) is divided into (the denominator)
- how many of the pieces you are given (the numerator).

Individual work: To consolidate the relationship between tenths, hundredths and their decimal equivalents, give each child a 'Blank 100 square'. Ask them to colour in 1/10 of the 100 square (that is, 10 squares) in a colour of their choice. Repeat with 2/10 in a different colour, then 3/10, then 4/10 (which will complete the 100 square). Ask the children to cut the square into the four different-coloured strips and use them to write the first four entries in this table:

1/10	=	10/100	=	0.1
2/10	=	20/100	=	0.2
3/10	=	30/100	=	0.3
4/10	=	40/100	=	0.4

Now ask the children to complete the table up to 10/10.

Differentiation

Less able: Encourage the children to put each fraction into the calculator in order to check the equivalent decimal value.

More able: Ask the children to include in their table some fractions that have equivalent hundredths but not tenths, such as 65/100 or 32/100. They should use a calculator to check the place value.

Plenary & assessment

Ask the children to use their knowledge of hundredths to write the fraction equivalents of the following decimals on their whiteboards: *0.7, 0.4, 0.6, 0.65, 0.25.* Then ask: *Which of those decimals cannot be represented as tenths?* (The ones not divisible by 10.) Demonstrate this on the board – for example, 70/100 = 7/10, but 65/100 does not have a tenths equivalent. Ask the children to use their calculators to investigate whether other fractions have tenths equivalents – for example, ask them to try 2/5 and 6/20. Discuss the relationship between tenths and fifths, and between tenths and twentieths.

Lesson 2

Starter
Indicate the list of ten multiples of 50 on the board. Ask the children to write down, against the clock, the numbers that add to them to make 1000 (for example: 200 + 800, 350 + 650, 550 + 450). Ask for answers around the room.

Main teaching activities
Whole class: Explain to the children that since we can quickly and easily write the decimal equivalents of tenths and hundredths, it is helpful if we can see that other fractions can be converted to tenths if we want to convert them to decimals. For example, 1/5 can be converted to tenths by multiplying the numerator and the denominator by 2: 1/5 = 2/10 = 0.2.
Likewise, 2/5 can be converted to 4/10 = 0.4. Ask: *Can anyone think of any other fractions that can be multiplied up to make tenths?* The children may suggest halves: ½ = 5/10 = 0.5. *What about dividing? Can you divide 5/50 down to a tenths fraction?* (Divide the top and bottom by 5: 5/50 = 1/10 = 0/1.) *What about 6/20?* (Divide the top and bottom by 2: 6/20 = 3/10 = 0.3.)
Individual work: The children can continue to investigate fractions that can be simplified to make tenths or hundredths in order to reveal their decimal equivalent. Encourage them to use both division and multiplication, and to record their findings in this way:
- 6/20 divide both numbers by 2 = 3/10 = 0.3
- 4/5 multiply both numbers by 2 = 8/10 = 0.8
- 50/100 divide both numbers by 10 = 5/10 = 0.5.

Differentiation
Less able: Give this group easier starting fractions to convert, such as 2/20, 4/20, 2/5, 1/5, 4/5, 10/20, 10/50, 5/50, 30/100, 60/100, 4/25.
More able: Encourage this group to convert fractions with low numerators and higher denominators, such as 4/200 and 6/100.

Plenary & assessment
Ask: *What is the decimal equivalent of 4/5… 30/100… 20/20…? What other fraction/decimal equivalents do we know?* The children may suggest: ¼ = 0.25; ½ = 0.5; ¾ = 0.75. *How can these help us to find some other equivalents?* Discuss how some fractions can be simplified to ¼ or ½ so that the decimal can easily be found (for example, 4/16 = ¼ = 0.25). Write the fractions ¼, ½ and ¾ on the board, then ask the children to contribute as many equivalents as they can. For example: ¼ = 0.25 = 2/8 = 4/16 = 8/32 and so on.

Lesson 3

Starter
Repeat the starter from Lesson 2, using a new list of ten multiples of 50. Can the children improve their score against the clock?

Main teaching activities
Whole class: Explain to the children that we can use our knowledge of decimal equivalents to find percentages. 'Per cent' means 'out of 100', so 75% is the same as 75/100 or 0.75 and 25% is the same as 25/100 or 0.25.
　　Use a set of 'Fractions, decimals and percentages' cards to play a matching game. Spread the cards face up on the floor or table, so that all the children can see them. Invite the children to look for trios of equivalent cards (for example: ½, 0.5, 50%). Attach each trio to the board with Blu-Tack. Explain that knowing these equivalents means we can either find fractions of numbers from

percentages or vice versa, since they are interchangeable. Demonstrate by asking: *What is half of 60?* Most children should be able to answer '30'. Now ask: *What is 50% of 60?* Repeat this with other fraction/percentage equivalents, such as: ¼ and 25%; 1/10 and 10%.

Individual work: Ask the children to find percentages of numbers and amounts of money using even amounts and percentages in multiple of 10, and 25%.

Differentiation

Less able: The children may need adult support to link finding percentages and fractions of numbers to using division. Ask questions such as *How can we find ¼ of 8?* (8 ÷ 4)

More able: Give the children harder problems which require working out percentages that have decimal number answers (for example, 25% of 49).

Plenary & assessment

Ask some simple percentage questions such as *50% of 90* and *25% of 16*. Then ask: *Can we find all percentages, from 1 to 100%, by using fractions? What about 20% or 75%?* Discuss what fraction/ percentage equivalents the children know. They can find 20% of a number if they remember that 20% = 0.2 = 1/5, so they can divide the number by 5. Likewise 67% is just over 2/3 (0.66). 75% of a number is ¾, so it can be worked out by finding ¼ and multiplying by 3 (or finding 50% and 25% and adding them).

Lesson ④

Starter

Hold up a number card (1–100) and state 'doubling' or 'halving'. Ask the children to recite the doubles to 100 or beyond, or the halves to zero. Start with numbers such as 6, 12, 24, 48, 96, 192.

Main teaching activities

Whole class: Explain to the children that to find some percentages, we need to use two or more stages. For example, to find 5% we could find 10% and then halve it:

5% of 60   →   10% of 60 = 6

So   5% of 60 = 3

Ask the children to suggest ways of finding 15%, 75%, 30%, 90% and so on. Demonstrate some examples of methods on the board.

Individual work: Distribute your prepared sheet of percentage problems. Ask the children to calculate the percentages and show how they found them.

Differentiation

Less able: The children can use a version where the percentages are of multiples of 10.

More able: The children can use a version with more complex numbers and percentages.

Plenary & assessment

Ask: *How would I find 35% of 70?* Demonstrate a method:

1. Find 10% of 70 = 7
2. Multiply by 3 to find 30% = 7 × 3 = 21
3. Halve 7 to find 5% = 3.5
4. Add 30% and 5 % = 21 + 3.5 = 24.5

Ask similar questions, encouraging the children to explain their answers:

- *How would you find 12% of 96?*
- *How would you calculate 5% of 150?*
- *If a pair of trainers costing £55 has been reduced in price by 8%, how would you calculate the new price? Can anyone suggest a different method?*
- *How could I quickly calculate 95% of 300?*

Lesson ⑤

Starter
Give a child a digit card (1–9) and ask the children to double it as they pass it on around the room (for example: 7, 14, 28, 56…). When they bridge 100, they should reverse the process and halve until they reach zero. Repeat with other digit cards.

Main teaching activities
Whole class: Remind the children that shops often use percentages when they advertise their price reductions in sales. Distribute the 'Sally's Sports' activity sheet. Explain that the prices in a sports shop have been reduced by the percentages shown. The children have to find the new sale price for each item. Work through one example. Remind the children that to find the sale price, they have to subtract the discount from the original price.
Individual work: The children use the activity sheet to work out the sale prices.

Differentiation
Less able: The children can use the version of 'Sally's Sports' with simpler prices.
More able: The children can use the version with more complex prices and percentages.

Plenary & assessment
Ask: *Can anyone suggest some different ways I might calculate 70% of a number, or 35%, or 12%?*
Methods for finding 70% might include: find 10% and multiply by 7; find 50% and 20% and add them; find 50%, add 10%, then add 10%; find 75% and subtract 5%

Play 'Percentage consequences'. Give each child a whiteboard and pen. Ask them to write a number smaller than 100 on their board. Now write on the classroom board a series of percentage additions or subtractions for them to apply to the number – for example: *Add 10%. Add 25%. Add 60%. Take off 5%. Add 100%;* and so on. After each new percentage has been added or taken away, they should pass their board to the next child, who continues. The first player to pass 500 holds up their board for the class to check.

Name	Date

Sally's sports

Each of the items in the table below is available at a discount.

Use the sales offer signs to work out the sale prices. You can use another sheet of paper for your working out.

Item	Original price	Sale price
Football club logo shirt	£45.00	
Football shorts	£22.00	
Football socks	£8.50	
Tennis racquets	£52.00	
Tennis dress	£38.00	
Tennis balls (6)	£16.40	
Boy's swimming shorts	£8.10	
Girl's swimming costume	£10.30	
Snooker cue	£109.80	
Hockey boots	£45.00	
Rugby boots	£62.00	
Running trainers	£35.00	
Aerobics trainers	£38.00	
Gym shoes	£16.00	

SALE 20% OFF football kit

BARGAIN 10% OFF swimwear

£££££ 25% OFF SUMMER SPORTS EQUIPMENT

SAVE 75% OFF snooker cues

DISCOUNT 35% OFF all boots & shoes

Ratio, proportion and percentages

Children use ratio, proportion and percentages in practical applications such as in cooking, shopping or in advertisements.

LEARNING OBJECTIVES

	Topics	Starter	Main teaching activities
Lesson 1	Ratio and proportion	● Use doubling or halving, starting from known facts.	● Solve simple problems using ideas of ratio and proportion ('one for every…' and 'one in every…').
Lesson 2		As for Lesson 1.	As for Lesson 1.
Lesson 3		● **Know by heart all multiplication facts up to 10 × 10.**	As for Lesson 1.
Lesson 4		● Partition (eg 47 × 6 = (40 × 6) + (7 × 6))	As for Lesson 1.
Lesson 5	Ratio and proportion	As for Lesson 4.	● Solve simple problems using ideas of ratio and proportion ('one for every…' and 'one in every…').
	Percentages		● Begin to understand percentages as the number of parts in every 100.

Lessons   overview

Preparation
Make ratio cards (1:5; 1:6 and 1:4), one for each pair of children; make an OHT or A3 copy of 'Cat food advertisments'. For Lesson 4, prepare a second ratio and proportion sheet similar to the activity sheet.

Learning objectives
Starter
● Use doubling or halving, starting from known facts.
● Know by heart all multiplication facts up to 10 × 10.
● Partition (eg 47 × 6 = (40 × 6) + (7 × 6))
Main teaching activity
● Solve simple problems using ideas of ratio and proportion ('one for every…' and 'one in every…').

Vocabulary
ratio, for every, proportion, in every, to every, as many as

You will need:
Photocopiable pages
'Cat food advertisement', see page 181, copied to A3 or OHT; 'Ratio and proportion', see page 182, one for each child;

CD pages
'Number fans cards' and '0–9 digit cards', both for teacher's/LSA's use, (see General resources, Autumn term). 'Cat food advertisement', 'Ratio and proportion' (see Summer term, Unit 5).

Equipment
Disposable cups; squash; measuring jugs or cylinders; coloured cubes; coloured pencils; 6-sided dice.

Lesson ①

Main teaching activities

Whole class: Tell the children that they are going to make a drink of squash, since drinks during the day are said to rehydrate the brain and so will improve their concentration! However, they must make the drink in a particular ratio. Remind the children that *ratio* means 'for every': if I make squash in the ratio 1:5, I will need 5 parts of water for every 1 part of squash. Demonstrate this using coloured cubes. Explain that this ratio can be used to calculate amounts – for example: 5ml squash to 25ml water; 50ml squash to 250ml water; 10ml squash to 50ml water. Work through a number of these examples with the children to help them understand the relationship. Repeat with ratios of 1:4 and 1:3.

Paired work: Give each pair a ratio card and the equipment needed (see above). Ask them to make up their drink in the ratio given on the card. Explain that they need to measure the capacity of their cup and mark the 'full' line (approximately 150–200ml) in order to calculate the correct amounts in millilitres. Then they should mark their cup with the level of squash needed before the water is added to fill up the cup. This will enable you to check the accuracy of their calculations. Once you have done this, they can make the squash and drink it. Expect to see improved concentration!

Differentiation
Differentiate by the level of support needed, particularly with measuring and calculation.

Plenary & assessment
Ask: *Were all the drinks the same strength? Which were stronger?* (The ones with more squash and less water.) *How many millilitres of squash did you use? How much water? Did you think your squash was too weak, too strong or just right?* Discuss how tastes differ and then take a vote on the children's preferences. Is there a favourite ratio that makes the best squash drink? Explain that this ratio could be expressed as a proportion – for example, 1:4 would mean that 1/5 of the whole drink was squash. You can demonstrate this by creating a fraction from the amounts:

200ml in the ratio 1:4 means 40ml squash and 160ml water
Proportion of squash = 40/200 = 4/20 = 1/5

Lesson ②

Main teaching activities

Whole class: Explain that a ratio is a comparison of numbers or amounts. Work through some examples, such as adults to children or chairs to tables in the classroom. Use the latter context to show that sometimes ratios can be simplified in a similar way to fractions. If you have 32 chairs and 8 tables, this is a ratio of 4:1 (dividing both numbers by 8). Explain that some ratios cannot be reduced to x:1. For example, a mixture of pens and pencils might be in a ratio of 3:2.

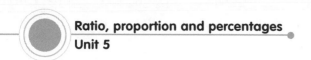

Individual work: The children represent some ratios by drawing or writing. Discuss a first example: 10 cats in a ratio of 1:4 ginger to black. The children must draw 2 ginger cats and 8 black ones.

Differentiation

Less able: The children can use coloured cubes to help them visualise the ratios suggested by the teacher. They may need adult support.

More able: The children could write and draw some ratios of their own.

Plenary & assessment

Check the children's answers and understanding by working through the questions on the activity sheet. Ask: *If I have a box of chocolates with a ratio 1:4 white chocolate to dark chocolate, how many chocolates could there be in the box?* (Any multiple of 5.) *Explain how you know.* (The ratio has 5 parts.)

Ask: *Can you explain in words what a proportion is? Can you explain what a ratio is?* Give 20 coloured cubes to each group: 10 in one colour and 10 in another. Explain that you are going to say a ratio or a proportion, and that you would like the children to represent it with coloured cubes. Say: *Show me a proportion of 7 out of 10... 1/6... 6/7... 8 out of 11. Also show me a ratio of 1:6... 3:4... 6:7... 8:5.* Use this game to assess the children's understanding.

Lesson

Starter

Ask quick-fire multiplication fact questions. Say: *8 × 4; The product of 7 and 6; Show me a multiple of 9; Show me a factor of 27; Multiply 6 by 5* etc. In the event of a repeated digit answer, eg 55, join with a partner to show the answer. The children use their number fans to respond when you say *'Show me'*.

Main teaching activities

Whole class: Display the A3 or OHT copy of 'Cat food advertisement'. Look at the first example. Ask the children: *What does this mean? How many cat owners did they ask?* Some children may answer '18', which will need to be corrected by explaining that a multiples of 10 must have been asked. 8 out of 10 can be expressed as the fraction 8/10, which can be simplified to 4/5 by dividing the top and bottom numbers by 2. Explain that this is a proportion. The ratio of cat owners who said their cats liked 'Yummy Kit' cat food to those who didn't is 8:2. This can be simplified to 4:1, which is less impressive-looking in advertising terms. So the ratio is 4:1 and the proportion of owners who said their cats liked the product is 4/5.

Individual work: Distribute the 'Ratio and proportion' activity sheet. Explain that the children must convert these proportions to ratios in their simplest form.

Differentiation

Less able: The children could use coloured cubes to help them visualise the proportions and ratios. They may need additional support.

More able: The children could create some similar proportion/ratio problems of their own, then swap with a friend to work out the answers.

Plenary & assessment

Explain that you are going to play the 'Make a ratio or proportion' game from Lesson 2, but this time you are going to say ratios and proportions that the children need to simplify before making them out of cubes. For example, a ratio of 3:6 can be simplified to 1:2. Distribute the cubes as before and say: *Show me a ratio in its simplest form of 6:8… 8:4… 2:10… 3:9. Now show me a proportion in its simplest form of 3 out of 12… 5 out of 10… 2/6… 4/12.* Look out for errors in simplifying. Ask for a volunteer to show each arrangement of cubes and explain how he or she simplified the ratio or proportion.

Lesson

Starter

Ask for two volunteers to create a two-digit number with the digit cards (0–9). They hold them up, explaining which digit is the tens and which is the units. Roll a six-sided dice to find a multiple. The other children use partitioning to find the answer and display it on their number fans when you say '*Show me*'. Continue with more two-digit numbers.

Main teaching activities

Whole class: Explain that we use ratio and proportion quite often in daily life for comparison, even if we don't realise it. Show the children the 'Cat food advertisement' sheet again; can they suggest any other examples? Every time we vote or express a preference, a ratio can be created – for example, say: *8 out of 32 children in our class want to stay in at playtime. What is the ratio of children who want to stay in to children who want to go out?* (8:24 or 1:3.) *6 out of 24 children choose baked beans instead of spaghetti at lunchtime. What is the ratio of those who chose baked beans to those who chose spaghetti?* (6:18 or 1:3.)

Individual work: Distribute your prepared ratio and proportion sheet. Explain that these are more ratio and proportion problems for the children to solve. Encourage them to show their working.

Differentiation

Less able: As before, the children can use cubes to help them visualise the groups.
More able: After completing the given problems, the children can go on to create their own scenarios and questions, then swap with a friend to work out the answers.

Plenary & assessment

Ask: *If 6 out of 30 children say they do not watch the TV news, what proportion do watch it?* (24/30 or 4/5.) *Explain how you worked that out. What is the ratio of children who watch the news to those who do not?* (1:4.)

Explain that the order a ratio is expressed in is important to the meaning. Demonstrate this by asking three children with brown hair and two with blond hair to stand up facing the class. Ask the rest of the class to express this as a ratio. They may say, correctly, that there is a ratio of 3:2 brown hair to blond. Write this on the board, then ask the volunteers to change places. Ask: *What is the ratio now? Can we simply say 'There is a ratio of 3:2 or 2:3', or do we have to explain what is in ratio with what? Who can tell me the proportion of children who do NOT have brown hair?* Repeat with other examples.

Lessons overview

Preparation
Provide some ratio and proportion questions that start with a percentage.

Learning objectives
Starter
- Partition (eg $47 \times 6 = (40 \times 6) + (7 \times 6)$)

Main teaching activity
- Solve simple problems using ideas of ratio and proportion ('one for every…' and 'one in every…').
- Begin to understand percentages as the number of parts in every 100.

Vocabulary
ratio, for every, proportion, in every, to every, as many as

You will need:

Equipment
Paper and pencils.

Lesson

Starter
Repeat the starter activity from Lesson 4: TU × U multiplication by partitioning. Use word problems to pose the question such as: *I have five bags of sweets and there are 24 in each bag. How many sweets do I have altogether?*

Main teaching activities
Whole class: Explain that this lesson links proportion and ratio with percentages. Give an example: if 80% of people asked are happy with their car, that means 80 out of 100 or 80/100, which can be simplified to 8/10 or 4/5. Ask: *What proportion is unhappy?* (20%, which means 20/100, which can be simplified to 2/10 or 1/5. *What is the ratio of unhappy to happy people?* (1:4.) Explain that if you know the size of the sample, you can then work out the actual numbers involved. *If 200 people were asked, how many were happy with their car?* Demonstrate the calculation:

$$4/5 \times 200 = 800/5 = 1600/10 = 160$$

Individual work: The children should be given some questions that begin with a percentage linked to proportion. They should use proportion out of 100 to find the answers.

Differentiation
Less able: Provide simpler calculations using only 100 people for each question.
More able: The children could devise their own percentage or proportion questions, then swap with a friend to work out the answers.

Plenary & assessment
Share some of the children's answers. Invite some of the children who have made up their own questions to challenge the rest of the class to solve them.

Ask: *How would you explain the difference between ratio and proportion to someone? How are they linked to percentages? Does it matter that the number in the sample is not 100 when you are converting to a percentage? How much is 100%?*

Name

Date

Cat food advertisement

8 out of 10 owners said that their cats preferred *Yummy Kit*

SCHOLASTIC
photocopiable

All New 100 Maths Lessons
Year 5

181

Name	Date

Ratio and proportion

Convert these proportions to ratios.

The first example has been done for you..

1. 8 out of 10 owners say their cats prefer Yummy Kit'.

   Ratio of Yummy Kit to other brands is [4.5]

2. 6/9 dogs are brown.

   Ratio of brown dogs to other colours is [ ]

3. 7 out of 20 boys like football.

   Ratio of boys who like football to those who don't is [ ]

4. 1 out of 10 coins are 5p pieces.

   Ratio of 5p pieces to other coins is [ ]

5. 8 out of 12 birds are sparrows.

   Ratio of sparrows to other birds is [ ]

6. 7/21 children love maths.

   Ratio of children who love maths to those who don't is [ ]

7. 90/100 teachers need a holiday

   Ratio of teachers who need a holiday to those who don't is [ ]

Data handling

Children carry out three or four different (but related) data handling activities which involve investigating and evaluating the school visits undertaken by one school in a year. They are given opportunities to choose the appropriate graph to present their results.

LEARNING OBJECTIVES

		Topics	Starter	Main teaching activities
Lesson 1			● Order a set of fractions such as 2, 2¾, 1¾, 2½, 1½, on a number line.	● Solve a problem by representing and interpreting data in tables, charts, graphs and diagrams, including those generated by a computer… first where intermediate points have no meaning, then where they may have meaning.
Lesson 2			● **Relate fractions to their decimal representations.**	
Lesson 3			As for Lesson 1.	
Lesson 4			● Continue to derive quickly decimals that total 1 (eg 0.2 + 0.8) or 10 (eg 6.2 + 3.8).	● Find the mode of a set of data.
Lesson 5			As for Lesson 4.	● Develop calculator skills and use a calculator effectively.
Lesson 6			As for Lesson 2.	
Lesson 7			● Continue to derive quickly division facts corresponding to tables up to 10 × 10.	
Lesson 8			As for Lesson 7.	

Lessons overview

Preparation
For Lesson 1, write a random set of fractions on the board, such as 1/2, ¾, , 2/7 and 1/9. For Lesson 8, copy the children's graphs created during the week onto OHTs.

Learning objectives
Starter
● Order a set of fractions such as 2, 2¾, 1¾, 2½, 1½, on a number line.
● Relate fractions to their decimal representations.
● Continue to derive quickly decimals that total 1 (eg 0.2 + 0.8) or 10 (eg 6.2 + 3.8).
● Continue to derive quickly division facts corresponding to table facts 10 x 10.
Main teaching activity
● Solve a problem by representing and interpreting data in table, charts, graphs and diagrams including those generated by computer, first where intermediate points have no meaning and then where they may have meaning.
● Find the mode of a set of data.
● Develop calculator skills and use a calculator effectively.

Vocabulary
database, line graph, bar chart, bar line chart, tally chart, frequency, mode, range, maximum/minimum value, outcome, Carroll diagram, group, set, list, classify

You will need:
Photocopiable pages
'The Archimedes Science and Technology Centre', see page 189; 'Thrills and spills', see page 190; 'Fair's fair?', see page 191 – all for each child.

CD pages
'Number fans'; '0–9 digit cards'; 'Fractions, decimal and percentage' cards (see General resources, Autumn term) and 'Decimal point card', both for teacher's/LSA's use (see General resources). 'The Archimedes Science and Technology Centre' and 'Thrills and spills'– less and more able; 'Fair's fair?', less able version (see Unit 6).

Equipment
Graph paper; individual whiteboards and pens or paper and pencils.

Data handling
Unit 6

Lesson ①

Starter

Have a random selection of fractions displayed on the board. Ask the children to order them, starting with the smallest. Ask: *Can you explain **how** you decide which fraction is the smallest?* The children may suggest looking for the largest denominator. *What else do you have to consider when you are comparing fractions?* Make sure the children understand that the size of the numerator is also important – for example, 7/10 is a **larger** fraction than 3/5. If in doubt when comparing two fractions, they can convert them to decimals.

Main teaching activities

Whole class: Explain to the children that in this unit of work, they will carry out three (or four) different (but related) data handling activities. These activities are all about investigating and evaluating the school visits undertaken by one school in a year. Revise the way in which different graphs are used for different types of data: bar charts or bar line graphs for comparisons of discrete (separate) data, line graphs for continuous data.

Explain that there are three types of value we can use when talking about a set of numbers:

1. Mode: the value that occurs most often. Write this list of numbers on the board: 3, 4, 7, 7, 8, 1, 2, 3, 3, 8, 1, 1, 2, 3, 3. Ask for a volunteer to come and reorder these in ascending order. Now ask the class to decide which value occurs most often. In this case the mode is 3.

2. Median: the middle value of a sequence of numbers arranged in ascending order, or the average (add together and divide by 2) of the two middle values if there is an even number of values in the sequence. Ask the children to look at the reordered data again and find the median value. In this case it is also 3.

3. Mean: this is what we would call the 'average' in everyday life. It is normally calculated by adding all the numbers together and dividing their sum by the number of numbers. Write the following on the board: 3, 17, 13. Ask the children to add these numbers together and divide by the number of numbers: $33 \div 3 = 11$, so the mean of these numbers is 11. Repeat with other sets of numbers such as 5, 3, 4, 3, 5 (mean = 4) and 9, 2, 3, 10 (mean = 6).

Individual work: Set groups of children to work as individuals on the activity sheets. Talk through each activity with the group beforehand. Most children will complete all three of the following activities in six days; others may need an extension activity such as writing (and answering) their own questions to append to the graphs. You may wish to set up a 'carousel' of simultaneous activities and work with different groups each day.

ACTIVITY 1

Use the table of data on the activity sheet 'The Archimedes Science and Technology Centre' to create a bar line graph showing the monthly number of visitors to the Centre in a year. Label the vertical axis with two squares for every 10 000 people. Use your graph to answer the questions.

Notes: The children's answers should reflect some reasoning about the changing seasons – for example, 'Fewer people go to outdoor places like parks when the weather is bad.' The higher numbers of visitors between May and August is probably a consequence of children being on school holidays and therefore being able to visit the Centre with their families. Encourage the children to see that the information extracted from a graph can be used to make hypotheses and even to predict. They need to think of the data in a 'real life' context in order to draw conclusions from it.

ACTIVITY 2

A Year 5 class visits the Speed and Sound science fair each year. Their favourite features are the rides demonstrating speed. Look at the Thrills and spills activity sheet, which has a line graph showing the speed of the Rocking Roller Coaster during its 3-minute ride. Draw a similar line graph for the Hill and Dale Dipper using the data in the table. Use the two graphs to answer the questions.

Notes: 1. 'A graph to show the speeds reached by the Rocking Roller Coaster at different points in the ride.' **2.** To find the mean speed of each ride, add up all the readings shown on the graph (including 0 readings at the beginning and the end). Mean speed for the Rocking Roller Coaster = 192 ÷ 10 = 19.2mph. Mean speed for the Hill and Dale Dipper = 25mph; mean speed = 25.5mph; mean speed = 25.7mph. **3.** To find the speed at a particular time, read it off the y-axis of the graph. For the Rocking Roller Coaster, speed at 70 seconds is 25mph and speed at 30 seconds is 11mph. For the Hill and Dale Dipper, speed at 70 seconds is 32–33mph and speed at 30 seconds is 10mph.

ACTIVITY 3

Look at the Fair's Fair activity sheet. Use the data from the tables showing the average waiting time and the duration of the ride for each of five rides at the Speed and Sound fair to draw **one** comparative bar chart showing all the information. Use all the data to compare the rides. List them in order of value for money and write a report commenting on the waiting times, the ride times and the value for money of each ride.

Notes: Look for the use of two different colours to represent the two sets of times on the graph. The children's decisions about value for money should use all of the available data, not just one or two parameters. The Wall of Fear is the best value for money at 27p per minute with only 10 minutes' waiting time and a 10-minute ride. Squashed costs 60p per minute and is a 5-minute ride, but has a very long waiting time. The Hill and Dale Dipper costs 76p per minute and has a very short waiting time, so may be considered better value than Squashed. The Rocking Roller Coaster costs 83p per minute, with 15 minutes' waiting time, so comes fourth. The poorest value for money is the Hole of Horror, which costs 90p per minute with 18 minutes' waiting time, and is the shortest ride.

Differentiation (Lessons 2–7)

Less able: The children can use the versions of the activity sheets with simpler numbers and graph frames with axes and divisions provided.
More able: Expect the children to work with greater independence. They can use versions of the activity sheets with more difficult numbers and more challenging questions.

Plenary & assessment

Each day, check the progress of each group and correct misconceptions. Ask questions such as:
● *Why does this activity use a bar line chart when this activity uses a line graph?*
● *Look at these numbers: 8, 4, 7, 8, 9, 2, 8. Find the mode and the median. Find the mean of the numbers. What advice would you give to someone calculating a mean?*
● *When would you use a calculator? Have any of you needed a calculator to answer the questions?*

Lesson ②

Starter

Write a mixed selection of decimal and fraction pairs on the board. Ask for volunteers to match and link them with a coloured line (for example: 2/10 = 0.3, 29/100 = 0.29, ¼ = 0.25, ¾ = 0.75, 1/5 = 0.2).
Present a selection of fraction and decimal cards and ask the children to order them on a 0–1 number line. Discuss how the cards can be ordered, and especially how knowing equivalents can help. For example: *I have to decide which is smaller, 0.25 or 1/3. I can recall that 0.25 = ¼, so it is less than 1/3.*

Main teaching activities

The children continue with the carousel of activities (see Lesson 1). Revise when a bar or bar line graph is appropriate and when to use a line graph. (The latter measures something over a period of time, eg temperature of a person in 24 hours.)

Ask the children to consider when finding the mean of a set of data might be useful. (It gives an overall 'snapshot' or measure of data, for example average rainfall in July or 'mean' number of visitors to a zoo each day.)

Plenary & assessment

Ask a group who have been working on 'The Archimedes Science and Technology Centre' to share their work so far. Ask: *What was difficult about drawing this graph? Why would it have been inappropriate to draw a line graph for this? Why do you think there were more visitors in some months than in others? How might a graph like this help the Centre to organise its publicity and 'special events'? Who might be interested in this data?*

Lesson

Starter

Ask a child to select two digit cards at random and create a decimal number with them, using the decimal point card. Ask the class: *What number would I need to add to this to make 10 or 1?* (For example: $3.7 + 6.3 = 10$; $0.3 + 0.7 = 1$.)

Main teaching activities

The children continue with the carousel of activities (see Lesson 1). Revise 'mode' or most represented or popular result or data. When might this have practical use, for example to find the most popular chocolate bar sold in a shop or the most representative shoe size of height?

Plenary & assessment

Ask a group who have been working on 'Thrills and spills' to report back about their work to the rest of the class. Then ask: *What sort of graph did you draw? Why? Which of the questions would you have been unable to answer if you had drawn a bar chart?* (The ones that involve reading intermediate points.) *Who might find this information of value?*

Lesson

Starter

Repeat the starter from Lesson 4, but ask the children to create numbers with two decimal places (for example, $4.17 + 5.83$). Discuss strategies for working out these additions. Remind the children that the same place value rules apply to decimal numbers as when adding whole numbers. The smallest digit, ie the hundredths, will add up to 0.10 or ten hundredths, that is one tenth and the other digits must add up to 9.
$0.07 + 0.03 = 0.1$, so $0.1 + 0.8 = 0.9$ and $4 + 5 = 9$
When recombined: $9 + 0.9 + 0.1 = 10$

Main teaching activities

The children continue with the carousel of activities (see Lesson 1).

Plenary & assessment

Ask a group who have been working on 'Fair's fair?' to report their findings and views. Some other groups who have looked at this activity may have different views, and can be invited to discuss these. Ask: *What facts do we need to look at when deciding which is the 'best' ride? Does it depend on your own preferences? Do some people value the thrill of a longer ride more than not having to wait a long time? How can you calculate the price per minute of a ride?*

Lesson ⑤

Starter

Use a set of fraction, decimal and percentage cards to play 'trios' with the class. Place all the cards face down (or stuck loosely to the board). Ask for volunteers to come and turn over three cards, so that everyone can see them. If they are a matching trio (such as 0.25, ¼, 25%) then they can be removed from the board. If not, they are turned face down and another child attempts to find a trio.

Main teaching activities

The children continue with the carousel of activities (see Lesson 1).

Explain that the children's data handling work will be displayed, and that they need to be able to present their findings to the class as if they were telling the owners of the Science Centre or the Speed and Sound Fair. They will thus need to have clear results and explanations, and be ready to answer questions. They should prepare a statement to go with each activity sheet. A statement might be a comparison of length of ride or value for money or popularity. Ask the children to consider how data can be presented to show the same results in different lights, for example by increasing the vertical scale on a bar chart, differences can be made to look visually bigger. Demonstrate using differences of waiting time on a vertical scale of 1 square = 1 minute and compare this to a vertical scale of 1 square = 5 minutes.

Plenary & assessment

Distribute individual whiteboards and pens. Ask the children to calculate the mean of each set of numbers that you write on the board. Write: 13, 11, 12; 4, 5, 3, 2, 4, 2, 1; 7, 8, 4, 6, 10, 1; 2, 3, 1, 4, 3, 2, 2, 1, 1, 1. The children in each group should work together. At the end of all the calculations, they should try to spot what the mean numbers all have in common. (They are all factors of 12.)

Lesson ⑥

Starter

Ask fraction questions related to division, such as *1/4 of 32 or 1/5 of 35, 48 sweets divided into eighths, one half of 90*, etc. The children hold up the answers on their number fans when you say *'Show me'*.

Main teaching activities

The children continue with the carousel of activities (see Lesson 1). With any children who have finished the carousel already, revise or teach other types of diagrams that represent and sort information – for example, Carroll diagrams.

Tell the children: *A group of children were asked what rides they preferred at the fairground. Each child was asked whether they had chosen fast rides or slow rides, with queues of more or less than 15 minutes.* Copy this diagram onto the board:

	Slow fairground rides	Fast fairground rides
Rides with queues of more than 15 minutes	5	35
Rides with queues of less than 15 minutes	40	10

Ask: *How many children were prepared to queue for longer than 15 minutes for any ride? How many children were questioned altogether?*

Ask the children who have completed the main activities to consider some types of information that a Carroll diagram could sort, such as the contents of lunchboxes on a school trip: egg sandwiches and other sandwiches; brown bread and white bread. Can they draw Carroll diagrams to sort this information?

Plenary & assessment

Ask the children who have been working on Carroll diagrams to display their charts. Ask the class: *What kind of information does this chart give us? Would it be suitable for displaying the number of visitors to a museum each month? Would it be suitable for sorting the number of people visiting the Archimedes Centre or the Speed and Sound Fair? How could we do this?* Demonstrate on the board, using a simple survey:

(SEE LETTER.)	Have visited the Archimedes Centre	Have not visited the Archimedes Centre
Have visited the Museum of Speed, Light and Sound	190	120
Have not visited the Museum of Speed, Light and Sound	214	400

Lesson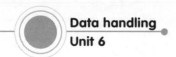

Starter

Ask questions about fractions of quantities, such as ¾ *of 1 litre or 2/3 of 300g.* The children raise their hands to answer.

Main teaching activities

Whole class: This lesson should be the culmination of the children's unit of work. Before the lesson, if possible, select a variety of the children's graphs to copy onto OHT sheets. Use these to share the children's results and findings. Compare the appearance of some graphs that are showing the same information, but look different due to a larger or smaller scale being used on the *y*-axis.

Group/individual work: Ask various groups to present their findings as if they were either the science center or science fair owners or visitors waiting in a queue. Invite the class to ask each group questions.

Plenary & assessment

Use this session to gather and reinforce all the children's learning about data handling in this unit of work. Ask:

● *Why are graphs and charts useful? When are they most often used? Who might find these graphs and charts useful?*

● *What action might the owner of the science centre want to take after seeing this data? Should visitors be given this kind of data as part of their guide book? Would it encourage or discourage visitors?*

● *Can you think of any other information about the science centre that would be useful? (For example, a line graph showing price increases over the last 5 years.) Who might be interested in this?*

● *Can the 'picture' conveyed by a graph sometimes be deceptive? How? Why might someone want to manipulate the data?*

● Give the children strips of paper to write down what they have learnt from this work, or what they know now about data handling that they didn't know before. Display these, or store them as a record.

Name   Date

The Archimedes Science and Technology Centre

Use the information in the table below to draw a bar line graph on a sheet of squared paper, showing the number of visitors to the Archimedes Science and Technology Centre in each month of a year.

Month	No. of visitors	Month	No. of visitors
January	25 000	July	40 000
February	20 000	August	45 000
March	18 000	September	30 000
April	25 000	October	25 000
May	40 000	November	17 000
June	38 000	December	15 000

Use your graph to answer the questions below.

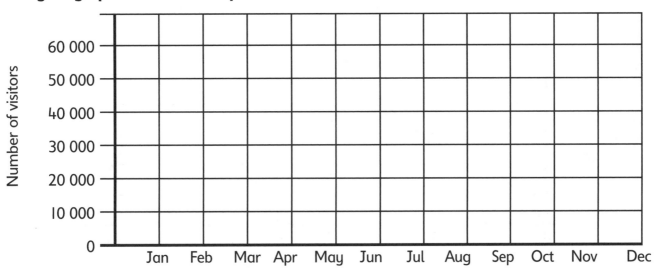

1. Which was the most popular month for visiting the centre? Can you explain why?

_____

2. Which was the least popular month? Why?

_____

3. How many more people visited the centre in the most popular 3 months than in the least popular 3 months?

_____

4. What is the range of this data?

_____

5. Why would it not be appropriate to represent this data as a line graph?

_____

Name	Date

Thrills and spills

Look at this graph for the Rocking Roller Coaster.

On the same set of axes, plot a line graph to show the speeds reached by the Hill and Dale Dipper, which also lasts for 3 minutes. The data you need is in the table below.

A graph to show  _____

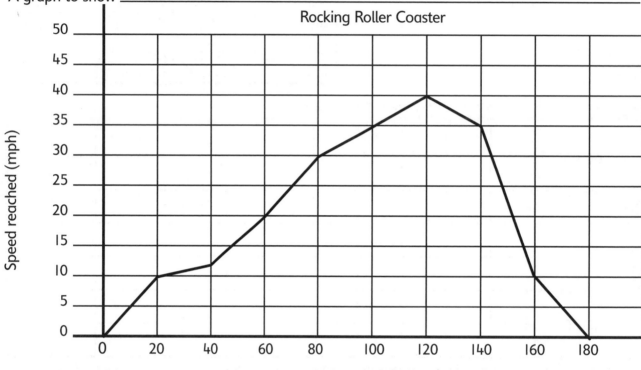

Rocking Roller Coaster

Speed reached (mph)

Time elapsed (seconds)

Hill and Dale Dipper

Time (secs)	Speed (mph)
0	0
20	5
40	15
60	28
80	38
100	42
120	42
140	50
160	30
180	0

Use the information on the graph to answer these questions.

1. Give the graph a title.

2. Use a calculator to find the **mean** speed for each ride. Show how you did it.

3. What was the approximate speed of each ride at 70 seconds?

4. What was the approximate speed of each ride at 30 seconds?

Name	Date

Fair's fair?

Look at the table of data below.

Draw one comparative bar chart to show the average queuing time and the ride length for five rides at the Science Fair. Use one big square of graph paper for every five minutes.

Ride	Queuing time (minutes)	Length of ride (minutes)	Cost
Rocking Roller Coaster	15	3	£2.50
Hole of Horror	18	2	£1.80
Squashed	25	5	£3.00
Wall of Fear	10	10	£2.70
Hill and Dale Dipper	5	3	£2.30

Now consider the cost of each ride. Use all your data to write a short report, comparing the rides in terms of value for money. List the 5 rides in order of preference, stating your reasons.

Child's report

Reflective symmetry

Children name and classify 2D shapes by their properties and lines of symmetry. They create symmetrical patterns by reflecting shapes in mirror lines and using the vocabulary 'parallel' and 'perpendicular' to describe its position.

LEARNING OBJECTIVES

	Topics	Starter	Main teaching activities
Lesson 1	Shape and space Reasoning and generalising about numbers or shapes	● Read and write whole numbers in figures and words.	● Recognise reflective symmetry in regular polygons. ● Make and investigate a general statement about familiar numbers or shapes by finding examples to satisfy it.
Lesson 2		● Round any integer up to 10 000 to nearest 10, 100 or 1000.	As for Lesson 1.
Lesson 3		● **Multiply and divide any positive and negative integer up to 10 000 by 10 or 100 and understand the effect.**	● Complete symmetrical patterns with two lines of symmetry at right angles.
Lesson 4		● **Multiply and divide any positive and negative integer up to 10 000 by 10 or 100 and understand the effect.**	As for Lesson 3.
Lesson 5		● Know and apply tests of divisibility by 2, 4, 5, 10 or 100.	● Recognise where a shape will be after reflection (sides not all parallel or perpendicular to mirror lines).

Lessons overview

Preparation
Shapes cut out of card (or commercially made 2D shapes), variety of triangles, square, rectangle, regular hexagon, pentagon etc.

Learning objectives
Starter
● Read and write whole numbers in figures and words.
● Round any integer up to 10000 to nearest 10, 100 or 1000.
Main teaching activity
● Recognise reflective symmetry in regular polygons.
● Make and investigate a general statement about familiar numbers or shapes by finding examples to satisfy it.

Vocabulary
reflective symmetry; mirror line; parallel; perpendicular; polygons; regular; irregular

You will need:
CD pages
'0–9 digit cards', for teacher's/LSA's use (see General resources, Autumn term).

Equipment
Mirrors; OHP; large sheet of paper to make a recording chart; strips of paper for children's statements.

Lesson ①

Starter
Human numbers: Create 5 digit numbers using digit cards. Ask 5 children to hold one card each. The rest of the class read the number and reorder it by giving the human digits instructions, ie *'The tens number moves to the thousands'* etc. Create the largest, smallest, odd and even numbers. Repeat with other children and digit cards.

Main teaching activities

Whole class: Establish what is meant by 'reflective symmetry'. Demonstrate by folding card shapes along lines of symmetry. Ask: *How many lines of symmetry has an equilateral triangle or a square? Why does a square have diagonal lines of symmetry when a rectangle does not?*

Using card shapes, revise reflective symmetry of regular polygons such as equilateral triangles and squares. Revise symmetry of a rectangle and discuss why it only has 2 lines of symmetry instead of 4, as in a square. (2 longer sides, not a regular shape.)

Demonstrate how lines of symmetry can be checked using a mirror or tracing paper. Remind the children that a reflected shape 'flips' over on the opposite side of a mirror line.

Individual work: Ask the children to investigate the lines of reflective symmetry of a variety of polygons. They could draw around the shapes and then find the lines of symmetry using a mirror.

Differentiation

Less able: This group could fold regular card shapes to find the lines of symmetry. These could be stuck down for recording purposes.

More able: This group should investigate patterns in lines of symmetry of regular polygons. Is there a relationship they could spot and predict for other many-sided polygons?
They might also investigate non-regular polygons.

Plenary & assessment

Begin a 'results table' on the board or on a large sheet of paper for display purposes.

Regular shape	Number of sides	Lines of symmetry
Equilateral triangle	3	3

Ask: *'Can anybody spot a pattern? Can anybody predict how many lines of symmetry a 20-sided regular polygon might have?'* Ask: *'Is the same true for irregular polygons?'* Continue in Lesson 2.

Lesson

Starter: Human numbers
Repeat the activity from yesterday but also round the numbers created to the nearest 10, 100, 1000.

Main teaching activities
Whole class: Continuing from Lesson 1. Explain that we suspect that there may be a relationship between the number of sides and the number of lines of symmetry but it is unlikely that enough samples were tested in one lesson.
Individual work: Continue the investigation encouraging children to 'fill the gaps' in the recording table from yesterday.

Differentiation
Less able: Continue to find lines of symmetry by folding but also check by using the mirror – moving towards finding lines of symmetry using the mirror alone.
More able: Look for patterns in other irregular shapes, ie do all triangles or shapes with one right angle have the same number of lines of symmetry?

Plenary & assessment
Continue the recording chart from yesterday and ask the children to write a statement about the relationship between the number of sides and the number of lines of symmetry in regular shapes. Ask: *Are there any other patterns we noticed, ie in triangles or all shapes with one right angle?* Distribute strips of paper to groups of children and ask them to write a statement of their observations. Display these with the recording chart.

Lessons   overview

Preparation
Mirror axes on OHT on squared paper. OHT of 'Blank axes'.

Learning objectives
Starter
● Multiply and divide any positive and negative integer up to 10 000 by 10 or 100 and understand the effect.
Main teaching activity
● Complete symmetrical patterns with two lines of symmetry at right angles.

Vocabulary
Quadrant, reflection, reflective symmetry, mirror line, parallel, perpendicular

You will need:
Photocopiable pages
'Symmetrical patterns', see page 198, one for each child.

CD pages
'Blank axes', one for each child; 'Decimal point card', one for teacher's/LSA's use (see General resources).

Equipment
Lots of coloured counters.

Lesson

Starter

Build and read 'human numbers' as for Lesson 1. This time ask the children to multiply or divide the numbers by 10 or 100 and direct the human digits to move accordingly. You will need a 'decimal point' person!

Revise the rule for x and ÷ by 10 and 100.

	x	←2	←1	x	
			1↓		
			2↓		
			2↓		
			1↓		
	x	←2	←1	x	

Main teaching activities

Whole class: Draw the following mirror lines onto an OHT of squared paper.

Explain that the dark lines represent mirrors and that any shape in any quadrant will need to be reflected vertically and horizontally.

Demonstrate this by using a coloured counter or colouring in a square. Reflect, by counting the squares to the mirror line and then by counting the same number *away* from the mirror line on the opposite side. Repeat with the other mirror line. Repeat with the reflected shape so that the pattern or counter appears in all 4 quadrants. Repeat as necessary.

Individual work: Distribute the 'Blank axes' general resource sheet. Explain that this is a similar grid to the one on the OHT. Give the children counters to practise reflecting from square to square into all four quadrants. Then ask them to create a coloured pattern which should be reflected square by square in both mirror lines.

Differentiation

Less able: This group may need more adult support to complete the activity.
More able: Encourage this group to use unusual shapes in their pattern such as diagonal lines, where each corner needs to be counted for reflection.

Plenary & assessment

Display the activity sheet 'Symmetrical patterns'. Ask the children what is wrong with the reflection shown. Ask for volunteers to check by counting the squares or corners to the mirror lines.
Then ask for a volunteer to create a pattern using coloured counters or crosses. Ask the children to reflect the pattern in both mirror lines.
    Ask the children: *'What rule would you write to help others know how to reflect shapes in a mirror line?'*

Lesson

Starter
 As for Lesson 3.

Main teaching activities

Whole class: Develop the pattern making ideas from Lesson 4. Introduce the vocabulary 'parallel' and 'perpendicular' as they refer to orientation of lines on a set of axes.
Parallel: Lines or planes continuously at the same distance from one another.
Perpendicular: At a right angle to another line or surface.

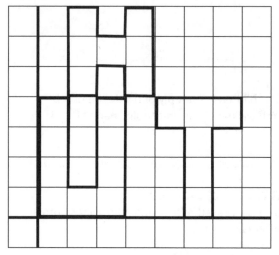

Use an OHT and copy of the activity page 'Blank axes' on which you have drawn a 2D-shape such as a 'T' or 'H'. Ask for 2 volunteers, one to describe the position of the lines and another to attempt to draw them on the OHT. The person describing should give instructions using the words 'perpendicular' and 'parallel', for example there is a line, one square in from the mirror line 'y' which is parallel to the mirror line. It is 4 squares long starting at coordinate (1,1). There is a second line perpendicular with the first line starting at (1,5). Finally ask for another volunteer to reflect these lines into all four quadrants.

Pairs work: Ask the children to use the General resources page 'Blank axes' to plot some lines on the first set of axes and to describe them to a partner, using the vocabulary 'parallel' and 'perpendicular'. The second child should attempt to follow the instructions and draw duplicate lines on their second set of axes. This could take the form of a sort of 'Battleships' game. A line of four squares represents a battleship, three, a submarine, two, a tug etc. Remind the children that the lines must be along the lines marked on the squares. Roles of describer and scribe are reversed and then both sets of lines are to be reflected into all four quadrants.

Differentiation

Less able: This group may be more confident giving the coordinates of the line first before being encouraged by an adult to think of a line parallel or perpendicular.

More able: Ask this group to describe letters on their grids such as H or T or U.

Plenary & assessment

Check understanding of the terms 'parallel' and 'perpendicular' by asking: *Hold your hand parallel to the table/floor/door etc. Now hold it perpendicular to the table, walls, board.*

Now use the OHT and point to lines asking the children to describe them in terms of parallel or perpendicular to the mirror lines.

Lessons ⑤ overview

Learning objectives

Starter
- Know and apply tests of divisibility by 2, 4, 5, 10 or 100.

Main teaching activity
- Recognise where a shape will be after reflection (sides not all parallel or perpendicular to mirror lines).

Vocabulary

Quadrant, symmetry, symmetrical, reflection, mirror line

You will need:

CD pages
'Blank axes', one for each child (see General resources).

Equipment
OHT of 'Blank axes'.

Lesson ⑤

Starter

Use the digit cards to create 2 or 3 digit numbers. Revise and apply knowledge of the tests of divisibility for 2, 4, 5, 10 or 100. Decide as a class whether the number you are holding up is a multiple of 2, 4, 5, 10 or 100 and ask the children how they know. Check using a calculator, ie 245 – multiple of 5; 245 ÷ 5 = 49.
ICT Opportunity: 'Becta' materials from DfE. Use 'Counter' to set a regular counting pattern such as counting in 4s. Stop the counter randomly and ask: 'What are the next 3 numbers in the pattern? If I left the counter running, what number should I start at to reach 102? Explain how you worked it out.'

Main teaching activities

Whole class: Use OHT of 'Blank axes'. Draw an equilateral triangle in one quadrant. Label the corners ABC and reflect, by counting the distance from the mirror line. Repeat for all four quadrants. Label the reflected points A1, B1 C1, A2, B2, C2 etc.

Individual work: Distribute copies of the 'Blank axes' general resource sheet. This time use the 2 sets of axes to draw a right-angled triangle and a rectangle to reflect in all four quadrants.

Differentiation

Less able: May need adult support to ensure accurate reflection of shapes.

More able: Encourage this group to draw a 4- or 6-pointed star and an irregular polygon of their own creation to reflect. Each reflective point should be relabelled A1, B1, C1; A2, B2, C2 etc.

Plenary & assessment

Ask: *What do you notice about the pattern created by your 4 shapes?* (They make a symmetrical pattern.) Ask: *What observations could you make about reflecting a shape?* (It 'flips' over.) This is distinct from a translation which 'slides' along to a different position.

Use a 2D shape and a blank set of axes on the OHP to demonstrate this.

Draw around the shape and ask for a volunteer to reflect it in one of the mirror lines. Label the reflection R. Next demonstrate how a shape may be translated by simply sliding it by 5 squares to the left or 7 squares downwards. Label this shape T. Ask the children to tell you the differences they can see.

Name   Date

Symmetrical patterns

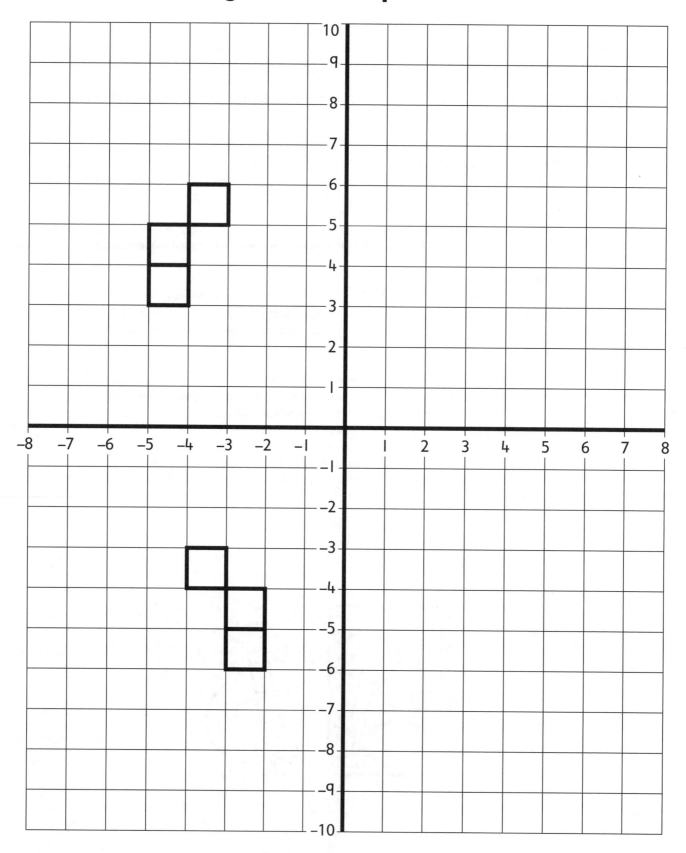

Summer Term
Unit 9

Translating and reflecting shapes and using timetables

The children use coordinates and simple formulae to translate shapes across axes and also to use the axes as mirror lines for reflections.

They use a timetable to practise calculating with time.

LEARNING OBJECTIVES

		Topics	Starter	Main teaching activities
Lesson	1	Shape and space Measures	● **Order a set of positive and negative integers.**	● Recognise where a shape will be after translation.
Lesson	2		● **Relate fractions to their decimal representations.**	As for Lesson 1.
Lesson	3		As for Lesson 1.	As for Lesson 1.
Lesson	4		● Begin to understand percentage as the number of parts in 100 and find simple percentages of whole numbers.	● Use timetables. ● Use units of time; read time on a 24-hour digital clock and use 24-hour notation.
Lesson	5		As for Lesson 4.	As for Lesson 4.

Lessons overview

Preparation
'Blank axes' grid onto OHT.

Learning objectives
Starter
● Order a set of positive and negative integers.
● Relate fractions to their decimal representations.
Main teaching activity
● Recognise where a shape will be after translation.
● Recognise where a shape will be after reflection.

Vocabulary
mirror line; refection; translation; x axis; y axis, quadrant; movement; slide

You will need:
Photocopiable pages
'Translations', see page 204, one for each child.

CD pages
'Number fan cards 0-9', 'Fractions, decimals and percentages', 'Number cards 1-20', one for the teacher's/LSA's use (see General resources, Autumn term); 'Negative number cards', one for the teacher's/LSA's use (see General resources, Spring term); 'Blank axes', one for each child (see General resources, Summer term). 'Translations', less able and more able versions (See Summer term, Unit 9).

Equipment
2D shapes; rulers.

Lesson ①

Starter

Show the children one of the negative number cards; explain that this represents a temperature eg –5°. Display the card on the board. Show the children another card and ask: *'Is this number larger or smaller?'* Place it accordingly. Repeat and order other positive and negative numbers.

Main teaching activity

Whole class: Define translations or translated shapes as shapes that slide up or down, left or right, as opposed to reflected shapes which turn over as they cross a mirror line. Demonstrate this using a blank coordinates grid on the OHP and a 2D shape. Slide the shape along from coordinate to coordinate.

Revise the use of coordinates, reminding the children that the x coordinate is always given first and that coordinates are written using brackets, eg (2,6)

Ask for three children to name a coordinate. Mark each one and join it up to create a triangle. Ask the children: *If I translated this shape two squares to the right what would be its coordinates now?* (The x coordinates plus 2, the y coordinates as before.)

Repeat with another shape.

Individual work: Distribute the 'Blank axes' General resource sheet. Indicate the negative numbers that continue along the line beyond zero. Explain that we can use these to move our shape into another quadrant.

Write up the following coordinates on the board (2, 4), (2, 7), (5, 5). Ask the children to mark these points and join them up using a ruler. Label the points A, B and C. Now ask them to translate the whole shape 6 squares to the left, into a different quadrant. Re-label the points A1, B1, and C1 and list the coordinates. Repeat the process by translating the original shape downwards by 7 squares. Label A2, B2 C2 and record the coordinates. Emphasise that when translating the shape to the left or right it is the x coordinate that will change and when translating a shape up or down the y coordinate is affected. A point translated left crossing the y axis line will become negative. Likewise a point translated down the y axis and crossing to the x axis will be come negative.

Differentiation

Less able: This group might need help to ensure that points move only in one direction along a line.
More able: This group should be able to draw and translate an additional shape of their own.

Plenary & assessment

Ask the children to look at the coordinates of the original and translated shapes. Ask: *Can anybody notice a pattern in these coordinates? How many squares did we move the shapes? What has happened to the coordinates?* (For the first translation the x coordinate has had 6 taken away from it and for the second, the y coordinate has had 7 subtracted from it.)

Now ask: *What do you think we would have to do to this shape to translate it into the empty quadrant?* (Move 6 to the left and 7 down or (x – 6, y – 7).)

Do so on the OHT, by counting squares and marking the points A3, B3, C3 and recording the coordinates.

Lesson ②

Starter

Use 'Fractions, decimals and percentages' to play a 'pelmanism' matching game using only decimals and their equivalent fraction cards. As the children turn over the pairs of cards ask questions such as, *'Are they an equivalent pair? What fraction/decimal would match this card? Can you remember where the 0.5 card was?'* etc.

Main teaching activity

Whole class: Remind the children about their observations about how coordinates change to match the number of spaces moved left or right, up or down, of a point. On a blank OHT of 'Coordinates grid', draw a square with coordinates (–2,1), (–6,1), (–2,4), (–6,4). Ask the children: *If I want to translate this shape to the right, which coordinates will change?* (The *x* coordinates.) Say: *I want to translate this shape 7 spaces to the right, how will the coordinates change?* (Add 7 to each *x* coordinate.)

Write the coordinates like this:

A (–2,1)	→	A1 (5,1)
B (–6,1)	→	B1 (1,1)
C (–2,4)	→	C1 (5,4)
D (–6,4)	→	D1 (1,4)

Explain that this can be written as a formula ($x + 7, y$), which means add 7 to the *x* number whilst the *y* number stays the same.

Ask for a volunteer to plot these new points and draw the translated shape. Ask the children if they think it is accurate. Count the squares to check.

Individual work: Distribute more copies of the 'Blank axes' general resource sheet. Ask the children to draw a shape such as a rectangle or a triangle to translate, starting at point (–7, 1) for point A. Keep the shape within one quadrant. Ask the children to label and list the points with their coordinates. Now ask them to calculate the new coordinates if they were to apply the formula ($x + 8, y$). Draw the new shape and label and list the coordinates.

Now ask them to apply a new formula to the original shape ($x, y–6$). Repeat the process as before.

Differentiation

Less able: Will need adult support to ensure accuracy.
More able: Could draw an irregular 2D shape such as: and translate each point.

Plenary & assessment

Say to the children, '*We have one quadrant with no shape in it. What do we have to do to our coordinate numbers to translate our original shape into that quadrant?*' (Add to the *x* coordinate and subtract from the *y* coordinate at the same time, ie ($x + 8, y – 6$).)

Ask the children to calculate the new coordinates for translated shape A3, B3, C3 etc. Ask for a volunteer to test the theory by drawing the shape based on the new coordinates. Ask: '*Why are these translated shapes not reflections?*' (They have moved by sliding and have not 'turned over' or been reflected in a mirror line.)

Lesson ③

Starter

Repeat the pelmanism game from Lesson 2 but include the percentage equivalent cards (from the 'Fractions, decimals and percentage' cards) and play 'Pelmanism trios'.

Main teaching activity

Whole class: Revise with the children the effect of adding or subtracting numbers to coordinates. Ask: *If I want to move a shape to the right, what must I do to the formula?* (Add to *x*) Ask: *What about moving to the left?* (Subtract from *x* coordinate.)

Ask: *What about moving a shape downwards?* (Subtract from the *y* coordinate.) *Or upwards?* (Add to the *y* coordinate.) Ask: *In what direction would a shape move if I applied this formula? (x + 4, y – 2)* (Right and down.)

Individual work: Distribute the activity page 'Translations' to the children. Explain that there are some shapes which need formulas applying to them to translate them to elsewhere on the grid (*x* + 2, *y* – 1) means add 2 to the *x* co-ordinate number and take 1 from each *y* coordinate number, for each point. Remind them that they must label each point and record the coordinates.

Differentiation

Less able: Use the differentiated page which contains simple shapes to translate, initially in one direction only.

More able: Use differentiated page which uses more complex shapes for translation.

Plenary & assessment

Ask: *Can anybody explain the difference between a translation and a reflection?*

Ask: *What is the formula used for, when translating points?* (A shortcut way of finding the position of a translated shape without counting squares.)

Compare and share translations. Ask the children to check each other's work for accuracy.

Lessons   overview

Preparation

OHT or copies of train or bus timetables (you need to seek permission from the company to use or reproduce in school) or make some of your own. Also prepare some questions to ask about the timetable.

Learning objectives

Starter
● Begin to understand percentage as the number of parts in 100 and find simple percentages of whole numbers.

Main teaching activities
● ● Use timetables.
● Use units of time; read time on a 24-hour digital clock and use 24-hour notation.

Vocabulary
digital notation; 24-hour clock; analogue; hours; minutes

You will need:

CD pages
'24-hour clock face', one for each child (see General resources).

Equipment
Timetables

Lesson

Starter

Use 'Show me' number fans to give answers to quick fire percentage questions, such as 10% of 60, 5% of 80, 25% of 36, 50% of 32, 20% of 50 etc.

Main teaching activity

Whole class: Display OHT of clock face. Revise reading time in 24-hour notation, for example, Ask: *What time is 20:30, 18:15, 21:45? Tell me the time you go to bed/getup/ watch your favourite soap in 24 hour notation.*

Remind the children that during 24 hours of every day, the hands of an analogue clock travel twice round the clock face. Hence in 24-hour digital notation, the first circuit is written using the first 12 hours, 10:15, 08:20 etc. and the second set of 12 hours continue the counting, ie 13:25 etc. Remind the children that in the 12-hour clock, 'am' stands for 'anti meridian' or 'before midday'; 'pm' means 'post meridian' or 'after midday'; hence morning or afternoon. Write some times up on the board and invite the children to translate them into the 24-hour clock equivalent times: 9.45 pm (add 12 to the hour time for the second time around the clock) → 21:45; 8.10 am → 08:10; 7.10 pm → 19:10.

Demonstrate the difference in notation for the 24-hour clock, including **:** between the hours and minutes.

Pairs work: In pairs, create an ideal day of television viewing using 24-hour digital notation. Write the start and finish times and the length of each programme.

Programme	Start	End	Duration
Football Focus	07:45	08:15	30 Minutes

Differentiation

Less able: Support this group with a 24-hour clock face to help with the hours and calculating the duration of programmes.

More able: Stipulate that this group must allow for advertisement breaks, trailers etc. Hence no programme will end exactly as another starts so:

Coronation Street 19:30 – 19:58.

Plenary & assessment

Using the children's ideal television planners, ask questions such as: *What would you be watching at 08: 50, 11:25, 13:18, 02:30?* From this create a class ideal viewing plan and ask related questions such as: *'If a programme started at 13:20 and ended at 14:10, how long was the programme?'*
'A film starts at 16:25 and lasts for 2 hours and 50 minutes – what time does it end?'

Lesson ⑤

Starter

As Lesson 4.

Ask more complicated percentages, which need greater calculation and ask the children to explain how they would calculate them: 30% may be found by adding 10% + 10%; 12% by finding 10% +1% +1% or 90% by subtracting 10% from the whole number. Discuss strategies.

Main teaching activity

Whole class: Show the children the OHT of a timetable. Spend some time asking the children to read the times and calculate travelling times etc. Ensure that everyone understands how a timetable works.

Individual work: Using the given timetables, ask the children to answer the questions and pose some of their own.

Differentiation

Less able: Provide a simplified timetable of your own making.

More able: Use a larger, more complex timetable to pose questions for a partner to answer.

Plenary & assessment

Share answers to some of the timetable questions and correct misconceptions. Ask the children to volunteer some questions of their own and ask the others to solve them. Ask: *What is the longest journey or the shortest journey?* etc.

Now ask some mental time calculations, for example: *A car arrives at its destination at 14:18. It had been travelling for 2 hours and 45 minutes. What time did it set off?*

Our postman says it took him 5 hours and 15 minutes to complete his round today. He left the sorting office at 06:35 – what time did he finish his round? Discuss ways of counting on and counting back to solve these questions.

Name	Date

Translations

Apply these formulae to translate the shapes. Record the coordinates here:

1. (x + 11, y)	2. (x + 12, y – 5)	3. (x – 2, y – 12)
A (–9 , 8) → AI (2 , 8)	E (–5 , 2) → EI (7 , –3)	I (–4 , 8) → II (–6 , –4)
B (–7 , 8) → BI (,)	F (,) → FI (,)	J (,) → JI (,)
C (–9 , 2) → CI (,)	G (,) → GI (,)	K (,) → KI (,)
D (–7 , 2) → DI (,)	H (,) → HI (,)	

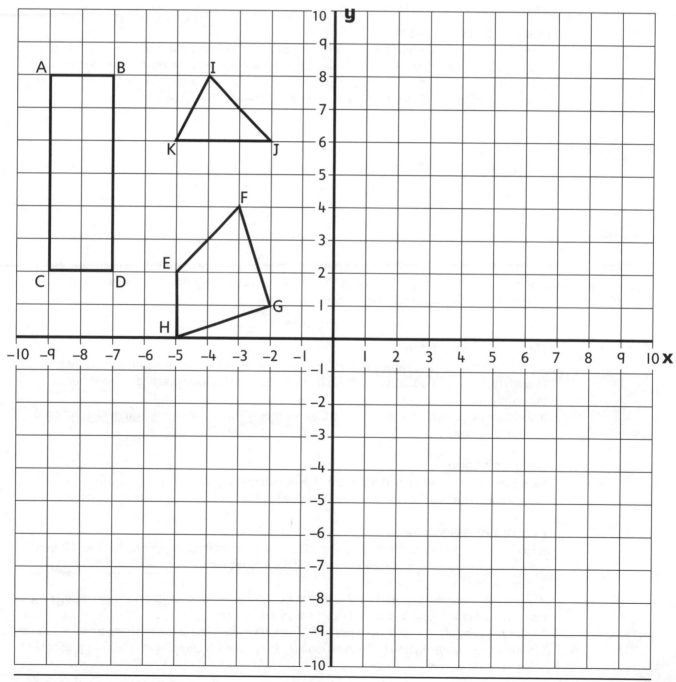

◼ SCHOLASTIC

photocopiable

Word problems using measures

The children use coordinates and simple formulae to translate shapes across axes and also to use the axes as mirror lines for reflections.

They use a timetable to practise calculating with time.

LEARNING OBJECTIVES

	Topics	Starter	Main teaching activities
Lesson 1	Measures Problems involving 'real life' money and measures; Making decisions	● Derive quickly all 2 digit pairs that total 100.	● Use read, write standard metric units. ● Suggest suitable units and measuring equipment to estimate or measure length, mass or capacity. ● Record estimates and readings from scales to a suitable degree of accuracy.
Lesson 2		● Order a set of fractions.	**● Use all four operations to solve simple word problems involving numbers and quantities.**
Lesson 3		● Order a set of numbers or measurements with the same number of decimal places.	**● Use all four operations to solve simple word problems involving numbers and quantities.** ● Choose and use appropriate number operations and appropriate ways of calculating.
Lesson 4		● Use, read and write standard metric units. Convert larger to smaller units.	**● Use all four operations to solve simple word problems involving numbers and quantities** including making simple conversions of pounds to foreign currency. ● Choose and use appropriate number operations and appropriate ways of calculating.
Lesson 5		As for Lesson 4.	**● Use all four operations to solve simple word problems involving numbers and quantities** including making simple conversions of pounds to foreign currency.

Lessons overview

Preparation
Give the children suggestions of items to estimate, weigh and measure, appropriate to your classroom and surroundings.

Learning objectives
Starter
● Derive quickly all 2 digit pairs that total 100.
Main teaching activity
● Use read, write standard metric units.
● Suggest suitable units and measuring equipment to estimate or measure length, mass or capacity.
● Record estimates and readings from scales to a suitable degree of accuracy.

Vocabulary
miles; pints; gallons; metres; kilometres; centimetres; millimetres; kilograms; grams; litres; millilitres; equivalent; conversion

You will need:
CD pages
'Number fan cards 0–9', one for each child; 'Number cards 1–100', for teacher's/ LSA's use (see General resources, Autumn term).

Equipment
Scales, metre/cm rulers, jugs/measuring cylinders for measuring millilitres and litres; Provide items to weigh and measure.

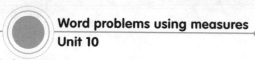
Lesson ①

Starter

Ask the children to find the pair to make 100 of a number you hold up and hold up their number fans when you say 'Show me.' eg You hold up 15 and the children make 85 using their number fans.

Main teaching activity

Whole class: Discuss with the children all the units of measure that we use in our daily lives. Make a list on the board. Kilograms and grams for weighing or measuring quantities of food in shops, centimetres and metres when estimating measures, drawing lines etc. Millilitres and litres for measuring liquid, drinks and petrol.

The children may also mention pints – still used for milk and beer, and miles when referring to distance.

Help the children to understand that metric and imperial units are two distinct systems of measuring and do have equivalents, ie 568ml = 1 pint, but they are awkward numbers to convert and often it is easier to round and estimate, ie 1 litre is just under 2 pints. Explain that because in this country we have held onto both systems, it is important to be aware that they exist.

Pairs work: Give the suggested items to each pair to first estimate the mass/length/capacity of and then use the equipment provided to accurately measure.

Remind the children to be aware of the different scale divisions on weighing scales and measuring jugs to ensure accurate measurements.

Differentiation

Less able: You may choose to differentiate the items to be weighed or measured or provide an easy to read scale, depending on your equipment availability. Alternatively, provide adult support to assist with accuracy.

More able: On completing the set tasks these pupils should go on to find other items to estimate, measure and order.

Plenary & assessment

Ask questions relating to suitable units for measuring, such as: *What unit of measure would you use to weigh a chair; find the height of a door; the length of a corridor or the capacity of a mug?*

Also, ask comparison questions, *Which would you expect to be heavier, a school chair or a table, your maths book or an atlas? Which is taller, the cupboard or the bench?* Ask about mixing units: *Is it possible to measure the height of the door only using metres? Who used mixed units, ie metres and centimetres? How could these be written as just metres or just centimetres?*

Lessons ② ③ ④ ⑤ overview

Preparation

Copy a newspaper table of exchange rates copied onto OHT. Prepare a chart with the headings 'Holiday destination', 'Local currency', '£ to exchange' and 'Amount received'.

Learning objectives

Starter
- Order a set of fractions.
- Order a set of numbers or measurements with the same number of decimal places.
- Use, read and write standard metric units. Convert larger to smaller units.

Main teaching activities
- Use all four operations to solve simple word problems involving numbers and quantities including making simple conversions of pounds to foreign currency.
- Choose and use appropriate number operations and appropriate ways of calculating.

Vocabulary
kilometres, centimetres, millimetres, cm^2, m^2, currency, conversion, equivalent

You will need:

Photocopiable pages
'DIY at Number 32', see page 210, one for each child.

CD pages
'DIY at Number 32', less able version (see Summer term Unit 10).

Equipment
Materials for making games in Lesson 5.

Lesson ②

Starter

On the board, write up the set of fractions below, some of which need to be simplified for the children to order them.

3/3, 2/6, 3/9, 1/3, 1/5, ¼, 2/4, 1/9, 1/6

Ask the children to order them, smallest first. Ask them to explain how they know which is smaller.

Main teaching activity

Whole class: Explain that weights and measures are important to our daily lives and we cannot avoid using them whether shopping or doing home decoration. Introduce the concept of a house, Number 32 which is in need of some redecoration before the new owners can move in.

Distribute activity sheet 'DIY at Number 32' and go through the various measurements. Explain that sometimes the measurements may need converting to smaller units in order to calculate, ie Sally wants three new shelves in her room. Her shorter wall measure 2.8m. Shelving is sold in 300cm or 10m lengths. Which is the best buy for Sally's shelves? How much would be wasted?

Ask: *If we have measurements in both metres and centimetres what must we do to calculate the problems? How many centimetres in a metre?*

Individual work: Use the measurements on activity sheet 'DIY at Number 32' to calculate the home improvements needed at Number 32. Think carefully about standardizing measurements before calculating.

Differentiation

Less able: Use differentiated activity page with simplified numbers and questions.
More able: Work independently and then create more measurement questions and calculations of their own.

Plenary & assessment

Go through some of the questions asking individuals what operation they chose and how they created a calculation to solve the problem.

Work through some of the examples on the board to iron out misconceptions and confusion. Encourage the children to draw a diagram of anything they cannot visualise.

Lesson ③

Starter

Write up a list of mixed measurements on the board. Ask the children to sort these into sets of measurements and then order them, smallest first.

1.2 litres; 250g; 4000g; 1.5kg; 1.8km; 350m; 650cm; 2000ml; 3500ml; 2.5 litres; 700m; 40g;

Main teaching activity

Whole class: Explain to the children that mixed units can sometimes be used in 'real life' problems. Floors might be measured in m² whereas tiles are measured in cm². In order to calculate how many tiles may be needed, a common unit of measure needs to be used. Ask: *If a floor area measures 3m x 4m, how do you calculate how many 30cm² tiles you need?* Convert area to 300cm x 400cm. You can fit 10 x 30 in tiles across and 13 1/3 down. Since you have to buy whole tiles the calculation would look like this: 10 x 14 = 140 tiles.

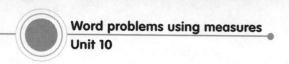
Individual work: Continuing problem solving from Lesson 2. Ask the children to calculate the area of carpet needed for each room. Calculate the number of tins of paint needed for each room. A tin of paint covers 1½ walls and costs £9.80. Sally wants one wall pink and the rest green. Mum wants the kitchen to have a different colour on each wall. Dad wants their bedroom all cream and the sitting room has one wall covered in wallpaper which Mum doesn't want to change. How much in total will they spend on paint?

Differentiation

Less able: Use differentiated activity page from Lesson 2 with simplified numbers and questions. These children may experience difficulty in visualising the problem and may need added adult support. They should be encouraged to sketch out the different aspects of the problem, for example draw the tin of paint per room or draw a sketch of the floor area.

More able: Work independently and then create more measurement questions and calculations of their own. These children might like to sketch and redecorate an imaginary bedroom of their own, making up the dimensions The computer simulation of painting a room on the *'Dulux'* website, might be starting point.

Plenary & assessment

Ask questions such as *What are the clues in these questions to help you decide on the operation to use? What formula did you use to calculate area? Why can't you calculate using mixed units?* Ask: *Think of a question, linked to Number 32 which could be solved using this sum: (4.1 × 2.8) ÷ 2'* (Sally wants half of her bedroom floor carpeted.)

Ask the group of children who made up their own measures questions, related to number 32 to challenge the rest of the class.

Lesson

Starter

Use the mixed measures used in Lesson 3, convert to smaller units: 1250ml = ? l, 1½kg = ? g; 440cm = ? m; 50mm = ? cm. Revise 1000g = 1kg; 1000ml = 1 litre; 100cm = 1m etc.

Main teaching activity

Whole class: Ask the children if they can think of any currencies used in other countries, ie Euro, UK pounds, US Dollar, Australian dollar, Japanese Yen etc.

Explain that when you travel from one country to another it is necessary to convert your money from one currency to another. Ask where they could find out about exchange rates ie banks, newspapers, Internet.

Use the current exchange rate to calculate simple conversions, ie if £1.00 = 1.5 Euros, how many Euros would I receive for £10.00 or £100.00 or £150.00?

Individual work: Choose six destinations to visit on your world tour and fill them in on the prepared chart. Ask the children to use the exchange rates on your OHT to calculate how much local currency they would receive at the current exchange rate. Fill in the chart.

Differentiation

Less able: You might wish to round the exchange rates for simpler calculations.
More able: Extend the number of currencies to calculate.

Plenary & assessment

Share as a class the results of the currency conversions. Ask:*'Which currencies were the most difficult to convert? Did you have to use a calculator? If you were on holiday and trying to calculate the cost of things would you be as exact as this?*

Also pose questions such as: *If I receive 1.5 Euros for each £1.00, how do I calculate 50p? I want to buy a vase for 32 Euros, how much is that in pounds sterling? A flight to New York costs £250 – how much is that in Euros? US dollars? Yen?* etc.

Lesson ⑤

Starter: Converting hours and minutes

Ask questions such as, 'How many minutes are there in an hour and a half, 2 hours, 12 hours? What fraction of an hour is 15 minutes, 30 minutes?'

'A bus journey lasts 53 minutes, how much less than an hour is this? My exam lasts 135 minutes, how long is that in hours and minutes?'

Main teaching activity

Display a fractional exchange rate such as 4 orbs = £1.00 sterling. Write up: 2 orbs, 6 orbs, 1 orb, 16 orbs, 18 orbs. Ask the children to convert the amounts to £ sterling and explain their strategies for doing so.

Whole class: Explain to the children that they are going to design a game based on exchange rates. This could be a board game, such as 'Snakes and ladders' but introducing a currency exchange or a card game such as 'Pairs' or 'Snap'. To simplify the fluctuating exchange rates, the game could use foreign currency to pounds sterling or some imaginary currencies. Advise against having too many currencies or the game will become unmanageable.

Pairs work: Design a game using the concept of exchange rates. Plan the look of the game and the rules. Decide on the materials that will be needed to construct it.

Differentiation

Less able: Encourage this group to plan a simple card game such as 'Snap'. This might simply feature different currency cards to match.

More able: This group may be able to create a game requiring exchange calculations and penalties, or a 'Snap' type game where the equivalent sum of money is matched, ie 1.5 Euros match with £1.00.

Plenary & assessment

Invite each pair to explain the basis of their game, the rules and where the exchange rate element occurs.

Name	Date

DIY at Number 32

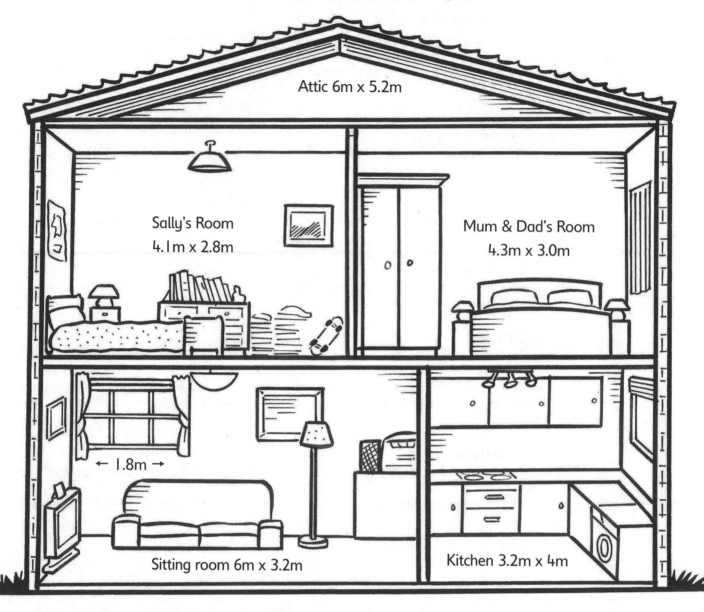

Attic 6m x 5.2m

Sally's Room
4.1m x 2.8m

Mum & Dad's Room
4.3m x 3.0m

← 1.8m →

Sitting room 6m x 3.2m

Kitchen 3.2m x 4m

1. Sally wants 4 shelves in her bedroom. The wall measures 2.8 wide. Shelving is sold in 300cm lengths costing £2.40 each or 10m lengths costing £9.00. Which is the best value for money? How much will be wasted?

2. The sitting room curtains need replacing. The material chosen is £8.20 per metre. They need to buy 4 times the length of the window. How much do they have to buy? How much will it cost?

3. The attic needs new floor boards. Floor boards can be bought in 6m lengths, each 20cm wide. How many are needed?

4. The kitchen floor needs tiles, what is the area of the floor?

Strategies for adding and subtracting

This unit gives children the opportunity to recognise and use patterns in number and various mental strategies to estimate and predict the size of possible answers, then to go on and calculate, using either the expanded or compact written methods, according to ability and confidence.

LEARNING OBJECTIVES

	Topics	Starter	Main teaching activities
Lesson 1	Mental calculation strategies (+and -) Pencil and paper procedures (+and -) 'Real life' problems Making decisions and checking results	● Continue to derive quickly decimals that total 1 or 10.	● Add several numbers. ● Use known number facts and place value for mental addition and subtraction.
Lesson 2		● Continue to derive quickly all pairs of multiples of 50 with a total of 1000.	● Use known number facts and place value for mental addition and subtraction. ● Use knowledge of sums and differences of odd or even numbers.
Lesson 3		● Continue to derive quickly division facts corresponding to tables up to 10 × 10.	● Extend written methods to: column addition/subtraction of more than two integers less than 10 000.
Lesson 4		● As for Lesson 3.	● Extend written methods to: column addition/subtraction of more than two integers less than 10 000; addition or subtraction of a pair of decimal fractions both with one or more decimal places.
Lesson 5		● Continue to derive quickly division facts corresponding to tables up to 10 × 10. ● Use all four operations to solve simple word problems involving numbers and quantities.	● Use all four operations to solve simple word problems involving numbers and quantities. ● Choose and use appropriate number operations and appropriate ways of calculating.

Lessons   overview

Preparation
List of 10 decimals on the board. For Lesson 2, prepare a sheet of varied calculation problems including addition and subtraction of two HTU numbers and addition and subtraction of numbers with one decimal place.

Learning objectives
Starter
● Continue to derive quickly decimals that total 1 or 10.
● Continue to derive quickly all pairs of multiples of 50 with a total of 1000.
Main teaching activity
● Add several numbers.
● Use known number facts and place value for mental addition and subtraction.
● Use knowledge of sums and differences of odd or even numbers.

Vocabulary
add; addition; more; plus; sum; total; altogether; subtract; units boundary; tenths boundary

You will need:
CD pages
'0–9 digit cards', for teacher's/LSA's use (see General resources, Autumn term).

Equipment
Pencil and paper or white boards for informal jotting; dice.

Lesson ①

Starter: 'Pairs to make 10 Bingo'

Indicate the list of decimals on the board. Ask the children to jot down any 5 of them. Call out the pair to make 10 of one of the numbers on the board, ie if 6.2 is on the board, say '3.8'. The children who have the matching pair on their board, ie 6.2, cross it out. Repeat. The winner is the first to cross out all their numbers.

Main teaching activity

Whole class: Mental addition strategies

Throw a dice to generate 5 single digit numbers. Discuss and revise possible strategies for adding these numbers together, eg doubles, making 10, near doubles etc. Given the set of digits, ask the children which two numbers would they choose to add first. Are there any pairs of numbers that make 10? (7 + 3, 6 + 4, 8 + 2, 9 + 1) Are there any doubles, or near doubles (6 + 6 or 6 + 5). Ask: *In which order would you add these numbers?* 6, 8, 3, 6, 7

$$6 + 6 \quad = \quad 12 + 8 \quad = \quad 20 + \quad (7 + 3) \quad = 30$$

double   makes   makes 10
            whole ten

Take the children's suggestions for an alternative order. Or:

$$3 + 7 \quad = \quad 10 + \quad (6 + 6) \quad = \quad 22 + 8 \quad = 30$$

makes 10   makes   makes
        double   whole ten

Repeat to build confidence. Next use the dice to create multiples of 10, ie 5 = 50 and repeat strategies.

Pairs work: Using a dice repeat the activity demonstrated in the main teaching activity. Calculate five, single digit calculations and five, 2-digit multiples of 10. Record informally.

Differentiation

Less able: Use only 3 single digits to begin with.
More able: Use multiples of 10 and multiples of 100.

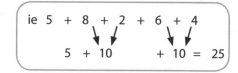

ie 5 + 8 + 2 + 6 + 4

5 + 10   + 10 = 25

Plenary & assessment

Revise the strategies for adding mentally.

Ask the children: *In a number sentence such as 50 + 20 + 70 + 30 + 20, what would you add together first?* Take a variety of strategies and record them for all to see. Ask: *Who can see a different way? Which way is the most efficient? Why do you think that?*
Repeat with other number sentences.

Lesson ②

Starter: 'Pairs to 1000 Bingo'

Repeat the game from Lesson 1 but start with multiples of 50, ie 150, 250, 350, 500, 450 etc.
Give the pair to make 1000. Children cross off the corresponding number on their sheet or board.

Main teaching activity

Whole class: Odd or even

Explain to the children that they have a number of strategies, including estimation and knowledge of odd and even numbers which will assist with accuracy in calculation, ie 470 + 380 – odd or even?

Previous knowledge should inform children that an even + even = even number. Estimation will bring the calculation closer, ie 500 + 400 = 900 (even). So calculating should be easier:

$$400 + 300 = 700$$
$$70 + 80 = \underline{150} \text{ (near double)}$$
$$850$$

Repeat with differences. 810 – 380 → Odd or even? Even – even = even.

Estimate → 800 – 400 = 400

Calculate: 380 + (20) = 400
         400 + (400) = 800
         800 + (10) = 810

Therefore the difference is 430. Ask the children if anybody can suggest an alternative method? Ask them to explain why they find this more logical. Does it work with decimal numbers? How efficient are these strategies?

Repeat strategies with decimal number. ie 81 – 38 or 8.1 – 3.8. Or 7.4 +9.8 etc.

Individual work: Present the children with the varied calculation problems. The children should use their knowledge of odd and even numbers and estimation to aid calculation of numbers given.

Differentiation

Less able: Use differentiated calculations using 1 and 2 digit numbers – multiples of 10.

More able: Use differentiated calculations using 2 and 3 digit odd and even numbers.

Plenary & assessment

Write 3.52 + 3.58 on the board.

Ask: *How would you calculate this: 3.52 + 3.58?*   = 6.00 + 1.00 + 0.1
                            = 7.1

Can you suggest a strategy for helping someone to calculate using decimals? Should it be any different to HTU if you have a good grasp of place value? Explain why.

Now calculate 0.01 + 0.02 + 0.14. Take alternative suggestions for strategies. Ask the children to explain why it works for them. Discuss with the children the method that is the most efficient, and lead to the least number of possibilities for error. Encourage children to make informal jottings to avoid errors. (Do hundredths first = 0.03 + 0.14 = 0.17.)

Generate new calculations by picking random digit cards and discussing ways to solve them.

Lessons   overview

Preparation

Prepare a range of HTU addition problems for children to solve using their chosen method.

Learning objectives

Starter

● Continue to derive quickly division facts corresponding to tables 10 × 10.

Main teaching activity

● Extend written methods to: column addition/ subtraction of more than two integers less than 10000 addition or subtraction of a pair of decimal fractions both with one or more decimal places.

Vocabulary

add, addition, more, plus, sum, total, altogether, subtract, take away, minus, decrease, difference, units boundary, tenths boundary

You will need:

CD pages

'Number cards 1–100' and 'Number fan cards 0–9', both for teacher's'/LSA's use (see General resources, Autumn term).

Equipment

Pencil and paper or white boards for informal jotting.

Lesson

Starter

Hold up a number card such as 7. Children volunteer division facts to match it, ie 42 ÷ 6 = 7. They collect the card, for their group, if they are correct. The first group to collect 5 cards win.

Main teaching activity

Whole class: Write up the sum 349 + 269. Ask children to first round and estimate, and then solve it on their white board using their chosen methods. Some children may use the expanded method:

```
  349
 +269
  500
  100
   18
  618
```

Some may use compact standard method:

```
  3 4 9
 +2 6 9
 ₁61₁8
```

Some children may round and adjust, eg 350 + 270 – 2 = 350 + 250 + 202 = 618.

Check progression and use this as an opportunity to assess and decide on groups ready to progress to the standard method. Discuss when a written method is most efficient and accurate. Repeat using 567 – 243 and 422 – 187. Check methods and accuracy as children *'show me'*.

Individual work: Ask the children to solve the range of HTU addition problems using their chosen method or alternatively you may wish to move a group on to a more compact method.

Differentiation

Less able: Written addition using 2-digit numbers.
More able: Written addition using decimal numbers.

Plenary & assessment

Spend some plenary time checking answers by demonstrating both the expanded and compact method. Write up:

```
   206
 + 347
   543
```

Ask the children what is wrong with this calculation.

Remind them that using the compact method involves remembering to 'carry' up one into the next place value. This then needs to be included into the calculation: 6 units + 7 units = 13 units. That is one ten 'carried' or put with the tens and three units recorded in the units column. Discuss where this should be put in order not to forget it.

Lesson

Starter

Quick Fire Table Fact 10 × 10.
Use number fans to 'show me' quick fire multiplication facts.

Main teaching activity

Whole class: Write up the following question:
School fund makes a profit of £1524 on a sponsored event. It is decided to spend £257 on a visiting theatre group. How much money remains in the school fund?
Ask: *'How would you calculate this?'* Encourage rounding and estimating first and then written responses such as:
Estimate: 1500 – 250 = £1250

```
£1,524 =   1000 + 500 + 20 + 4
 – 257 =          200 + 50 + 7
```

readjusted to: Or:

```
=> £1,524 =1000 + 400 +110 +14       £ 1 5⁴ ¹2¹ ¹4
   – 257 =         200 +  50 + 7       –   2  5  7
   £1,267 = 1000 + 200 +  60 + 7       £ 1 2  6  7
```

Compare both methods and look for similarities, ie 14–7 for the units. Readjusted number actually reads the same for both calculations.

Also revise written addition methods with

```
Either:   Or:
£171.28   £171. 28
+138.64   +138. 64
200.00    3₁09.9₁2
100.00
  9.00
  0.80
  0.12    Again, compare similarities.
309.92
```

Individual work: Give the children money problems of HTU sums with two decimal places.

Differentiation

Less able: These children are to complete simpler 3-digit calculations. Some subtractions may still be completed using a number line.
More able: These children should be able to use only compact methods to solve a variety of written and number calculations.

Plenary & assessment

Ask: *If I have £1072 per month but my house rent costs £350 per month and my supermarket bill is £421 per month, how much do I have left to spend on bills and treats?' Ask: How would you solve this?* Some may add £350 and £421 together and take it away from £1,072. Others may subtract separately. Ask for volunteers to demonstrate their chosen method and discuss the relative merits and margins of error for each. Ask: *How could you estimate first?*
Repeat with a similar example.

Lessons overview

Learning objectives

Starter
● Continue to derive quickly division facts corresponding to tables 10 × 10.
● Use all four operations to solve simple word problems involving numbers and quantities.

Main teaching activity
● Use all four operations to solve simple word problems involving numbers and quantities.
● Choose and use appropriate number operations and appropriate ways of calculating.

Vocabulary

add, addition, more, plus, sum, total, altogether, subtract, take away, minus, decrease, difference, units boundary, tenths boundary, estimate, even, odd, units/tens/hundreds boundary

You will need:

Photocopiable pages
'A mixed bag of problems', see page 217, one for each child.

CD pages
'Number fan cards 0–9', for teacher's/LSA's use (see General resources, Autumn term). 'A mixed bag of problems', less able and more able versions (see Summer term Unit 11).

Lesson

Main teaching activity
Whole class: Remind the children about the checking and estimating techniques practised earlier in the week, ie even number + even number = even number or odd number + odd number = even number etc. Also remind them that rounding and estimating gives the relative size of answer. Also remind the children that not every calculation needs to be written, as in the case of 140 + 150 = 290. However care must be taken if numbers become more complicated or bridge 10/100/1000 such as 497 + 836. This would be difficult to calculate accurately using a mental calculation. So written methods become more accurate:

E   500 + 800 = 1300
E + 0 = 0

```
Either:        Or:        H T U
  H T U                     4 9 7
    4 9 7                  +8 3 6
  +8 3 6                   1 2 0 0
  13,3,3                    1 2 0
                              1 3
                           1 3 3 3
```

One or two children might be able to tell you as a mental calculation 500 + 800 + 36 − 3 but for the majority of the children, this should be a written calculation.
   Emphasise the importance of accurate place value.

Individual work: Distribute 'A mixed bag of problems'. Explain that there are a variety of calculations, some of which may be solved using mental or informal methods but many requiring a written calculation.

Differentiation
Less able: Use differentiated page using simpler numbers
More able: Use differentiated page using decimal numbers and 2 step problems.

Plenary & assessment
Ask: *If I were to calculate £741.71 − £314.28, would I expect an odd or an even answer?* (Odd. This can be calculated by mentally counting on from 8 → 11− a difference of 3.) Ask: How would I round and estimate this calculation? (£750 - £300 → £450.)
   Now ask for volunteers to talk through their methods of calculation.

```
  £ 741.71    =      700 + 40 + 1 + 70p + 1p
 −£ 314.28    =      300 + 10 + 4 + 20p + 8p
```

Readjusted to:

```
  £ 741.41    =      700 + 30 + 11 + 60p + 11p
 − £ 314.28   =      300 + 10 +  4 + 20p +  8p
  £ 427.43    =      400 + 20 +  7 +.40p + 3p
```

Emphasise the position of the decimal point and how it remains in the same position.

An alternative calculation would be:
```
  £ 7 ³4 ¹1 .⁶7 ¹1
  − 3  1  4 . 2 8
  £ 4  2  7 . 4 3
```

Name	Date

A mixed bag of problems

Copy and complete:

1.
```
  £420.10
+ £361.40
```

2.
```
  £372.81
+ £721.34
```

3.
```
  £814.42
- £113.12
```

4.
```
  £417.14
- £288.37
```

5. **Ellie had saved £48.57 from her birthday money and then received £78.50 for Christmas.**

How much money had she saved?

_____

6. **165 boy scouts join 145 cubs for a camping trip.**

How many children attended?

_____

7. **I have 6m 52cm of pink ribbon and 4m 47cm of green ribbon.**

How much ribbon have I in total?

_____

8. **My garden measures 15m in total. The path stretches as far as 7m 28cm.**

How much more path do I need before I reach the bottom of the garden?

_____

Strategies for multiplying and dividing

Children investigate patterns in multiples and factors in order to enhance and extend their understanding about number.

LEARNING OBJECTIVES

		Topics	Starter	Main teaching activities
Lesson	1	Properties of numbers and number sequences Reasoning and generalising about numbers	● Use doubling and halving starting from known facts.	● Find all the pairs of factors up to 100.
Lesson	2		● Use doubling and halving starting from known facts.	● Find all the pairs of factors up to 100.
Lesson	3		● Know by heart all multiplication facts up to 10 × 10.	● Make general statements about odd or even numbers, including the outcome of sums and differences.
Lesson	4		● Use factors.	As for Lesson 3.
Lesson	5		● Partition.	● Explain a generalised relationship (formula) in words.

Lessons   overview

Preparation
Two lists of numbers to a) double and b) halve, eg:
a) 3; 6; 12; 50; 12; 15; 43; 48; 37; 21; 29; 18; 36; 46; 43; 16; 17; 24; 25; 44.
b) 60; 50; 74; 32; 42; 86; 92; 96; 84; 100; 98; 88; 72; 70; 48; 36; 64; 28; 22; 18.

Learning objectives
Starter
● Use doubling and halving starting at known facts.
Main teaching activity
● Find all the pairs of factors up to 100.

Vocabulary
predict; pattern; pair; rule; formula; relationship; factor; square number; strategy; prime number

You will need:

CD pages
'Blank 100 Square', one for each child; 'Multiplication square' and 'Blank 100 square', for teacher's/LSA's use (see General resources, Autumn term).

Equipment
Pencil and paper or white boards for informal jotting calculations; colouring pencils; stopwatch or similar for timing.

Lesson

Starter

Ask the children to jot down both lists of numbers from the board. Explain that they have 1 minute to double or halve them. How many can they do in the time? Discuss strategies for getting as many done as possible, ie do not sit trying to work one out, go through and do all the ones you know first.

Main teaching activity

Whole class: Revise what a factor is. (Numbers multiplied together to give a multiple.) Ask the children to find factors of 16, 28 or 35. Use a multiplication grid to show the children how to work out a factor. Explain that a multiplication grid is slightly limiting because it only shows factors up to 10, ie it would not give 2×14 for 28. Remind the children that factors of a larger number can be found by partitioning the larger numbers into multiples of known factors, eg $28 = (2 \times 10) + (2 \times 4)$ thus 2×14 are factors of 28. Revise prime numbers, ie numbers only divisibly by themselves and 1, such as 17. Ask the children to suggest other prime numbers.

Individual work: Distribute a copy of a 100 square to each child. Ask them to work through the numbers and to colour all the prime numbers in one colour. A calculator can be used to check.

Next, work through the remaining numbers and to record all the factors of the first 30 numbers on the bottom or back of the sheet, eg factors of 6 are 1, 2, 3, and 6.

Differentiation

Less able: This group may be glad of the support of a copy of a multiplication grid to begin to find factors and a calculator to check higher factors. They may only find factors of numbers 1–50.
More able: This group should be able to find all the factors of 1–50 mentally. They might take the investigation further, to 100, if there is sufficient time.

Plenary & assessment

Ask the children to share their findings of the prime numbers from 1–100. Ask: *Would the same pattern be true of the next 100 from 101–200? ie 1, 2, 3, 5, 7 etc are prime numbers, so would 101, 102, 103, 105, 107 also be prime numbers?* (No, not the even ones such as 102, which is divisible by 2, or 105, which is divisible by 5.)

Remind the children that they can use their knowledge of tests of divisibility and a calculator to work these out. Work through together identifying further prime numbers:

| 101 | 103 | 107 | 109 | 113 | 127 | 131 | 137 | 139 | 143 | 149 | 151 |
| 157 | 163 | 167 | 173 | 179 | 181 | 191 | 193 | 197 | 199 | | |

Lesson

Starter

Multiplying by 4 by doubling and doubling again. Ask the children questions such as 8×4; 16×4; 20×4; 25×4; 32×4 etc.

Ask them to explain to you their double doubles. Divide the class into two teams and have a quick fire competition where you call out a question, ie '*18 x 4*' and the first team to put up their hand and say '*72*' gains a point. The first team to 10 are the winners.

Main teaching activity

Whole class: Revise square numbers. (A number multiplied by itself gives a square number.) Ask the class to identify the square numbers they know up to 100 by chanting $1 \times 1 = 1$, $2 \times 2 = 4$, $3 \times 3 = 9$ etc. List these for all to see. Ask the children to extend this list with any other square numbers they can calculate, eg $20 \times 20 = 400$ or $13 \times 13 = 169$. It is sometimes easier to children to visualize if you actually draw a square with 2 across 2 down = 4, a square number.

Conversely, the square root of a number is the factor that when multiplied by itself gives the square number, ie $8^2 = 64$ $64 = 8$.

Individual work: Find all the square numbers on the 100 square from yesterday and colour them a different colour from the prime numbers. Is there a pattern?

Continue to find further factors of numbers up to 100 as before.

Differentiation

Less able: This group will need support in listing all the factors of their numbers, especially to understand that, for example, 28 has factors of 1, 28, 2 and 14 as well as 4 and 7. Point out the relationship, double one factor and halve the other.

More able: This group should extend the prime number, square numbers and factor investigation to numbers 101–200. Fill in the numbers on a blank 100 square and colour and highlight as before. Which numbers follow the same pattern?

Plenary & assessment

Ask the children to look at the square numbers they have highlighted. *Is there a pattern?* (Yes, they run diagonally across the page.) Is the same true for the next 100, ie 101–200? (Yes, 11 × 11, 12 × 12, 13 × 13 numbers also run diagonally.)

Ask them to look at their prime numbers. *Is there a pattern?* No, not really and the arrangement is different for numbers 101–200.

Finally, *Are there any other generalizations or observations that we can make, for example, even numbers have generally more factors than odd numbers.*

Lessons overview

Preparation
A sheet of 20 single figure multiplication and division questions.

Learning objectives
Starter
● Know by heart all multiplication facts up to 10 × 10.
● Use factors.
Main teaching activity
● Make general statements about odd or even numbers, including the outcome of sums and differences.

Vocabulary
odd, even, predict, sequence, pattern

You will need:
Photocopiable pages
'Investigating odd and even numbers', see page 224, one for each child.

Equipment
Pencil and paper or white boards for informal jotting calculations; stopwatch or similar for timing; large piece of paper for recording.

Lesson

Starter

Challenge the children to complete a page of 20 single-figure multiplication problems and division problems where the answer is a single number – in less than 3 minutes. As children call out 'Finished!' give them their time – so you will have to keep a close eye on the clock. This will give you an idea of who really knows their tables instantly and those for whom speed compromises accuracy.

Main teaching activity

Whole class: Revise what is already known about odd and even numbers, ie evens are divisible by 2, and even + even number gives an even answer etc. Ask the children if, given their knowledge, they can predict: *What happens if you add 3 even numbers together or 4 or 5? What about subtraction? What happens if we subtract 3 even numbers in a row or 3 odd? Or 4 or 5?*

Take suggestions and record these on a large piece of paper. Explain that the children are going to pose a question, make their own prediction and test the theory to find out the answer.

Individual work: Choose one addition or subtraction question to investigate, ie *Do all even numbers give an even answer, irrespective of the number of numbers being added. If I start with an even number and subtract an odd number, what do I get? What happens if I continue to subtract odd numbers until I reach zero? Is there a pattern?*

Use the recording sheet 'Investigating odd and even numbers'. Encourage the children to make a prediction: 'I think… because...' and then investigate using a number of examples.

Differentiation

Less able: This group should attempt to investigate a question chosen by the teacher. The level and difficulty will be dependent on the prior knowledge and understanding of odd and even numbers, and will be at the teacher's discretion. A possible question might be to investigate what happens when adding two even numbers together, or two odd numbers, or the outcome of adding one odd and one even.

More able: These children should be able to investigate a question that they have posed independently and then extended to investigate *'What if …'* They should be able to show their mathematical thinking, working in a logical way.

Plenary & assessment

Share findings of addition and subtraction investigations. Ask: *Did any of the results match the predictions that we wrote at the beginning of the lesson? Did anyone not agree with the results of the majority? Why? Are these 'rogue' results which need checking and retesting?* 'Rogue' results are ones that do not fit in with a general pattern, and therefore may be incorrect and need checking. Ask: *What is the next question we should investigate?* This may be subtraction for some and multiplication/division for others.

Lesson

Starter

Write up on the board the following calculations: 35×50; 32×40; 48×30.

Ask the children to simplify these calculations by breaking them down into their constituent factors and reordering them for easier multiplying, for example 35×50:

$= (7 \times 5) \times (5 \times 10)$ $= (5 \times 5) \times 7 \times 10 = (25 \times 7) \times 10$ $= 175 \times 10 = 1750$

Main teaching activity

Whole class: Ask the children to pose a question that could be investigated as before but looking at the effect of either multiplication or division, eg *Do all even numbers multiplied together give an even answer?* Using 2 even numbers, 3, 4, etc? or if even numbers are divided by an even number does it always produce an even answer? What if it is divided again, etc.

Again, use a range of predictions on the board or a sheet of paper for later reference in the plenary.

Individual work: As for Lesson 3. Pose questions. The children should use a further recording sheet 'Investigating odd and even numbers' to note down questions, predict and investigate.

Differentiation

Less able: These children should investigate a question set by the teacher. It should be based on the children's current level of understanding and ability to calculate. It might be to investigate repeated subtraction from a given starting number or, more simply, to investigate what happens when an odd number is subtracted from another odd number or from an even number. The children should be encouraged to look for a pattern and make a generalized statement about their findings.

More able: These children should be able to pose a further question to investigate, based on their prior knowledge and understanding of patterns in odd and even numbers. They may already observe that subtracting an odd number from another odd number always results in an even answer. From there they should be able to extend their thinking to: *What happens if I repeatedly subtract odd numbers? Is there a pattern?* Alternatively they might investigate the behaviour of odd and even numbers when multiplying. These children should be able to predict and then investigate, explaining their results with clear reasons.

Plenary & assessment

Share findings of investigations by asking individuals to present their evidence to the rest of the class giving reasons for their original prediction and what they found out.

Compare with original predictions. Listen out for clear mathematical reasoning. Ask: *If 2 even numbers multiplied together give an even answer, is this true for all even numbers of even factors? ie 2 even factors 4, 6, 8 etc.? Why?*

Lessons overview

Preparation
OHT for 'Generalisations about odd and even numbers'.

Learning objectives

Starter
- Partition.

Main teaching activity
- Make general statements about odd or even numbers, including the outcome of sums and differences.
- Explain a generalised relationship (formula) in words.

You will need:

CD pages
'Number fan cards 0–9', for teacher's/LSA's use (see General resources, Autumn term).

Equipment
Pencil and paper or white boards for informal jotting calculations; large piece of paper for recording.

Lesson

Starter: Multiplying using partitioning
Ask the children to calculate mentally a sum such as 18 × 6; 19 × 4; 21 × 6; 23 × 5 etc, using partitioning and use their number fans to display their answer when you say: 'Show me'.

Main teaching activity

Whole class: Explain that in this session the children are going to draw together everything they have learnt about calculating using odd and even numbers. Explain that to avoid constantly writing odd and even, it is easier to use letters, ie E = even, O = Odd. In this way we can write a number sentence or formula which shows our findings.

Display on OHT or large sheet of paper to summarise findings about odd and even numbers.

Starting with addition, demonstrate how they might record:

E + E = E	Or:	O + O = E
E + E + E = E		O + O + O = O
E + E + E + E = E etc		O + O + O + O = E etc.

Individual work: Create own information page giving generalisations about odd and even numbers, with sections for 'Addition', 'Subtraction', 'Multiplication' and 'Division'. Children record their own results as a formula in the appropriate section. As the children work, ask individuals to put up one or two of their results up on the class recording sheet for others to use and test for themselves.

Ask the children to try an example of any of the formulae copied from the class record to ensure that they understand and agree:

$$E \times E = E \qquad\qquad O \times O = O$$
$$2 \times 6 = 12 \qquad\qquad 7 \times 3 = 21$$
$$E \times E \times E = E \qquad\qquad O \times O \times O = O$$
$$2 \times 6 \times 4 = 48 \qquad\qquad 7 \times 3 \times 3 = 63$$

Differentiation

Less able: Adult support may be needed to ensure that this group understand and can apply the formulae. You may decide that they should use addition and subtraction only.

More able: This group should be able to rigorously test some of the formulae and detect possible anomalies.

Plenary & assessment

Ask: *Are there any odd and even combinations that do not produce a consistent result?* (No, there should be reliable patterns.) *How can this knowledge assist with the accuracy of our own calculations?* (It's not a complete answer, but another checking strategy.) Discuss how consistent application of a rule should produce reliable results in this instance.

Turn the children's findings into a game. Explain that you are going to call out a formula or code calculation such as O + O. The children consult their investigations and put their hands on their head if they think the answer will be odd or stand up if they think the answer might be even.

Name	Date

Investigating odd and even numbers

Questions to be investigated:

My prediction:

Testing to produce evidence:

What I found out:

The next question I want to investigate:

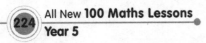